4-7-2011

Up From the Deep
The Return

Keith & Darla,

    You can read how the other
half lives although we both
can end up in the brig

       Bob

Up From the Deep
The Return

Robert K. Harmuth

Riverdale Books
Cumming, Georgia

Up From the Deep: The Return

Riverdale Books
an imprint of

Riverdale Electronic Books, Inc.
4420 Bonneville Drive
Cumming, GA 30041
http://riverdaleebooks.com

ISBN: 978-1-932606-21-8

To my shipmates in the USS *Growler* (SSG-577), all the submariners in the First Nuclear Weapons Deterrent Submarine Force, and in memory of the USS *Growler* (SS-215).

Dedicated to William Gunn, Captain, USN (Ret)

Contents

Photos follow pages 68 and 168

Preface

A cold drizzle fell as the 60-yen taxi came to an abrupt stop near the head of the main pier in the turning basin of the U. S. Naval Station, Yokosuka, Japan. High pitched car horns honked and bicycle bells rang to warn the taxi and passenger of passing traffic as a young American naval officer pulled a huge B-4 bag and duffle bag from the trunk of the well worn Toyota taxicab. He stiffly returned the driver's bow of thanks as he lifted his luggage and started walking across the road toward the pier. He glanced behind him at the tall limestone cliffs and walked past a large tunnel used by the Japanese for storage and shelter during World War II. He paused for a moment, reminded himself everyone drove on the wrong side of the street, looked in both directions, and then continued toward the pier.

It was a typical April day in Japan; cold, wet, gray, and windy with a heavy fog hanging over the harbor. He walked a few yards up the pier, then, stopped to readjust the bags in his hands. He looked down the pier but saw nothing of any ship or submarine through the dense fog. Slowly, he continued down the pier and the silhouette of a huge submarine bow began to take shape a few hundred feet ahead. With a grunt, he continued his walk and an enormous submarine began to take shape through the fog, the likes of which he had never seen. The submarine sail (often erroneously called the conning tower) appeared to extend into the sky and disappear in the fog. A great deal of activity was in progress along the entire length of the submarine. Shipyard workers were building a scaffold up the side of the sail and the After Battery Compartment hatch was a beehive of activity with crew and shipyard workers coming and going.

The naval officer stopped at the foot of the gangway, straightened his tie and tried to smooth his wrinkled khaki uniform. Then he briskly walked up the gangway, dropped his bags to salute the Ensign (United States flag), turned toward the Topside Watch and, "Request permission to come aboard, sir!"

1

His salute was returned with permission to board so he lifted his bags again and stumbled off the end of the gangway onto the main deck aft of the sail. He had arrived! The Petty Officer of the Watch was deluged in work; checking identification of workers and vendors coming and going while keeping track of the crew as they arrived and departed the boat. His white hat was cocked on the back of his head with the sides curled with a few well-placed black smudges from fingerprints. His blue dungarees were clean but not pressed, black shoes well soiled, and a .45 Colt pistol hung from his right hip akin to John Wayne.

The young officer informed the Topside Petty Officer of the Watch, FTG2(SS) John Anderson, that he was reporting aboard for duty. Anderson warmly welcomed him aboard and called below to report the officer's arrival, forgetting the officer's last name in the process.

"Control, Topside, a Mr. Ahh, shit, a Mr. H. is topside reporting for duty. Inform Lieutenant Breeding." Anderson then informed the officer someone would be topside shortly to take him below. Unwittingly, the young officer's name was coined as "Mr. H," a name that was to remain with him for the following couple of years. He looked around topside and was thoroughly impressed by the submarine's size. It was the largest American diesel submarine in commission displacing close to 3,500 tons submerged. He marveled at the two huge missile hangars astride the bow and wondered how difficult it must be to maintain depth control with such a mass of metal forward.

Lieutenant Donald Breeding came topside to greet Bob, the young officer, and welcomed him aboard the U.S.S. *Growler* (SSG-577). Anderson told Mr. H to leave his bags and lay below with his paperwork with Don Breeding. They climbed down the After Battery hatch and as Bob stepped onto the well-polished, linoleum-covered deck of the crew's mess and drew in the smell of the submarine. A smile creased his face as he inhaled deeply and smelled the odor associated only with a submarine, diesel or nuclear. It was a combination of oils, paints, electronics, body odors, and then something very special that only a Submariner appreciates. "My God, I have finally made it."

Chapter One
The Regulus Nuclear Deterent Weapon Submarine Force

This is a story about the Regulus Nuclear Missile Submarine Force, centered on the submarine, U.S.S. *Growler* (SSG-577). It is a story about submarines and Submariners who carried strategic nuclear weapons—the strategic Regulus I Missile.

There were five Regulus Missile Submarines: the U.S.S. *Halibut* (SSGN-587) was the only nuclear powered submarine and carried five missiles; the U.S.S. *Tunny* (SSG-282) and U.S.S. *Barbero* (SSG-317) were World War II vintage diesel boats that carried two missiles; and U.S.S. *Grayback* (SSG-574) and *Growler*, converted to Regulus boats during new construction in the late 1950s, which carried four missiles each. The five boats formed four units; *Barbero* and *Tunny* deployed together as one unit. The five boats were Submarine Division Eleven (SubDiv 11) in Submarine Squadron One (SubRon 1) and were directly supported by GMU-10 (pronounced GUM-U meaning guided missile unit). There were a number of other GMUs located throughout the United States. The most active in the development of the Loon and Regulus missiles was GMU-55 located at Point Mugu, Naval Air Station, California and operating on the Pacific Missile Test Range out of the port at the U.S. Naval Construction Battalion Center, Port Hueneme, California.[1]

The Regulus missile started development in 1947, when the Regulus I first deployed in the Pacific on the U.S.S. *Los Angeles* (CA-135) followed by the U.S.S. *Helena* (CA-75), U.S.S. *Toledo* (CA-133) and U.S.S. *Macon* (CA-132). In the mid-1950s, the aircraft carriers U.S.S. *Hancock* (CV-19) and U.S.S. *Randolph* (CV-15) deployed with the missile in the Pacific and Mediterranean Sea.[2]

The first deployed Regulus submarine was U.S.S. *Tunny* (SSG-282), built and modified by Mare Island Naval Shipyard (MINSY). A small hangar was built aft of the sail that carried two missiles. The U.S.S. *Barbero* (SSG-317) was similar. U.S.S.

Grayback (SSG-574) and U.S.S. *Growler* (SSG-577) were designed as fast attack submarines of the *Tang* class with new, light weight, high-speed Fairbanks Morse diesels for main propulsion. The diesel engines were a disaster on all submarines installed, surpassed in poor performance only by the General Motors "pancake" engine. They were the first boats with main engines sound mounted except for the smaller submarine killer submarines of the "K" Class. They were large boats, with a submerged displacement of about 3,500 tons. During construction the submarines were cut in half, a missile compartment inserted between the Forward Torpedo Room and the Forward Battery Compartment, and two hangars added above the hull over the bow. U.S.S. *Halibut* (SSGN-587) was nuclear powered and displaced 5,000 tons. She carried five missiles in one hangar/missile space forward, powered by 6,600 shaft horsepower.[3] *Halibut* would later gain world fame as the submarine that worked with Howard Hughes' *Glomar Explorer* in the partial recovery of a USSR sunken submarine. She also was portrayed at great length in *Blind Man's Bluff* as a covert operator, tapping Soviet communication cables.[4]

The diesel boats transited to their patrol station from Pearl Harbor to the Soviet Union's East Coast. The trip took two weeks, thus a deployment was a month long just in transit times. The Regulus concept initially included a number of other submarines, diesel and nuclear, that guided the missile further than the launching submarine's capability.

The Regulus predecessor, Loon, was almost identical to the German V-1 "buzz bomb." Loon was a simple, almost foolproof missile, 27 feet long, weighing 5,000 pounds, and capable of delivering a 2,000 pound warhead at a range of 150 miles. It was identified by the pulse jet engine, which looked like a stovepipe atop the main body. It flew at 380 knots at a 5,000 foot altitude. The first Loon was launched from USS *Cusk* (SS-348) on 12 February 1947.[5]

Loon and Regulus boats operated out of Port Hueneme, California and utilized the Pacific Missile Range operated by NAS, Point Mugu. A humorous Loon incident occurred on the Pacific Missile Range in the early 1950s. Each launch resulted in a consistent three-mile error from its target, Navy owned San Nicolas Island. Investigations found the island target was plotted inaccurately on the charts.[6] The missile had operated perfectly.

During the Korean conflict, operational use of Loon was seriously considered but it was not deployed. One of the Loon connections to *Growler* was Pat Garrett, who was an ETSN at Point Mugu, NAS in the Loon Program in 1952. His involvement wasn't as much with the Loon Missile as it was ensuring the Pacific Missile Test Range was clear of fishing boats prior to a launch. He appeared on the *Growler* in the early '60s as a spook—an intelligence rider during patrols. One of the lessons learned by new riders on submarines was how to properly operate the head. The spooks didn't attend submarine school and on their first ride, often found themselves the victim of the "howling head" and became a "speckled trout." The sinks and heads drained into one of two sanitary tanks. During the mid-watch, or earlier if required, the sanitary tanks were blown to sea by high-pressure air. The deeper the submarine, the higher the air pressure to blow the tanks clean. All sinks and heads were tagged with a sign when blowing tanks but the signs were sometimes overlooked when the call of nature was urgent, and an embarrassing blowback occurred.

As Trident and Polaris overshadowed Regulus, so did Regulus overshadow Loon. Each system contributed to the success of the Free World. The plan for Regulus was deployment by submarines in the frigid waters of the Northwest Pacific Ocean and the Bering Sea. The Regulus submarines conducted launches and exercises in the cold northern waters off Dutch Harbor, Alaska preparatory to actual deployment. The crews were familiarized and acclimated to the tough-ness of the northern waters by the exercises.[7]

The Regulus boats' namesakes represent a wealth of history and honor in the Submarine Force. The best known was the original U.S.S. *Growler.* Follow-ing a number of successful war patrols in World War II, she attacked a Japanese destroyer by ramming it on the surface. She received intense machine gun fire from Japanese surface units, severely injuring her skipper, Commander Howard Gilmore, who was unable to reach the bridge hatch. He pushed his quartermas-ter, Dutch Schultz[8], down the conning tower hatch and ordered *Growler* to sub-merge, thereby leaving himself on the bridge but saving the submarine and crew. He was posthumously awarded the first Medal of Honor in the Submarine Force. She failed muster following a wolf pack attack west of Mindoro with submarines *Hake,* and *Hardhead* three patrols later. She is considered "still on patrol."[9]

The World War II *Halibut* was a member of the famous "Roach's Raiders," which included *Haddock* and *Tuna.* Under the command of Commander Galan-tin, she was attacked by a Japanese antisubmarine group south of Formosa. The boat was nearly bashed to destruction by a multitude of depth charges that dim-pled the hull, caved in the Conning Tower, and literally destroyed the Forward Torpedo Room. She survived but was retired upon return to Pearl Harbor. A veteran of many battles, she sank 12 ships for a total of over 45,000 tons.[10]

Grayback was lost with all hands in November 1943 following a heroic and successful war patrol career. She was credited with 14 sinkings in ten patrols, including a submarine, destroyer and light cruiser. She also remains on "eternal patrol."[11]

Tunny and *Barbero* conducted successful war patrols near the end of World War II. *Tunny* was outfitted with the newest of sonar arrays and was instrumental in the development and use of sonar and radar.[12] She was converted and recom-missioned on 6 March 1953. Many of the crewmembers had been in the Loon

Missile Program. She launched the first Regulus missile by a submarine and conducted the first OST (Operational Suitability Test) under wartime conditions in 1955. *Tunny* was in on the ground floor of the Regulus Missile evolution and a source of officers and enlisted men who manned Regulus submarines for the duration of the program. She was the first to operate in the ice packs of the North Pacific and Bering Sea. *Tunny* participated in a SEATO demonstration exercise in 1958 with the Seventh Fleet and shared the Regulus stage with the U.S.S. Toledo (CA-113). It was one of the few times a submarine operated with a surface fleet, resulting in humorous situations for the *Tunny*. "I suggest you get the hell out of their way before they run over you," was one instruction from the DivCom, and illustrative of a submarine in a surface fleet environment.[13]

Tunny was the first Regulus submarine to deploy on a patrol with Regulus Missiles on board, on 23 October 1959. The first actual Strategic Strike Deterrent Mission, with assigned targets, was conducted by the *Grayback* a few months later. *Tunny* was utilized in her initial patrol to scope out the patrol area for navigation, weather, and hostile conditions. Commander Marvin Blair and *Tunny* launched the first thermo-nuclear warhead by a submarine.[14] She launched her 100th missile on 27 October 1964, the last Regulus fired by a submarine. She went into overhaul in April through August 1965 and was redesignated LPSS-282, serving as a troop carrier until decommissioning on 28 August 1969 at Mare Island. She was sunk on 19 June 1970 as a MK 37 torpedo target for the U.S.S. *Volador* (SS-490).[15]

Barbero was decommissioned after receiving severe damage on her last patrol of World War II. On 1 February 1955, *Barbero* entered MINSY for conversion to Regulus and recommissioned on 28 October 1955. She served NATO in the Atlantic Fleet. *Barbero* launched a Regulus above the Arctic Circle north of Norway. She participated in exercises against the Continental Air Defense Radar Network and responded to the Lebanon Crisis in 1958. She even demonstrated mail delivery by missile for the Postal Department and arrived in Pearl Harbor on 24 August 1959 to join SubDiv 11 along with *Tunny* and *Halibut*.[16]

She launched her 46th Regulus on 4 August 1960, the 1000th launch of the Regulus I. *Barbero* deployed on her first patrol on 30 September 1960, coincident with the U.S.S. *George Washington*'s (SSBN-598) first Polaris deployment in the Atlantic.[17] Following her 71 day second patrol, the tactical situation required four Regulus missiles on station so she joined *Tunny* to form a single deployment unit. *Barbero* was decommissioned on 30 June 1964 and sunk as an acoustic torpedo target by U.S.S. *Greenfish* (SS-351) on 7 October 1964.[18]

Grayback was the first submarine designed and built by Mare Island Naval Shipyard. Her design included added crew berthing ending the typical "hot bunking" by the crews. *Growler* had similar berthing facilities. She was the first submarine with an aluminum sail hinged on one side for rapid access to the masts and periscopes. The installation was a failure. *Growler's* sail was solid steel and not hinged. She incorporated new torpedo stowage and handling systems and was the first submarine to utilize an Attack Center that combined the uses of the Conning Tower and Control Room. While almost 80% complete, her design was modified to accept the Regulus Missile. Launched in July 1957, Admiral Charles Lockwood stated the striking power of *Grayback* (and *Growler*) "reduced by comparison the atomic bombs dropped on Hiroshima and Nagasaki to the level of 4th of July firecrackers."[19]

Grayback was a forerunner in experimenting and testing the W-27 thermo-nuclear warhead in freezing temperature operations. She deployed on her first patrol on 21 September 1959 and returned in December 1959.[20] She launched the only Regulus II missile from a submarine.[21]

Grayback was decommissioned on 25 May 1964, but in November 1967 under-went extensive work to remove the Missile System and replace it with amphibious equipment. She was recommissioned on 9 May 1969 and deployed to Subic Bay in the Philippines, where she served for 11 years as LPSS-574, including operations in Vietnam with Seal Teams.[22]

Halibut was the only Regulus Submarine built from the keel up. A modified Skate Class nuclear submarine built to accept the hangar and launcher system of Regulus, she was launched in July 1959 and designed to handle launches in heavy seas up to a State 4 sea. She joined the Regulus Division in November of 1960 and conducted her first patrol in February 1961.[23]

The new *Growler*, like *Grayback*, was an improved member of the 563 Fast Attack Class of submarine. Built at Portsmouth Naval Shipyard in Kittery, Maine, she looked like a huge, clumsy, and pregnant whale. Her bow didn't neatly cut through the waves but pushed the seas in front of her; just like the *Grayback*. Gilmore's words, "Take Her Down," were inscribed on the wardroom bulkhead of the new *Growler* in honor of Commander Howard Gilmore, and her passageways echoed with encouragement from the 88 *Growler* submariners of the past that went down with her in World War II.

Mr. H first saw Admiral Arleigh Burke at the Naval Academy in the summer of 1955 at the change of command for the Chief of Naval Operations (CNO). During his four years at the Academy, different color schemes were tried in a few Midshipmen rooms to get away from the dreary and typical light green of officer's country everywhere. Just before noon meal formation, during June Week 1959, Admiral Burke dropped into Mr. H's room unannounced to chat about the color schemes. Mr. H was just stepping out of the shower when the CNO knocked and entered the room. It was quite a moment, seeing the CNO and World War II destroyer hero face-to-face while standing at attention completely naked and wet. He was extremely cordial and pleased at our color approval as we watched the Brigade march by our window to noon meal. A better excuse for missing a formation was never made.

Prior to sea trials, the crew spent a lot of time in New London at the Submarine School undergoing team training. One of the requisites to graduation from the school was escape training in the diving tower. However, the entire crew was requalified in the escape method, including the Commanding officer, Lieutenant Commander Chuck Priest. As during school, the escapes were made in alphabetical order so RM1(SS) Pappy Powers was just behind the captain. With Steinke Hood on and the May West life jacket inflated, Captain Priest stepped out of the escape hatch into the tank—and disappeared downward. Pappy couldn't believe the sight; no one was that negatively buoyant. In a moment, Captain Priest reappeared strongly climbing the rope line upward toward the top of the tank, loudly shouting, "Ho. Ho, ho," to permit air to escape his lungs as divers watched his every move.[24]

The commissioning crew of *Growler* was unusual in that every member was Qualified in Submarines with one exception. It was an exceptionally qualified crew that placed into commission an exceptional submarine. Of interest, the one unqualified crew member seemed to attain the most notoriety. Lieutenant (jg) James Murphy first was noted during sea trials during the initial deep dives. A couple of hydrophone cable runs had been removed prior to "fast cruise."[25] Unfortunately, the cable penetrations were not plugged properly and welded shut. During the fast cruise, a thunderstorm passed overhead with large amounts of rain. Water began dripping through the holes in the hull. Epoxy resin was used to temporarily plug the holes above Sonar and Radio but promptly forgotten. During sea trials, the epoxy blew out near test depth of 500 feet, and the water began shorting out power in Sonar and poured into the Pump Room. Captain Priest immediately emergency surfaced the boat and the XO, Pete Burkhart, rushed to the scene. RMC (SS) Pappy Powers was in Radio, heard the "pop" when the plug gave way, and saw a stream of water coming through an empty conduit near Sonar. Jim Murphy noted the hole was the size of a nickel and QM3 Robert "Hymie" Hoffman, the duty quartermaster, grabbed a couple of nickels and pushed them into the hole, which slowed the leak to a dribble. SO1(SS) Tom Coffman, the senior sonar man, organized a bucket brigade to catch water and dump it into the galley. Carrol Miller, the Auxiliaryman of the Watch (AOW), quickly cut a circle out of rubber gasket material, placed it between two nickels, and the leak stopped. According to Herb Tibbits, a little "monkey shit" (a black, soft, putty-like material) didn't hurt stopping the leak either. From that day on, the Harvard graduate and nickels were thought of synonymously. Tom Crymes was a mess cook on board working in the Crew's Mess when he heard the Collision Alarm scream. Tom did his job and immediately slammed shut the bulkhead flapper and dogged down the watertight door. He heard a scream and looked through the deadlight (little round window in the watertight door) and saw a yard worker trying to get out of Control with water flying around him. Tom will never forget the look of absolute terror in the yard worker's eyes.[26]

During *Halibut's* initial dive to test depth, one of the crew members happened to be in the head in the After Torpedo Room. He must have had to go pretty bad to be in the head during the first deep dive. As the hull shrunk due to external pressure, the door to the head stuck and the submariner had to remain in the head until the boat went shallower.[27]

The majority of the officers on board were U.S. Naval Academy graduates and a friction began between the officers and Jim Murphy, an Ivy League graduate. One night while surface steaming with the temperature hovering around 31°F, Jim assumed the watch on the bridge wearing only a T-shirt. He had to prove to the officers and men he was as *macho* as any academy graduate. His tale was yet to be complete as his adventures continued for a couple more years.[28]

Like any new construction vessel, and in particular a submarine, the quality of the construction is directly related to the efforts of the commissioning crew. Jim "Hingejaw" Harrison remembers making four to five walks through the boat on a daily basis. Everyone in the crew made these walks. Invariably, numerous faults or omissions were detected and many were quickly corrected. The origin of "Hingejaw" is unknown but likely the rapid use of his mouth was coined during a shipyard overhaul in Pearl Harbor.[33]

The commissioning crew called the event the "Tongue of the Ocean." The boat was conducting sound trials with a Taylor Basin sound boat standing off a short distance recording any noise. COB Tom Stebbins had the hydraulic manifold and Jim Murphy was the Conning Officer in Control. Captain Priest was on the bridge with two lookouts and the boat was rigged for dive. Periodically, the ballast tank vents were cycled to reduce the freeboard thereby offering more hull noise to record. Due to the huge twin hangars on the bow, *Growler's* center of buoyancy was well forward of most submarines. The sound boat had drifted a bit askew from the submarine so Jim Murphy ordered, "All ahead one-third." Immediately, the huge bow began rising and as Murphy swung the periscope around to see why, he noticed the stern was submerging.

"Blow all main ballast tanks," Murphy shouted. "Shut the bridge hatch." Both lookouts were already on their way down at the order of Captain Priest and green water poured down both the upper and lower bridge trunk open hatches. Immediately, COB Stebbins took control and surfaced *Growler*. Seaman Frank Moll was one of the lookouts and managed to finally get the upper hatch shut. On the surface and holding, the upper hatch was opened for a wet and cold Chuck Priest.

Murphy had nothing signed off on his qualification card that day but a few erasers appeared on scene.[30]

Following the scare, the *Growler* anchored in the stream off Provincetown at the lower end of Cape Cod. The crew was granted liberty and went ashore mumbling about the near flooding incident and decided to do some serious drinking. They stopped at Auntie May's Restaurant to enjoy a good meal and some good brew. A guy of the night and his friends took a liking to Jimmy "Pappy" Hegg and the fight was on. Lieutenants Ted "Fussy" Hussy and Bob "Delicate" Duke maintained some calm and got the crew back to the barge before too many injuries were incurred but the restaurant was badly marred.[31]

Halibut was startled the first time they opened the inner and outer hangar doors at sea. There were no baffles to keep seawater from rushing into the void between the two doors. Ocean swells surged across the boat, over the doors, and into the hangar. When the inner door was closed, all the water caught in the saucer shaped door dumped into the hangar as well. Back in the shipyard, the doors were removed, worked on, and placed back on board, but not exactly the way it was planned. The large yard crane was busy so two small rail cranes were used instead. When they swung the door over the *Halibut*, one crane got ahead of the other and both cranes toppled. The door ended up on the crane booms on the deck of the *Halibut*.[32]

When Tom Crymes reported on board as a member of the commissioning crew, he just missed the launch of the submarine, an event that no sailor ever forgets. The COB, Jim Strahorn, welcomed him on board and asked him his name. Tom told him he would like to be called Tom since they wouldn't let him keep his name on *Barbero*. When he reported on her following Submarine School, the COB told him there were two "Toms" and one "Tommy" already on board and he had to pick another name—he chose "Larry," his middle name. Chief Strahorn welcomed him as a "Tom." Crymes became good friends with QM1(SS) "Moo" Marullo. Moo left *Growler* later to serve on board U.S.S. *Thresher* (SSN-593) and was lost with the boat a few years later. Moo met a beautiful local Portsmouth girl; they fell in love and were married. When world events changed the homeport of *Growler* from Puerto Rico to Pearl Harbor, Moo couldn't wait to get back to his wife on the East Coast. He managed a change of orders, unfortunately. MT2(SS) Tom Jones, not the singer with a sock in his jock, joined the boat during construction and was also looking forward to being home ported in Roosevelt Roads. Fortunately for Jones, he did not seek to leave *Growler*.[33]

Crymes narrowly escaped death himself following the first patrol when he was cleaning out the periscope well. Someone inadvertently failed to notice a red tag and lowered the periscope. Luckily, his screams were heard and the periscope stopped in time. It would not be the only periscope crisis.[34]

The Commissioning Crew was active in many community events while building in Portsmouth, New Hampshire. They participated in parades, helped charities, and generally were good citizens. One of the more popular groups on board was the boat's baseball/fast pitch softball team. Coached and managed by Bob Seay, the baseball team did very well against local teams although the submariners never did become acquainted with hitting the fast moving softball. One baseball game no member will forget was against a local prison in the prison yard. Many of the team swore off all crime, no matter how petty the crime—not that the crew was a police problem.[35]

Denny Sloan was a young Lieutenant (jg) when he reported aboard for duty shortly following sea trials. He was on the bridge when *Growler* arrived at the Weapons Station, Yorktown, Pennsylvania. He observed what every crew member on the boat would experience; the boat was terribly underpowered. The dinky Fairbanks Morse & Company "hotrod" engines that provided the boat with years of problems. The *Growler* sailed to Yorktown upon departing Portsmouth. The tide was ebbing and the boat was unable to power twist her stern into the wharf. A locomotive was called to pull in the stern.[36]

The crew had a great trip through the Panama Canal. Between the locks, Bob Duke and Bill Lindeman decided to make a photo reconnaissance run in a rubber boat and film the *Growler* at periscope depth, snorkeling, surfacing, then ramming out a missile and running up the missile engine. Everything was planned and made ready. The film crew was swamped with volunteers but the final four were chosen by Captain Priest: Lieutenant (jg) Bob Duke, Lieutenant (jg) Bill Lindeman, TM1 (SS) John Haney, and the cook CS3 (SS) Oscar Weigant. The *Growler* started her approach at periscope depth and slowly circled the rubber raft when a school of Great White Sharks decided to investigate the rubber raft. The paddles became a blur as the foursome left a large wake as they headed for the submarine. Captain Priest didn't immediately surface believing the waving was being made in joy and readiness. Luckily, rescue was achieved and the escape from the sharks made good. The size and number of sharks increased with each telling of the experience.[37]

A few hours later, Captain Priest decided to hold swim call for the crew. As the crew started jumping into the water, Ozzie Weigant seemed a bit hesitant. The CO observed this and shouted,

"Don't worry Ozzie, it's fresh water. Sharks don't live in fresh water," whereupon Weigant leaped off the bow into the water as the CO shouted again, "but keep an eye open for the alligators." Ozzie proved that submarine sailors could walk on water as he quickly returned to the submarine.[38]

As the crew was jumping off the boat in every direction in their birthday suits, holding a bar of soap, a cruise liner passed by. The tourists on the liner lined the rails and camera shutters blinked at the crazy submariners. Dave Straka swears they were not swimming nude—possibly the standard Navy issue tan swim trunks looked transparent when wet.[39]

An event few people are aware of was the launching of a dummy Regulus II missile. *Grayback* launched the only real Regulus II but *Growler* launched a dummy to prove her capability to handle the much larger missile. Following the successful launch, *Growler* headed south for missile training off Roosevelt Roads, Puerto Rico.[40]

About this time, the *Tunny* returned from her first patrol, which was termed a "scoping" patrol. It was designed to scope out (investigate) the patrol area and gather intelligence for the following missile patrols by the five boats. Her captain, Lieutenant Commander Marvin S. Blair, requested the patrol be considered an official Missile Deterrent Patrol since they did carry the Blue Birds. She had departed on the mission on 17 July 1958. Eventually, the mission was approved as an official patrol and her crew members, along with all the other Regulus crew members, were awarded the SSBN Deterrent Patrol Insignia.[41]

The USS *Carbonero* was deeply involved in the Regulus development and testing. She broke and holds a number of missile launch records. On one of her final launches, she registered the shortest flight of just a few feet and a couple inches, the shortest flight time airborne, and she was the only submarine to launch and land her own missile as well as the only submarine to land a Regulus. The bird came off the launcher and ended up on deck after starting the missile engine run-up test.[42]

About this time, the Navy began a Proficiency Pay System intended to pay a bonus each month to personnel in vital and skilled positions. It caused a great deal of conflict as crew members of the same rating, but a different NEC (Navy Enlisted Code), received different paychecks. One of the ProPay ratings was quartermaster and when Tom Crymes was on *Tang* prior to *Growler*, he stood the 04-08 watches. The XO/Navigator on *Tang* was an old mustang (commissioned from the enlisted ranks) and didn't believe in ProPay. The boat was returning to Pearl Harbor from Yokosuka via the Northern Route on the surface and stars were shot every morning. After a week of awakening the XO and shooting stars with him, the XO said,

"Crymes, you can shoot stars as well as any officer. Why are your star lines always all over the place?" Crymes quickly responded,

"Because a QM3 without ProPay doesn't have to use a sextant, sir." The point was made. Crymes got his ProPay and the XO slept in during morning stars.

Among *Growler*'s plankowners was Travis Bevans who was a Quartermaster that served aboard the famous USS *Missouri* (BB-63) prior to attending Submarine School in 1947. The battleship was anchored in Rio de Janeiro to host a Conference of the Americas. Bevan was assigned a small alcove on the forecastle to spot arriving dignitaries arriving by boat and signaling the Signal Bridge of their approach. Eventually, President Harry Truman arrived with Bess and Margaret. The President was invited to attend ceremonies on the "Surrender Deck" (01 Level Starboard side). Harry was an independent sort and decided to wander around the bow a bit and ran into Bevan.

"Hi son, I'm Harry Truman. Pleased to meet you." Bevan was beyond words, saluted, then engaged the President in conversation. The week of the conference, Bevan was assigned the 04–08 Anchor Watch to plot the ship's anchored position. Truman wandered into the Chart Room and asked for some coffee, having smelled it from the Admiral's Quarters where he was residing. Quickly, Bevan served him a hot cup of coffee and the two then sat to discuss every manner of subjects. For the remainder of the week, the length of the conference, every morning, the President awakened at 0500 and strode into the Chart Room for coffee and a chat with Bevan; insisting Bevan call him Harry. A couple years later, Bevan was still aboard *Missouri* although most of the crew had turned over. The battleship anchored in New York Harbor for a similar event with the United Nations. The President came aboard, was rendered appropriate honors on the quarterdeck, then pushed aside the Captain and strode to the alcove on the forecastle. He bent over and,

"Hi, Bevan, nice to see you again."

"Hi, Harry, nice to see you again, too." Bevan's stock on *Missouri* skyrocketed.[43]

Bevan assisted in navigating the *Growler* into Roosevelt Roads, which was the first ship to pay a call (visit) to the new naval facility. On one of his previous boats, *Torsk*, his XO was Charlie Priest who brought Travis with him when he had orders as the CO of *Growler*. Bevan was one of many shipmates that obtained a commission later, while serving in *Nautilus*. The arrival in Puerto Rico proved sailors will be sailors but nothing tops the humor of a submariner. The commissioning crew was difficult to top for tricks. Pete Burkhart, the XO, decided it would be fun to bring a little of the north down to sunny Puerto Rico. When they arrived, at a given signal, the crew moved topside and snowballed everyone on the pier. Half the freezer had been full of Portsmouth snowballs for months.[44]

Not to be outdone by his Executive Officer, Captain Priest decided to find out just how fast the F-8U Crusader Chase aircraft flew. During one of the first training missile shots, Priest ordered the missile speed increased to full power just to see if the chase aircraft could keep up—they could but weren't very pleased by the move. Following the exercise, the Crusaders dove on the *Growler* on the way home, breaking the sound barrier directly overhead. It scared the living hell out of the crew.[45]

Growler arrived in Pearl on 7 September 1959 and departed on her first deterrent patrol on 12 March 1960. She was awarded the Battle Efficiency "E" prior to her departure. It would be the only Battle Efficiency "E" awarded *Growler*, for she would either be deployed, or in an urgent state of repairs, for the remainder of her operational life. Preparatory to departing on her first patrol, all hands that would be standing watches topside were issued two pair of Army surplus wool shirts, thermal knit underwear, nylon skivvies, and wool socks. It was apparent the boat would be heading north—way up north.[46]

Shortly before *Growler*'s departure, a strange event occurred near the submarine piers. The tall escape training tank, taller than 100 feet in height, blew a bottom porthole. In front of the tower was a small parking area for Commanding and Executive Officers. One car caught the stream of water that lasted all night. The water was similar to regular pool water, chlorinated for health reasons. The next morning, the car was observed initially void of all paint and looking like polished steel. A couple hours later, the entire car was covered in powdered rust. So much for preferred parking spaces.[47]

Every ship has shipyard, construction, and overhaul stories but *Grayback* has one unlike any heard before. Due to the major change and modifications of *Grayback*, she spent a long time in the shipyard at Mare Island. A key rule is never let a submariner get bored. At Mare Island, the crew took a liking to the chrome shop and soon everything available was chromed. The ultimate was chroming the boat's commodes that would come back in play six years later. Bob Owens stated:

"One could inspect one's hemorrhoids every time Mother Nature called."

When at Mare Island, *Grayback* was moored astern of *Sargo* when *Sargo* conducted sea trails after her reactor became critical. One day, she tested main engines without alerting surrounding vessels and broke *Grayback* from her moorings. Again, Bob Owens had the quip of the day,

"*Nautilus* was underway on Nuclear Power but *Grayback*'s underway on no power."

Growler was to get underway without power 45 years later in New York.

During her first commissioned Christmas, Captain Priest rented four cabins on the North Shore of Oahu near Waimaha Bay for three days and nights for all his single shipmates. The cooks on board set up each cabin with all the food, condiments, and drink they could consume. The young singles became adept at swimming, surfing, and watching a multitude of beautiful bikinis gracing the beaches.[48] The custom would continue.

A noteworthy technique was developed by Lieutenant Commander Joe Ekelund who was the boat's Executive Officer and Navigator. Utilizing the built in stadimeter of the periscopes, he could estimate ranges from observed mountains and other physical objects on land. Observing more than one object gave him a fixed position and by following the sequence a number of times, the iterations provided a relatively accurate ship's position. The technique was called "Ekelund Ranging."[49]

One of the first shipmates to qualify in submarines during the patrol was Victor Pantoja who had reported from the Tunny via Tripler Army Hospital. Pantoja had broken an ankle on a dive on Tunny in April and was assigned to work with SKC (SS) Jim Terry as a storekeeper striker. He enjoyed the job, both under Chief Terry and his successor SKC (SS) Howard. He was promoted to SK3 (SS) and went to the *Archerfish* in 1962; the all bachelor crew submarine that would soon be home to a couple more shipmates, ET1 (SS) Lin McCollum and ET1 (SS) John Bowman.

Grooming standards generally went to hell in a hand basket on patrol and there really were no barbers on the boat, although most stewards knew how to cut hair and took care of the officers. Sometimes, the Chief of the Boat just appointed someone to do the job or maybe one of the crew would volunteer. Normally, the "barber" was given a minimum pittance for his work with some of the pay going into the submarine's recreation fund. Not caring to have his hair molested on patrol, Moose Gunderman had his head cut bald before departing on patrol. While the rest of the crew's hair grew long, some grew straggly looking beards and long hair. Moose remained bald. There is no medical reason for this but it is sworn to be true.[50]

The late winter/early spring patrol was wrought with a number of unique problems specific to the patrol area. As the weather warmed, ice began to melt and ice flows broke loose. It was late on the 0400-0800 watch and the boat was just completing a snorkel battery charge. Lieutenant John McDonald was the Conning Officer, Jim Murphy was the Diving Officer, and CS1 (SS) Oscar Weigant was delivering hot pastries to the watch section. John called the XO on the sound powered telephones,

"XO, John, sir. I'm pretty sure I saw something off our port bow sir. We hold nothing on sonar and I can't find it again."

"I'll be right there John. Secure snorkeling!" The XO raised the #1 periscope and he and John searched for any sign of a contact. No ice had been noticed for over a day. Morning twilight was brightening and only wave tops were noted. Suddenly, *Growler* lurched to starboard and a loud crunching sound screeched throughout the boat. Ekelund felt a strong jerk through the periscope handles.

"Lower all periscopes and masts." Captain Priest was immediately in Control. The watch section immediately brought him up to date.

"Raise #1 scope, waist high," ordered the CO. The periscope slid upwards with a rubbing and scratching sound. The Captain looked through the lens and saw nothing but drops and a white circle. "Down scope. We have a damaged #1 periscope XO. Let's plane up to fifty feet for a look around in #2 scope."

"Make my depth five zero feet aye sir," sang out Jim Murphy. The idea was to bring the sail out of the water so if ice or wreckage were in the water, the periscope would not be vulnerable. "Five Zero feet Captain."

"Very well, up #2 scope." It was now near sunrise and he gazed over a field of scattered ice flows, none of them large enough to endanger *Growler*, but obviously one had been large enough to put #1 periscope out of commission. "XO, let's get out of this area today and head south." The Quartermaster's Notebook entry for the same minute read: "Came to periscope depth. Raised #1 periscope, ice ahead, no #1 periscope."[51]

The boat spent the daylight hours heading for warmer waters. *Growler* suffered no more serious equipment failures and was looking forward to being homeward bound when Gary Powers' U-2 spy plane was shot down over the USSR. Not knowing what world reaction they faced, *Growler* was extended on station for a few days until world events stabilized.

A favorite watering hole for the *Growler* crew was the Dolphin Club in downtown Honolulu. As per usual, the party got a little rough one night and the manager asked them to go drink somewhere else. Indeed they did just that as the HASP (Hawaiian Armed Services Police) arrived. They picked up all the furniture, even potted plants, and moved across the street.

A month or so after returning to Pearl Harbor, Lieutenant Commander Robert Crawford took command. A few days earlier, the day Crawford reported on board for duty, a near disaster took place just a few berths away. While charging her oxygen tanks, USS *Sargo* caught fire. EN1(SS) Carrol Miller grabbed a few shipmates and headed to assist *Sargo* fight a fire that was virtually inextinguishable. A pure oxygen fed fire requires no fuel. Enter Jim Murphy, trained in explosive disposal, who also rushed to *Sargo* to see if he could be of assistance. The raging fire was furiously hot and no one could get near the fire or the shut off valves. The Duty Officer reacted quickly and correctly. He opened the vents to the after ballast tanks and flooded *Sargo*'s stern, sending a cascade of seawater into the Stern Room and extinguishing the fire. *Sargo*, an acclaimed submarine for her historic submerged transit between the Atlantic and Pacific Oceans via the polar route just weeks prior, became a wreck dockside. Miller and crew returned to *Growler* with singed hair and a great sea story to tell.[52] Sadly, MM3(SS) James K. Smallwood, USN, of *Sargo* gave his life in the accident and was later honored for his action in the fire. *Sargo* was overhauled and returned to active and successful duty, and she was known for her unofficial slogan, "Twin screws are better than one." *Sargo* was one of about six submarines modified as forward Regulus Missile Guidance submarines. They would take position closer to the target permitting the launching submarine to remain at a maximum range of about 500 nautical miles. It was like a relay team with the guidance submarine picking up and guiding the missile in the final phase.[53]

Commander Chuck Priest was selected to enter Admiral Hyman Rickover's next group of potential nuclear submarine commanding officers so a change of command was planned and conducted in record time. Lieutenant Commander Robert Crawford was a 1945 U.S. Naval Academy graduate after attending Dartmouth College. He went to Submarine School after serving on the destroyers *Roe*, *Greene*, and *Thomas*. He served on the submarines *Capitaine*, *Carp*, *Catfish*, and *Carbonero*. He was a well experienced submariner and well acquainted with Regulus by the time he took command of *Growler*.[54]

The *Sargo* had been scheduled to give the King of Thailand a tour and at sea demonstration prior to the fire. Instead, *Growler* was to take the honors including an at sea Regulus Operation. The crew was dressed in their Full Dress and manned the rail for the affair. The boat and the crew never looked better but it didn't come easily. George Larson was one of the painting crew and painted the entire bow and starboard side with a foxtail and a five gallon bucket just to get the job done. The CO was presented with a model of the royal barge, *Bhumibol Barge*, as a token of thanks. Forty years later, Jim Murphy presented the piece to the Intrepid Sea, Air, and Space Museum for display on board the boat in the port hangar along with the original *Growler* plaque and the "nickel plaque."[55]

The second patrol was a winter patrol and the submarine was kicked about by the rough weather of the Bering Sea and North Pacific. A common announcement on the 1MC was: "Stand by for heavy rolls; batten down all unsecured equipment; secure all gear adrift." Both aluminum cowlings over the missile hangar doors were lost off the Kamchatka Peninsula, to join and be joined, by Regulus submarine retrograde. The daily routine that often reached boredom was suddenly interrupted when a MK 27-4 torpedo experienced a hydrogen gas explosion that armed the warhead. TM2 (SS) C. R. Tucker had been charging the batteries in the torpedo while TM2 (SS) George Larson and TM1 (SS) Dave Bishop were conducting fire control transmission checks between Control and the Torpedo Room. The explosion scattered warhead material inside the torpedo as Bishop was sitting atop the torpedo. The MK 27 torpedo was an electric torpedo initially used in World War II. TMC (SS) Chief Bob Seay and Jim Murphy managed to disarm the broken warhead. Jim Hefferman remained at the rear of the Torpedo

Room and relayed messages to and from Control. The boat had surfaced with the entire crew in life jackets while venting the air outboard in the Torpedo Room. The crew mustered in the After Battery Compartment while Phil Coyle and John MacDonald, the Engineer, converted the Fuel Ballast Tanks to act as Main Ballast Tanks and blow to sea. The warhead was passed up through the Forward Torpedo Room hatch to be gently lowered into the sea. Needless to say, the entire crew was on edge with a broken warhead on board. TM1(SS) John Rauch received the warhead atop the missile hangars and quickly pitched it into the ocean, anxious to rid the boat of the danger. A few of the torpedomen didn't believe the warhead had actually armed but no chances were taken. Bob Seay was promoted to Chief and Jim Murphy to Lieutenant. They were the first two crew members to be awarded decorations.[56]

Whether he enjoyed the attention or not, Jim Murphy was constantly preyed on by the crew and officers. One of Murphy's "Murphyisms" was to wear a beret bedecked with medals, of unknown origin, when he was on the Conn. If he was on the periscope, he wore a black patch over the eye not looking through the lens—we hope. TM2 (SS) Wally Horseman managed to run off with the beret one night and it wasn't returned until the end of the patrol. Horseman also placed the Gooney Bird on his chest at Midway Island.[57] A fellow Harvard graduate on the *Darter* was quoted as saying, "You can always tell a Harvard Man, but you can't tell him much."[58]

The Adak episode on this visit included EN1 (SS) Ron Rintz, EN1 (SS) Marty Saxton, and others who "borrowed" a laundry truck for some ungodly reason—likely to steal the totem pole. They stacked all the laundry neatly in stacks before taking off but it wasn't long before the Base Marines were in hot pursuit. Now, there are not many places to run to or hide on Adak, Alaska, but the crew escaped with Rintz, Bill Daack, and Saxton hiding in a Dumpster until the coast was clear. When they got back to Pearl, Bill Daack got married with the reception at EMC (SS) Luther Samuel's house and John J. Galvin as his best man. That's almost like jumping from one dumpster into another.[59] Saxton went on to become ENCM and COB of a Polaris submarine.

When *Growler* returned to Pearl Harbor, a short and stubby Lieutenant was waiting for them. Lieutenant Robert Owens was reporting aboard as the prospective executive officer. He brought with him experience on World War II war patrols as an electrician on the U.S.S. Tinosa (SS-283) and a vast knowledge of missiles, especially Regulus.[60]

Growler's second patrol began on 10 November 1960. She performed admirably and returned on 18 January 1961 to Pearl with her superstructure fouled with fishing nets. The replenishment stop in Adak set a precedent of mischief that followed for many more patrols. In this case, it was the theft of a stuffed animal but the mischief soon centered about the symbol of Adak, a totem pole. *Growler* returned to Pearl on 12 May 1961 from Patrol #3 under the command of Commander Crawford. This time, Lieutenant Commander Donald Henderson awaited the return as the Prospective Commanding Officer. There was a change of command and then *Growler* went into drydock and overhaul at the Pearl Harbor Naval Shipyard with the primary purpose being to raise her sail ten feet and all the masts and periscopes.

Raising the height of the sail on *Growler* lessened the adverse results of the venturi effect between the top of the hangars and the seas by ten feet. The aluminum and wood decking topside was replaced with steel. She completed her repair and modification yard period in December 1961 and was on her way to patrol #4 on 11 February 1962.

Another important modification accomplished was simplifying the launcher by eliminating the ability to train the missile. The missiles would be launched straight ahead over the bow, reducing some flexibility but eliminating a labyrinth of valves and switches that had become a maintenance nightmare. With the Regulus II Missile no longer an option, the launcher was no longer required to pivot to accommodate the much longer missile.[61]

On Thanksgiving Day, QM1(SS) Don Curbow reported for duty, just in time to depart on Patrol #4. Facing another winter on station, *Growler* experienced a number of equipment failures, the worst of which was the main bearing on the #1 main engine/generator shaft. Don Curbow recalls with great respect the work accomplished by the enginemen, who overhauled an engine on station in less than 72 hours. He also recalls the Soviets reporting the *Growler* sunk, likely overheard by one of the spooks on board. The report may or may not have been synonymous with an attempted attack on Growler. She completed her patrol and traveled to Yokosuka, Japan on 24 April 1962 for a rest and repair period before departing on the second half of her back-to-back patrols. The crew remembers the royal welcome given them by the White Hat Club. The Japanese yard workers in Yokosuka ingeniously cast a new bearing and turned the bearing in place by rotating the shaft with air starting power.[62]

When *Grayback* arrived in Yokosuka for a refit period between her second and third patrols, the boat received a form letter from Commander, now Admiral, Jim Osborn who was the Commanding Officer of the U.S.S. George Washington (SSBN-598). It had been mailed at sea on the historic occasion of *Washington*'s first deterrent missile patrol. (He may have used a sea buoy) Lieutenant Commanders Pete Burkhart and Bill Gunn composed a letter back to the Washington that read:

"Dear Oz, We received your letter after returning to port from *Grayback*'s second patrol, and we had been relieved by another SSG who was maintaining continuous missile coverage of our targets, until *Grayback* returned to the SSG patrol area on her third patrol. We will relieve the boat on station and then be relieved after 60 days on station, and return to Pearl Harbor after about 99 days at sea, and a total deployment of about six months. We will be returning to station about 75 days later. And, we only have one crew which makes all the patrols. Kindly refer to NAVORD SWOP 27-1 and 27-4. Please feel free to call on us if you ever need real fire power."[63]

They never received an answer to the letter sent in jest to "Oz" who had been in the missile business for many years and was the first commanding officer of *Tunny* as a SSG.

Bill Gunn was Weapons Officer on *Halibut* prior to being ordered to *Growler*, and one of the few, if not the only, non-nuclear propulsion trained officers. His fun loving antics included: when he stood Conning Officer Watch and wanted more speed, he used to bang on the pipes. If there was a question about his banging, his reply on the 21MC always was, "More steam from the janitors!"[64]

◆   ◆   ◆

Submariners began their careers at the Naval Submarine School in Groton, Connecticut although commonly referred to as New London, Connecticut. Both officers and enlisted attend the school preparatory to assignment to a submarine. Rear Admiral Eugene B. Fluckey, of World War II fame and a Medal of Honor awardee, was instrumental in permitting Naval Academy Midshipmen to be assigned to submarines for their senior year cruises and Bob was in the group the first year submarines were utilized. The U.S.S. *Becuna* (SS-319), officers and crew, was a perfect training platform for future submariners. The attention, love, and care demonstrated by *Becuna*'s crew was a premonition to Bob and all students and crew who rode her of life aboard a submarine and instrumental in Bob's entering the Submarine Service; a feeling and devotion never lost to this day.

Submarine School provided the student with "hands on" experience that was vital when the "student" reported on board his first boat. The newly arrived "non-qual" on a submarine was a liability to the boat until he learned and earned his dolphins, officer or enlisted. Near the end of the school, officers selected "their" submarine, and Bob picked *Growler*. He knew she was a missile submarine and her unclassified operating schedule indicated local operations for the remainder of 1962. Having deployed to WestPac twice in two years, local operations seemed a godsend.

His family's arrival and reception in Honolulu by the wardroom wives and Division Commander was warm and indicative of the community he was entering. What was not welcome was the order to report in three days for a flight to Yokosuka to meet *Growler*. Deterrent Strategic Missile submarine operations were top secret and "local operations" covered their covert operating schedule. The *Growler* wives had done well, including reservations in a motel on Waikiki and all the paperwork completed for Navy housing.

◆　　　　　◆　　　　　◆

Growler was a beautiful boat below decks and more advanced than the first nuclear boats, *Nautilus* and *Seawolf*. Bob followed Don through the control room, still referred to as the control room on *Growler*, but as the attack center on many of the newer submarines without a conning tower. (The compartment between the bridge and control room on earlier submarines) A maze of colored indicator lights adorned switches, indicating the condition of valve openings, open or shut, engaged or off. A conning stand replaced the old conning tower, where the periscopes were viewed and a labyrinth of indicators and information repeaters were displayed. It was the heart and guts of the boat, where most decisions were made and reports concluded. It stood a foot and a half above the control room deck and was referred to as the "Conn."

Don led Bob through the watertight (WT) door into the forward battery compartment, which held the forward battery below the deck, chief's quarters, the ship's office, the wardroom and staterooms for officers, a small galley and even smaller shower for officers. The wardroom was the dining room, working space, submarine torpedo and missile plotting room and general living space for officers.

It was an adequate space for a few men but seated eight officers for meals and an equal number of men at Battle Stations. The Chief's Quarters consisted of four rows of bunks three high, plus a small table normally used for acey duecy and poker games. It was commonly and respectfully referred to as the "goat locker."

"Damn Don, this is the biggest boat I've been aboard except for *Triton* and she was still building."

"I'll be honest with you Bob, *Growler* is big but she shrinks a lot after a few months on patrol. She's a good boat and if you don't mind discomfort and hard work, you'll enjoy her. If that bothers you, you're facing a horror story." They walked into the wardroom and Don introduced him to the Executive Officer, Bob Owens. Lieutenant Commander Owens was a large man with a huge white beard and enormous grin.

"Welcome aboard, Bob."

"Thank you sir, I'm pleased to be aboard!"

"Hey, I'm Bob to you. Don't worry, no one will confuse us," as another large grin creased his face. "Sit down, Bob and have a cup of java with us." Owens had been an electricians mate and made seven war patrols on the USS *Tinosa*

(SS-283) during World War II. Following the war, he went to college, earned a B.S. Degree in Geology, and was commissioned an officer. He was involved with the Loon and Regulus Missile Programs from their inception. "XO Bob" was a walking, breathing encyclopedia of information on submarines and Regulus. Bob enjoyed his coffee and met most of the officers as they cycled in and out of the wardroom, conducting business.

The Chief of the Boat (COB) was Chief Stebbins who would later assist in the "recommissioning" of *Growler* at the *Intrepid* Sea, Air, and Space Museum. He had relieved Chief Jim Strahorn, the commissioning COB. Stebbins in turn was relieved by Chief Torpedoman's Mate Mike Powell, who learned of his advancement to chief enroute Adak on Patrol #2. COB Powell was the épitomé of a chief petty officer. He was built like, and as strong as, an ox, yet was soft spoken and fatherly to the young shipmates. However, if overcome with ire, he could be most impressive and terrorizing with his commanding voice and salty talk.

Bob was assigned to the middle stateroom of three and inherited the top bunk, along with a couple of drawers and a 10" wide locker for hanging clothes. His bunk permitted him about a foot of headroom below the hull and he found out he needed virtually none of the uniforms he carried halfway around the world. Don advised him to go to the exchange and buy "Levis," skivvies, and sweatshirts to carry him through the upcoming patrol. *Growler* was big, but without a laundry or washing machine. Bob was about to adjust to an entirely new lifestyle and standard of grooming.

After settling into his stateroom, Don asked him to meet his new commanding officer. Lieutenant Commander Don Henderson was also a Naval Academy graduate and spent his entire career in submarines except his first ship. Until 1960, officers were selected for submarine duty only after qualifying at sea on a surface combatant as an Officer of the Deck underway, a requisite subject to many discussions but certainly a benefit for the Submarine Force. Submarine officers were already conversant with surface warfare tactics and thinking. Captain Henderson was an impressive individual with pearly white teeth to accent his grin, an athletic build, and an unmistakable speech leaving little question to the listener as to what was desired. A handsome young man, he was a commanding figure who spoke in concise and precise sentences. There was no doubt he was in command.

Bob enjoyed lunch with the officers, then was given a tour of the *Growler* by Don Breeding. Don had been a Missile Technician and achieved a commission as a Limited Duty Officer so he really knew the Regulus Missile System. The *Growler* was a "bastard" boat, in that she was like no other submarine in the world, but similar to the *Grayback* in appearance. Both submarines had been under construction as fast attacks when the requirement for missile submarines took priority.

Both boats were converted to accept the Regulus I & II Missiles. The priority of construction was so high that valves and piping systems designated for nuclear fast attacks boats were robbed from the *Sargo* and *Skate*, building at adjacent berths. The final product worked out well, but she was a submarine with a multitude of bastard systems of varying valve types and operating sources.

Don gave Bob a tour through the boat, including the missile hangars. They were enormous, and the missiles appeared ominous. To avoid troubling the local Japanese populace, the hangars were advertised as containing only exercise missiles. *Barbero* had been more innovative earlier, explaining the hangar abaft the sail as a laundry for washing clothes. She was said to sail throughout the U.S. Seventh Fleet operating areas doing laundry for submarines and other vessels without clothes washing facilities; silly but effective.[65]

Following his tour, the XO assigned Bob to work directly for him on specific shipyard tasks, since he was familiar with the Yokosuka shipyard. The primary task was the replacement of a wiped main bearing, but a large number of other equipment needed repair or replacement. Japanese ingenuity built a lathe in place to resurface the shaft bearing and the bearing was rebuilt and a spare constructed by the shipyard while the other problems were resolved with equal competence.

Submariners, like SEALS and Top Guns, enjoy fun on the beach or liberty as much as they thoroughly expend effort on the job. Likely to be rated the top "funnyman," and fun person among a crew of jokers was the *Growler*'s navigator, Bill Gunn.

Lieutenant Commander William Gunn graduated from the Maine Maritime Academy, was commissioned, then graduated from Submarine School in 1954. He was assigned duty in U.S.S. *Sterlet* (SS-392) where he qualified in 1955. A year later, he met the U.S.S. *Pickerel* (SS-524) in Yokosuka, where he qualified for "Command of Submarines." He then spent a few years involved with Special Weapons and duty with GMU-10 and GMU-90. He returned to sea on the U.S.S. *Halibut* (SSGN-589) as Missile Officer, followed by duty on *Growler* as Navigator/ Operations Officer. He was a brilliant officer with an encyclopedic mind for naval history and absolutely thrived on jokes and laughing. A better shipmate no one could ask for.

The boat had no ship's flag so Bill Gunn, with design assistance from others, designed a ship's flag and a new patch with approval of ComSubRon One. He also designed a cap to be worn by officers and chiefs alike. It was a replica of the Japanese Defense Force insignia, except a red star was added in the middle of the insignia. The ship's flag was indoctrinated at the Yokosuka Naval Officers' Club one night, with a full house and floor show in progress. The flag became a table-cloth and was saluted by the officers during the floor show. The wardroom was admonished and discharged from the club by a very unhappy ComSeventhFlt in uniform next to the officers' table. Fortunately, Captain Henderson and his wife, Billie, had sufficient sense to depart the table before things got out of hand. Billie had flown out to visit during the four weeks the boat spent in Yokosuka. During the exodus, Bill literally ran into a Marine Colonel who took exception to being knocked down. The colonel pulled his false teeth from his mouth and placed them in his pocket as he faced Bill, ready to do battle.

Surveying the situation, Bill wasn't sure whether to kick him in the pocket or his empty mouth. They walked into the nearest head, everyone expecting to hear a horrific battle. But it remained quiet and a few minutes later, Bill walked out of the swinging doors of the head with all the Marine's medals and ribbons in his hands. The entire maneuver by Bill relieved the situation and the Submariners returned to *Growler* unharmed.

One of Bill Gunn's favorite stories took place in Yokosuka at one of the local watering holes. He was chatting with some of the local clientele when he was asked by a Japanese lady what other submarines he had served on. He replied he had previously served on the *Pickerel*.

"You mean like a small cucumber?" Bill had been on the *Pickerel* for the infamous battle surfaces, usually with a 30° up bubble. The crew in the forward torpedo room would trot back to control to see what the problem was only to find out the officers were deliberately surfacing at large angles. One time they lost control of the angle on the surface and arrived with a 72° up angle that threatened the boat sliding backwards into the sea. The *Queenfish* was nearby and filmed the surface, then sent a message to *Pickerel*: "Congratulations. What is the specific gravity of the after torpedo room bilge?"[66] (It inferred the angle was so steep the electrolyte would have run out of the batteries to the stern of the boat)

During sea trials on *Halibut*, she made her first dive and took a 57° down angle due to some pretty serious miscalculations by the shipyard on the "Rig for Dive" Bill. The huge hangar was built with a 15° down angle, which meant the personnel in the hangar/torpedo room actually were in a 72° down angle. The men were standing on the torpedo tube breech doors, which were closer to horizontal than the decks. The *Halibut* blew and backed out of the dive. When they returned to Mare island, engineers from David Taylor Model Basin informed the boat that engineering wise, the boat should not have been able to pull out of a dive angle greater than 45°.[67]

Grayback had the original boat's battle flag, which was flown each time she returned from patrol. The flag was to be flown if and when she had to go into battle and launch her missiles in anger.

Grayback had her share of characters, among them was Gilly Willy. His adventures ashore date back to World War II, and he made fourteen WestPac (Western

Pacific) trips before reporting aboard. Willy was a great shipmate and submariner but when the boat was in port, so was he. He relentlessly submitted a leave chit for the entire in port period and everyone knew he would not be seen until moments before the boat was ready to go to sea. He loved to stir up the pot; he must have had some of the same genes as Ron Rintz on *Growler*. In an Acey Duecy Club one night, he joined a chief with a young mother and her pre-school son. Willy tried to engage the lady in conversation but in vain. Finally, he told her in not a subtle way, the chief she was with was not interested in her but rather her little boy. The chief received a smack in the face and a kick to the shin—and the fight was on.[68]

Billie Henderson expressed a fearful story that had taken place in Pearl Harbor. *Growler* was enroute station for Patrol #4 via Midway Island when a lube oil line parted, causing a large fire in the Engine Room. Don Bosetti and Don Goldsberry quickly extinguished the fire, but the generator/engine set experienced a failed bearing and journal that could not be repaired underway or at Midway. Surprisingly, ComSubPac permitted the boat to continue on patrol with only two engines. The hot rods proved their unreliability, and severe and numerous problems plagued the patrol to the point where the CO radioed the Admiral to inform him of the problems. *Growler* was quickly ordered to Japan for shipyard repairs, thus departing station early. *Grayback's* crew was recalled from liberty and departed for station to relieve *Growler*. The *Growler* wives immediately heard the sudden recall of *Grayback's* crew and knew something was wrong on *Growler*. Rumors flew and grew, and soon the wives were in a state of panic about their husbands. Even the Base Chaplain tried to comfort them but that just reinforced the wive's worries. They were finally placated when the CO called Billie to say that they were safe and sound in Yokosuka, but Billie went out to see for herself.[69]

The *Growler* crew also upheld the reputation of the fun-loving wardroom. Led by Ron Rintz, the crew took on a Royal Navy destroyer crew in a bar outside the Naval Base. Unhappy with some of the destroyermen's remarks, Rintz roared, "the Queen sucks." Jim Bender was punched out by an Engineman named "Ty Ty." Ty Ty broke his hand on Jim's hard head.[70] They waged war to a successful conclusion that culminated in another free ride home courtesy of the Shore Patrol.

Meanwhile, back in Pearl Harbor, the officers of the *Grayback* matched the scene at the O' Club in Pearl Harbor. Preparatory to deployment the following morning, the officers and their wives enjoyed one last night of fun. For some reason, the party was held at the main officers' club vice at the submarine base and resulted in the *Grayback* being discharged from the club. The officers departed singing the praises of *Growler* as they departed. For the following years, both boats managed to avoid serious trouble by using the other boat's name.

Still in Yokosuka, the *Growler*'s wardroom enjoyed a night out at the Kanko Hotel with classic Japanese music and plays. Most of the junior officers enjoyed the "hotsi" baths and soothing massage in the basement of the hotel. Jim Murphy was with the officers in a stainless steel steam bath. One of the officers shoved a broomstick through the handles on the front of the steam bath and turned the heat to maximum. Red as a well cooked lobster and gasping for air, Murf broke out of the heat trap and chased the rest of the officers throughout the hotel, including across the main stage, with nary a thread of clothing on his body. As he chased his fellow officers, they ran back, one at a time, to the bath and took his clothes. The next morning, Murf, a very large officer, returned to *Growler*, clad only in a very tiny kimono in a Shore Patrol car. No one knew the entire story but the XO was heard to roar with laughter as the tale was told. He was truly fortunate—he missed the anti-nuclear protests taking place in Yokosuka and outside the main gate.[71]

Submarine officers established their own home away from home at the Naval Base, Yokosuka called the "Sanctuary." Atop the communications building, was a small wooden structure with a security-locked front door. One had to enter the *Grayback*'s hull number (574) to enter. It contained a galley, mess room, game room, a bar, three bunkrooms and a large head with showers. It was an excellent respite for submariners while off the boat. A nominal fee was paid for each meal and each officer restocked the bar when he departed the area for whatever he had consumed. Later, a similar facility was constructed at the Naval Base, Subic Bay in the Philippines, courtesy of the *Grayback* homeported there in its new role as a LPSS.

Bob found out from his former two ships, when reporting on board a new ship, it was most helpful to make friends with a few important crew members. One was the Storekeeper, SKC(SS) Jim Terry, but his first acquaintance that turned into friendship was *Growler*'s cook CS1(SS) Duane Heatwole. Not only was he a terrific cook, as most submarine cooks, he was a baker by trade and baked the most outstanding pastries ever made. Two of his best liberty friends were crew members we've already met, John Anderson and Ron Rintz. One night at the Dolphin Club, a submariners only bar in a back alley of Yokosuka, the three of them were at a table being entertained by a few local Japanese ladies. None of the men nor ladies were feeling much pain and laughter was the emotion of the moment. Duane stuck his hand down inside his pants and slipped a finger between a couple of the thirteen buttons. "Hot Doggie," exclaimed one of the girls, thus a new nickname was registered for the cook. "Hotdog" became his handle that would follow him for the rest of his life. The exception was when he was elected mayor of Page, Arizona.[72]

A week or so later, Bob was the duty officer—his first night on duty by himself. The watch was informed the U.S.S. *Oriskany* (CVA-34), an aircraft carrier, was scheduled to enter port later that evening. *Growler* was berthed at a nearby floating pier. An elderly Japanese yardworker who had worked in the shipyard since World War II walked up to Bob and, "*Konichiwa* (how are you) *konabaa gunkan ukie* (carrier come in tonight), *ne?*"

"*Konichiwa. Honto desu* (that is true)" answered Bob.

"*Anatomooto takusan.* Put more rope to submarine."

"*Doshite?*" (why) "*Funega mitsu oshu* (ship push much water), *ne?*" Bob responded, "carrier push much water and rip *Growler* from berth?"

"*Wakararimashita ka?*" (You understand) Bob bowed and thanked him for his advice. The elderly worker walked back down the pier and Bob ordered all lines tripled. That night, *Oriskany* entered port and *Growler*'s lines strained to the limit—but held. Bob was forever grateful to the old man and his advice. The actual conversation was considerably more difficult than described with many hand signs and head nods. Bob was anything but a Japanese linguist.

One morning, everyone's attention was caught by a tug and barge entering Yokosuka and berthing astern of *Growler*. The barge carried loads of "junk" with a definite smell of burned material wafting down the pier. The barge was met by a large group of officers and Shore Patrol who cordoned off the pier just aft of the submarine and no one was allowed beyond the line. Inquisitive submariners found out a merchant ship, carrying material for the Navy Exchange System, experienced a fire in one hold and the retrograde was going to be destroyed for insurance purposes. The crew sat topside watching with fascination as pallets of "stuff" were lifted onto the pier, crushed, and dumped into large Dumpsters. When a large steamroller came down the pier and began rolling over watches, some of them Rolexes, the crew could stand no more. The urge of thieves and cumshaw raced through their veins and soon it became a contest of whether the crew could grab more "stuff" than the exchange personnel could destroy. By the time the rape of the barge began, most of the expensive junk had been destroyed. However, this did nothing to dampen the enthusiasm of the crew as *Growler* was loaded to the waterline with chocolate, candy of all sorts, and a treasure of toiletry items. The crew would gain many pounds in the days ahead and sprout pimples for weeks; but they smelled better.

A sad note was the departure of QM1(SS) Shields who signed up for the U.S. Army Warrant Officer Program that accepted E-6 ratings and commissioned them as Warrant Officers. Shields received his commission and was ordered to a swift boat squadron on the Mekong River. He was likely killed by the Viet Cong in Vietnam. He never returned.

Another shipmate to receive a commission was SKC(SS) Jim Terry who was the first crew member to qualify/requalify on board *Growler*. A submariner had to requalify on each submarine assigned. Terry set up the spare parts system so brilliantly that the system lasted for the entire life of the boat. He was commissioned an Ensign by Captain Henderson. He was a key person to know if anything was needed, part or supply, and gives credit to Lieutenant Ken Cox for encouraging him to apply for a commission.[73]

The upcoming patrol was the second patrol of back-to-back patrols. The previous patrol had taken the crew away from their families and home for the holidays. Duane "Hotdog" Heatwole told Bob about the Christmas treat they had served the crew. The meal followed a special message from Captain Don Henderson:

> "SEASON'S GREETINGS! To you, the *Growler* crew. I wish to take this opportunity to extend my very best wishes. Deployed as we are on a war deterrent missile strike station, makes one easily forget this holiday season; and yet it also serves to drive home to each of us the reason for *Growler* being here. Each of us has loved ones that we sincerely hope will see many more peaceful and joyous Christmas seasons. Each of you is well aware of *Growler's* tremendous capability. You may rest assured that our presence here, although not realized by most Americans, is making a very significant contribution to preventing war." /s/ D. Henderson, Lieutenant Commander, Commanding Officer.[74]

Then came a banquet difficult to top, including shrimp cocktail, saltine crackers, stuffed celery stalks, assorted mixed pickles, assorted mixed olives, roasted tom turkey, snowflake potatoes, giblet gravy, sage dressing, cranberry sauce, Virginia baked ham, candied sweet potatoes, raisin sauce, buttered green peas, hot Parker House rolls, Waldorf salad, hot mincemeat pie, fruit cake, ice cream sundaes, fresh milk, hot coffee, mixed nuts, hard candy, cigars and cigarettes. The "fresh milk" was a bit of an exaggeration. It was powdered or reconstituted milk.

◆   ◆   ◆

One of Bob Owens' favorite tales took place a couple patrols earlier. Bob Owens settled in on board Growler temporarily as the Assistant Missile Officer but his real assignment was to prepare to become the Executive Officer. In mid-March 1961, *Growler* departed on her third patrol and the transit to Adak was uneventful. The Adak personnel eyed the boat warily but noted she was clean and shiny so was outbound. Shenanigans would be unlikely. The usual replenishment was quickly completed and *Growler* was bound westward toward station. They remained north of the Aleutian Islands in the lee of most of the bad weather but ran into severe fog. Bob and Bill Gunn were on the bridge at first light to obtain a star fix but were unable to get a position due to a thick and low hanging bank of fog.

"Bridge, ECM. Very loud radar contact dead ahead! It's as high as it gets, sir, way above signal strength five."

"Sonar, Bridge, do you have any contacts ahead of us?"

"Nothing, sir, but we are making way too much noise to hear much." Before anyone could react, Bob and Bill both looked up to starboard and saw a huge radar mast and antenna coming toward them but drawing right rapidly. They both ducked subconsciously to avoid being seen as a huge Soviet vessel passed down the starboard side at a range of less than fifty yards, completely unaware of the *Growler*'s presence.

"Bob, you can stay up here but my shorts are about as thick as this fog. I'm going to take a shit," he barked as he headed down the hatch in typical Gunn fashion.[75]

◆   ◆   ◆

A few mornings later, 24 May 1962, it was *Growler*'s turn to depart Yokosuka. It was an exciting morning for Bob as he climbed up to the bridge. As with most new officers, he was permitted to stay on the bridge to observe the boat get underway. He drew in a deep breath, "I'm here and we're getting underway for a patrol. This really isn't a dream!"

"Single up all lines," barked Don. It took a little longer after tripling the lines a few nights earlier. Minutes later, *Growler* was underway with a tug pulling her off the berth. With her bow headed seaward, she fell into a long line of ships moving from Tokyo and Yokohama to sea. The fog was thick and between all the ships and small islands, navigating was difficult. Bob volunteered to assist the Navigator, Bill Gunn, and run a radar plot since he had been in and out of Yokosuka many times on destroyers and was familiar with the area. This helped a little bit until the watch on the bow began yelling and pointing directly ahead. Ensign George Playdon reported a sand bar dead ahead. Sounding three blasts on the ship's whistle indicating she was backing and then five more to warn the vessels behind, *Growler* shuddered under an "All Back Emergency" bell. Knuckles turned white on the bridge as the boat passed over a large area of floating kelp with a huge merchant ship quickly closing from astern. She came down the port side, only fifty feet away and the fog was so thick, the bridge of the behemoth could not be seen. A few somewhat unkind words descended on the heads of the bow lookout and *Growler* resumed forward motion. Despite the thick fog and heavy shipping, *Growler* cleared Sagami Wan Strait and found the welcome open sea. The boat changed to course East to clear the Japanese home islands until sunset. A few moments later, Captain Henderson ordered the boat submerged and *Growler* left the busy world on the ocean surface and entered the quiet world below.

The boat was trimmed, systems and equipment checked out. The remainder of the day was spent getting acclimated to being at sea again and stowing the ship for sea. The first evening, the captain held a meeting for all officers. He described the patrol area and explained the patrol mission and what was expected of each officer. He turned and said,

"Bob, you are the new guy on the block and right now you are a liability to this crew and boat. It is your individual responsibility to become a member of the team and pull your own weight as soon as possible. You're a Naval Academy graduate and I know you have what it takes to be a good Submariner. Never hesitate to ask questions and you'll likely find some of the best answers from the enlisted members of the crew. You are going to start standing watches as Diving Officer under instruction. You'll be standing watch under a chief or another junior officer. They taught you at Canoe U the Chief Petty Officers are the backbone of the Navy. In the Submarine Force, that is a gross understatement. If you have any questions regarding your duties, ask the XO. Remember that number one is to become a member of this crew and number two to get qualified. Neither is easy. Good luck."

He was given the night off so he hit the sack early.

Chapter Two
Transit to Patrol Station

Bob barely stirred as the boat commenced snorkeling and awakened as the boat surfaced. The captain used the cloak of darkness to run on the surface and make good speed while he could. The sound of the sea rushing by his ear only a few inches away quickly settled him back into a deep sleep. His sleep was abruptly interrupted later by two blasts on the diving klaxon followed by "Dive, dive." It was 0600 so he decided to get up and get ready for a busy day. He slowly slid out of his warm bunk, he stretched and yawned.

"Hey, get off your ass mister, we're diving," shouted Wayne as he ran by the opening to the stateroom. Bob wondered why he yelled only to be yelled at again as Wayne headed aft on the run. Bob was certainly missing something. The boat submerged and the officers returned to the wardroom for coffee.

"Mister!" ordered a very unhappy XO as he glared at Bob. "What the hell do you suppose has to be done in the Forward Battery when we dive?" Bob stuttered a reply,

"Bulkhead flappers have to be shut, Watertight Doors shut… ah."

"That's correct and what did you do?"

"Ahhhh, nothing, sir."

"Everything on this submarine is everyone's responsibility, do you read me?"

"Yes, sir."

"I'm Bob, not sir!"

"Aye, aye, sirrr… errr, aye, aye." Then the XO explained any ship's evolution involved all hands. He then expressed in no uncertain terms it was time Bob get started learning the Rig for Dive Bills for each compartment.

"Aye, aye, sir!" Bob replied and all the officers had a good laugh

Growler cleared the shipping lanes the next day and training took place in earnest for Bob and other new crew members. Bob was tutored by the XO and the COB on the art of diving and trimming the boat. Soon, he no longer climbed down the hatch and ladder but flew through the air with hatch lanyard in hand and slid down the rails of the ladder. The trunk had been freshly painted by QM3 (SS) Dave Caswell and still reeked of light green paint. Bob marred the paint at one point as he flew down the trunk, hands on the rails—until his hands hit the only ladder support, about half way down. His hands flew loose and his back banged on the freshly painted trunk as his body fell to the grating on the main deck below.[1] His personal sweat joined the salt in the water as they drilled and drilled again until there were no inhibitions. The steward brought sandwiches as the practice continued. Following eight straight hours of training, the regular watch assumed the duties and Bob slowly dragged his tired buns back to the wardroom. His roommate, Don, was reading the message board when he sat down and stated,

"Its sure going to feel good to get a hot shower."

Don's head jerked at the word "shower" and he asked, "What's this about a shower Bob."

"I just said a hot shower will feel good."

"Hell, Bob, you'll be lucky if you get a shower at all during our patrol. The distillers barely keep up with the water demand for the engines. Bob looked down at his sweat-stained khakis and cringed. It was going to be a long patrol.

The captain ordered classified material placed on the conning stand for the officers to read. It consisted mostly of the Operations Order and Intelligence reports. Each officer had to know every type and number of Soviet vessel to expect, including naval and merchant vessels. There were aircraft, radar stations, harbors, islands, and the ocean bottom to memorize, as well as friendly forces they might encounter. The submariner's day was truly busy as the boat slowly moved to her classified patrol area.

The location and capabilities of American submarines have long been classified, going back to World War II. A visiting congressman asked an admiral why the U.S. was sinking so many Japanese submarines but the enemy was rarely successful in sinking American submarines. The admiral candidly explained American submarines dove deeper than Japanese submarines and their surface units set their depth charges too shallow to reach American boats. When the congressman returned to Washington, he couldn't wait to tell the story. Seven American submarines were sunk in the following month. Silence has been the key since then. The Submarine Force nickname, "Silent Service," was not coined because the boats ran quietly.

The crew was split into watch sections and Bob had the fortune of having EN1 (SS) Ron Rintz in his section as the Auxiliaryman of the Watch (AOW). The AOW handled the water and air manifolds, as well as numerous auxiliary equipments. Rintz was the Qualification Petty Officer for all piping systems in the boat, so he was a great resource for Bob. They hit it off well and so began a friendship and qualification competition between them that would last for the next four patrols. Ron's counterpart on the *Grayback* was MM1(SS) Valpoon, who was so dedicated to the boat he refused to leave the submarine after a patrol until all his equipment was working satisfactorily. When he did go ashore, he usually received a free ride home courtesy of the shore patrol.

The transit and patrol routine placed everyone on watch except the CO, XO, and navigator, so everyone went on watch for four hours and had eight hours off every day before going back on watch. When submerged, it made little difference whether it was day or night except Control was rigged for red lighting during hours of darkness; that helped one's ability to see in the dark. Everyone had his own routine to stand watch, accomplish his work, and to rest. In the wardroom, a nightly routine after evening meal was to play cards preparatory for the evening's movie. They played two card games, Hearts with two decks of cards plus three black queens of spades and "Oh Shit" or "Oh Shah. " Both games prompted raucous laughter from the cigar-smoking officers. No records were kept and the games were in fun, which provided a great way to relieve the strain of the patrol.

Captain Henderson utilized every opportunity to drill and train. From ECM contact reports while on the surface, to torpedo approaches, he honed the crew's skills to a fine edge. Each crew member reacted constructively and positively to every problem presented and almost automatically. There is no room for hesitation on a submarine in a casualty or shoot situation. Reaction did not replace thinking, but so many scenarios were exercised that almost every variable had already been practiced. The CO also enjoyed tactics and often prompted his officers into discussing tactical problems and solutions. He was famous for manipulating a junior officer's question into a solution. However, training was of paramount importance to all commanding officers, with repetitious exercises gaining instantaneous responses.

An excellent example played out on *Grayback* during local operations. She was on the surface for a lunch break with a missile hangar door open. The boat was to submerge at 1300 to resume exercises. Shortly before 1300, the Officer of the Deck (OOD) ordered the hangar door shut and at precisely 1300, he ordered the boat dived. Eight officers sprang from their seats in the wardroom and dashed to the control room to stop the dive. The officers had not heard a report from the Missile Center to the Attack Center that the hangar door was shut and locked![2]

Following about a week transit, *Growler* arrived on station. The boat slowed speed to minimum turns, secured snorkeling, and went to a depth conducive to good listening conditions. This was one of the last patrols conducted by the Regulus boats without a floating wire. However, *Growler* did have an experimental floating wire installed on a trial basis for the patrol. Since continuous communications were required for instructions and, God forbid, the order to launch, radio guarded the radio nets via a stub antenna on the #2 or Type 8B periscope. It required remaining at periscope depth constantly and a vigilant watch by the officers on the periscope. For hours, the Conning Officer rotated the periscope, warily looking for any contact or danger. No announcement was made but the boat became hushed and a sense of seriousness prevailed throughout the boat.

Chapter Three
Patrolling in the Soviets' Back Yard

For the seasoned crew members, it was a time to refresh the memory and look for changes that may have occurred since the last time *Growler* was on station, less than two months prior. Soviet activity varied from season to season, as in American fleets. Nicknames or acronyms were assigned to everything from seamounts to Soviet weapons. For the new crew members, it was a cram session of learning about a new place and the real enemy. Most of the new crew members were not "qualified in submarines," and none were qualified in *Growler*. They desperately learned the operational and emergency bills. Men "Qualified in Submarines" must re-qualify on each new boat assigned.

Bob's watches began with a question from one of his fellow watch standers, "What'cha working on today, Mr. H?"

His reply became the subject of conversation and the topic for the next four-hour watch. Questions on the subject flew about the watch section and often ended in heated arguments resolved only by personal inspections after the watch to confirm a correct answer. The watch section was a great teaching aid for Bob and the watch standers often reminded him of many details often overlooked or forgotten.

A whip antenna was raised periodically by Bill Gunn to obtain a navigation fix by Loran-C. The positions were difficult to determine, as the boat was on the extreme outer limit of Loran-C coverage. Navigation was often a seat of the pants operation, utilizing sounds from islands and ports, visual observations, and radio/radar direction finding by the electronics countermeasures equipment (ECM). Often times, the submarine, having received a launch order, would have had to obtain a radar fix prior to launch. The emission would have been immediately detected by the Soviets thus relegating the mission to a kamikaze effort.

Once on station, the crew became hushed and silent although no word was ordered for silence about the decks. Life took on seriousness and a bit of apprehension prevailed among the crew. After all, *Growler* was in Khruschev's backyard and he knew that Regulus boats were nearby. But then a deterrent missile mission was worthless if Regulus' presence was unknown. It was a subtle change in attitude by 85 professional sailors intent on making their effort result in a successful patrol by *Growler*, particularly since Khruschev was determined to sink any American submarine near the USSR.

Captain Henderson decided that Bob was qualified to stand Diving Officer (DO) watch by the time they arrived on station, following intensive training during the transit. The Conning Officer, Wayne Mehl, was also the Engineer and boat's Qualification Officer, regarded by most as best qualified on *Growler* of all the officers. During routine operations, he shared the periscope with Bob since "Waltzing Matilda" was a strain on the eyeball and very laborious. During one of Bob's first turns on the periscope, he managed to entangle *Growler* in a fish net. He received jovial congratulations from the crew for catching a net, for this was not a first for any of the Regulus boats. Snorkeling every night was mandatory to keep the submarine's batteries charged.

During the days, if a contact was sighted, *Growler* normally descended to the "layer" defined by a temperature gradient in the ocean water, maintaining communications on the floating wire. The boat could literally ride on the denser, cold layer at minimum speed, thus saving the battery. If the contact was a warship, the boat ducked beneath the layer to hide from the probing ears of enemy sonar. Astride the layer, sonar was also able to hear well and for thousands of miles under some conditions. It had been an exciting first watch on station for Bob but as the watch neared its end, "Hotdog" Heatwole strode into Control with hot, fresh spud nuts (glazed donuts), freshly baked. Hotdog had made the previous patrol and because of his great baking, the boat ran short of flour. A more than ample supply for this patrol had been loaded aboard. Bob was relieved of the dive and gratefully fell into his bunk, an exhausted but happy man.

The following morning arrived with a predicted huge storm topside, remnants of a typhoon that had swept up the coast of Asia. *Growler* rolled uncomfortably in the troughs and swells as Bob pondered the dilemma of his clothing. Even his skivvies must await changing for another four days. Water hours (no water available except for food and drink), plus no washing machines, would sorely test his personal hygiene habits.

A splash of water on his face following a brief scrubbing of the teeth and it was time for Bob's daily constitutional. He hopped out of his stateroom as he attempted to pull on his sea boots over still damp socks he had washed in the tiny washbasin the night before. As he stepped into the forward torpedo room, his feet slipped on the deck plates and he prevented a fall only by grabbing the oxygen generated indicator for the MK 16 torpedo bolted on the deck plates.

"Careful, Mr. H, there's ice on the deck with the outside sea temperature well below freezing." Bob shuddered at the thought and stepped into the head.

"Skin doesn't stick to plastic, does it?" he mumbled as he seated himself.

"Now man Battle Stations Torpedo," blared over the 1MC (general announcing system). Bob hustled off for the wardroom. Captain Don was conducting another exercise at periscope depth, tracking a small Soviet freighter as a target. The wardroom served as the plotting room, quickly becoming a beehive of activity, as the plot was set up and the target tracked. Within minutes, a solution was computed and firing a torpedo simulated. Bob's roommate was still trying to warm his buns on the Naugahyde (imitation leather) seats in his shorts when the exercise terminated. Bob managed to contribute virtually nothing and received a lesson resembling a lecture from the captain on what should have transpired.

"Okay, that's out of the way, how about a game of cribbage?"

"Sorry, Captain, I don't play cribbage."

"Oh, yes, you do. Now here's how it works..." The cards were dealt and between hands, the torpedo exercise was reviewed and Bob learned plenty about what he could have added to the plot of the target. The lecture ended as the captain pegged out.

The storm continued to build and *Growler* began to roll more than a little, even on the occasional excursion down on the layer and below to check for sonar contacts, and severely at periscope depth (65-feet to the keel). Bob's watch continued to be a training ground for qualification. Rintz was an old time Submariner who knew *Growler* like the back of his hand. A common practice in the watch section was to make bets on qualification questions and the standard unit of barter was a beer. Within a month of departing Yokosuka, Rintz bragged Mr. H owed him the Coors Brewery.

The ears of *Growler* were in sonar and in Bob's watch section, SO1(SS) Billy Bob "Scotty" Scott was in charge. He reported to *Growler* from instructor duty in Key West, which was a good indicator of his knowledge and skills. He not only provided the young officer a wealth of information about sound, but was key in keeping *Growler* out of harm's way. He had a "striker" on watch with him who had a reputation of being a bit clumsy and was given the nickname of "Blivet."

By the time Bob was relieved from the afternoon watch, it was time to snorkel charge and it was rough topside. The Conning Officer was a young Lieutenant (jg), David Butler, who had been a classmate of Wayne's at Stanford University. Dave completed his qualification requirements prior to departure on the previous patrol. His Diving Officer was George Playdon, also recently qualified, and was in the first group of officers permitted to attend Submarine School directly from college or the Academy without a tour of duty in the fleet first. Both were skilled submariners with patrol experience. *Growler* conducted a sonar search and returned to periscope depth to commence snorkeling. Within minutes, the heavy seas bested the skills of the officers and men and they broached (loss of depth control, placing the submarine in a semi-surfaced position). The CO returned to Control and quickly surveyed the situation.

"Dave, can you see the sea direction?"

"Just barely, sir. I think we're in or close to being in the trough."

"George, what's your orders to the planes men?"

"I've ordered full dive on both planes, sir."

"George, we're on the surface and both screws are doing nothing more than creating bubbles. The stern planes are trying to work in bubbles and full dive creates more bubbles. Ease the planes back to five or ten degrees dive and let them react. The same is true on the bow. Full dive does nothing more than create a plow. Ease up on the bow planes as well. Dave, come up a few feet and make it easier on yourself."

Within seconds *Growler* disappeared from the surface, adjusting course to starboard into the trough. Speed, and extra weight flooded into the forward trim tank, expedited the process but the wisdom of the CO proved successful. Everyone in control looked up at their CO in awe and stowed another piece of knowledge. The necessity to re-trim was avoided and they were back in the comforting shield of the sea. The ECM (electronics counter measures) mast went up as the boat broached to seek radars but there were none. The excitement receded and the snorkel charge was restarted as the boat took $10°-15°$ rolls with occasional rolls to $40°$. It was uncomfortable, but the batteries had to be charged. Like their surface counterparts, submariners learned to sleep on their stomach, legs spread-eagle with arms and hands clinging to the frame of their bunk. It was the sleeping pattern of the deep-water sailor.

The officers played Hearts and at 2000, a movie played in both the wardroom and crews mess preceded by a reel of "Victory at Sea." Every time one of the "Victory at Sea" reels were played, someone yelled that the opening scene with the credits was the same wave spliced together The sexiest thing the crew viewed on film was Angela Lansbury at an early age in a tight sweater.

Bob wasn't enthusiastic about returning to the dive. He stopped in Sonar, where the leading sonarman was on watch. Scotty had trouble with the audiometer test when he passed the exam for First Class Sonarman. This is crucial for a sonarman, since he relies on his hearing ability more than any other. He was sent to the Naval Hospital at Key West since he had been a sonar instructor at the Fleet Sonar School. The hospital recommended he be sent to a Survey Board in Charleston. At his hearing, a Captain asked him,

"Son, if you are hard of hearing, how do you think you can stand a Sonar watch?" Scotty answered,

"Sir, that is what the volume control is for." The board found him fit for duty.[1]

Bob found Scotty an excellent sonarman and when he heard something, one best listen to his report. He had an uncanny ability to analyze the presentation on the CRT (Cathode Ray Tube) of the BQS-4 and BQR-2b sonars on *Growler*. A patrol or two later, he received permission to install four hydrophones on the sail, one fore and aft, port and starboard. It permitted sonar to listen from the hydrophones on the sail above the layer while the boat was actually below the layer.[2]

Scotty gave Bob thumbs up and a smile indicative the situation was under control in sonar. *Growler* was snorkeling, so Bob stepped over to the ECM operator, ETC (SS) Charles Floyd. After a few minutes of watching and listening, he knew there was nothing to worry about.

"Who the hell would be out here on a day like this anyway?" Bob checked in with the Diving Officer, George Playton, and quickly relieved him. The planesman struggled to maintain depth control even though the boat was driving through the troughs that kept the weight of the seas equal fore and aft. The planesmen sat in comfortable upholstered seats and operated the planes with a yoke similar to aircraft. Wayne relieved Dave of the Conn.

"In Control, this is Mr. H and I have the dive." The watch standers acknowledged the fact he was the new Diving Officer. The boat remained difficult to handle and the two officers determined they weren't quite in the trough although it was dark and stormy. Wayne's best indicator of wind direction was watching the plume of exhaust exiting from the snorkel mast. Checking the chart with the Quartermaster of the Watch (QMOW) Don Curbow, and with the CO's permission, they came left ten degrees and depth control improved markedly. About 0200, Maneuvering called and reported the battery charge complete and they were zero floating, or trickle charging, the battery. Wayne secured snorkeling and *Growler* slipped a few feet deeper and the cycling vacuum in the boat ceased.

The watch rotated, Bob was relieved and he slept, ate, and studied. Then it was time for watch again. It was noon the following day and the storm had departed the area as quickly as it arrived. The seas settled down to sea state zero (no waves), with just the slightest swells running from the southeast. But the boat did have a problem. The heavy seas created such intense use of the bow planes, they literally ran out of grease. Movement of the bow planes caused a colossal howl that might be heard for miles underwater. The problem had to be remedied immediately... as deemed safe.

Two auxiliarymen, Jim Harrison and Pappy Hegg, with safety belts, were to go topside through the forward torpedo room hatch after dark, climb into the superstructure and pump Lubriplate grease into the bearings. It was a special type grease used liberally on moving surfaces open to sea water such as the launcher rails. The engineer could communicate with the team from within the escape trunk if the two enginemen, or the boat, experienced difficulties.

The seas were calm at nightfall; so calm one saw individual bubbles through the periscope. Then a heavy fog rolled in and visibility reduced to zero. The Captain came into Control, assumed the Conn, and asked, "Who wants to take her up?"

"I do Captain!" The operation sounded exciting and Bob wanted to be involved.

The CO's eyebrows lifted, then he said, "You've got it, Bob. Get into some foul weather gear. It's going to be cold up there."

The CO ordered the boat to 80' and carefully listened on sonar. The scopes were blank and speakers silent, indicative of nary a sound nor a whisper in the ocean. *Growler* moved to 65' and the CO looked around and lowered the scope.

"Fog is thicker than moose turds up there. (It's the first and only time he used the phrase but it was funny at the time.) Can't see more than a few feet. Raise the ECM mast. ECM, Sonar, report!" Both reported no contacts other than the distant early warning air search radar on the coast. There was no indication of a threat on sonar or ECM. It appeared clear to surface.

"Prepare to surface!"

Quickly the boat was ready. The CO stopped the screws and cleared the baffles (baffles is an area around the stern of the boat that has propeller and machinery noise that makes it difficult to hear astern and 15°–30° on either side), ordered Sonar to take one last look, and again Sonar detected nothing.

"Request permission to crack the lower hatch, sir," Bob called out.

"Permission granted." Bob cranked the hand wheel on the lower hatch of the bridge trunk. A hiss of air equalized pressure with the rest of the submarine and a cloud of fine mist and the musty smell of a closed space filled Control.

"Lower hatch indicates open, Captain," barked the COW.

"Request permission to open the lower hatch, sir."

"Permission granted, Bob. Keep a sharp eye out!"

"Will do, Captain."

QM1(SS) Taylor and Bob started up the trunk, careful not to slip on the wet stainless steel ladder. John Taylor was the Quartermaster of the Watch, who is normally the first man to the bridge with the OOD. It was cumbersome moving in the heavy A-1 foul weather gear and Bob pulled the hood off his jacket and let it fall to the Control Room deck. The visor was like Donald Duck's beak and flapped down over his eyes in the wind.

"Surface, surface, surface!" rang through the boat. Rintz blew the main ballast tanks and *Growler* moved upward slowly, then with a rush. Taylor and Bob awaited the order to open the upper hatch.

"Crack the upper hatch!" Taylor rotated the hand wheel a half turn. The two were covered in a rush of salt water spray.

"Open the upper hatch," and they replied by un-dogging the hatch. A gust of wind raced through the boat, pulling dust and small pieces of paper toward Control. A slight pressure had been in the boat when the upper hatch opened. One had to watch the internal pressure, for if it was too high the man opening the upper hatch could literally be blown out of the submarine like a pop gun cork.

"Upper hatch indicates open, Captain," reported the COW. Taylor rapidly turned the wheel counterclockwise and caught a free ride upward on the hatch lanyard as the spring-loaded hatch snapped to the open position. They scrambled the last few feet to the bridge and looked forward, then swept their binoculars from forward to aft.

Taylor called, "All clear to starboard, sir!"

"Roger. All clear to port!"

Suddenly, the 21MC barked, "Soviet surface search radar, Signal Strength-5, off the port quarter, sir!" shouted Jerry Bowman on the ECM set.

"Clear the bridge, Taylor," Bob screamed as he shoved him toward the upper hatch. On the 1MC Bob ordered, "Dive! dive! Get me down fast!"

The vents opened and water vapor blew 30' into the air. Bob leaped off the bridge down to a black pit below the bridge cockpit. At its bottom was the upper hatch and Bob glanced down the trunk to insure Taylor was on his way down. Things seemed to move in slow motion as he jumped into the trunk and grabbed the hatch lanyard on his way down. His feet hit the vertical ladder just as the hatch hit the hatch seat. Bob required no motivation to get the hatch secured as he heard waves slapping the side of the sail. He spun the hatch hand wheel clockwise to dog it shut. The dogs moved shut but the hatch didn't seat. The hatch had bounced off its seat and he had dogged the hatch "open." He froze in terror as he realized what happened. Frantically, he backed the hand wheel to reopen the hatch and seat it properly. As the hatch was un-dogged, icy seawater shot through the partially open hatch and poured onto his head. Ice ran down his back colder than the water pouring on him.

Then his panic disappeared. He remembered a mortally wounded Captain Gilmore on the bridge ordering the hatch shut to save the boat and crew.

"Shut the lower hatch!" Bob shouted to Taylor, who waited for him at the bottom of the trunk 30' below. If he couldn't get the hatch shut, the ocean could pour down the trunk and into the boat. With the lower hatch shut, only the trunk would flood... with him in it.

Fear returned as he seated the hatch and dogged it shut while deluged by cold salt water. "Damn it," he yelled at himself. His mitten was caught in the gears of the hatch. As the cold water poured on him, he didn't waste precious time to back off but continued to crank the hand wheel. The mitten and a piece of his ring finger fed through the gears but the hatch shut. "Thank God," he whispered as the water slowed to a trickle and then stopped.

"Straight Board, Captain," reported the COW as he watched the open circle indicator turn to a straight line. Older submarines had red and green indicators. Green indicated shut.

Bob looked at his mitten hanging from the hatch as his body slammed against the forward portion of the access trunk. The trunk vibrated violently as *Growler* took a large down bubble (angle) of about 10° and her screws drove her below the surface in a hurry. "Whew!" he whistled to himself as puffs of fog came out of his mouth and his heart pounded. *Growler* took a 10° down bubble, though it felt like 50° in the trunk.

Another shock tore through him; if they hit a Soviet ship, or whatever was radiating radar, sitting in the tube was not the place to be. He slid the 30' down the ladder and rapped on the lower hatch. Water in the trunk was quickly drained. The hand wheel on the lower hatch spun and the hatch sprung open. Bob looked down out of the dark tunnel like a captured rabbit in its hole and saw Taylor's smiling face. A very wet, cold, and frightened Bob stepped into the Control Room. Before Bob could answer a deluge of questions fired at him, he felt a searing pain in his ring finger. He pulled off his class ring in time to watch his ring finger knuckle swell to the size of a golf ball.[3]

The incident was reminiscent of January 1960 on board *Tunny*, when she flooded her conning tower during refresher training. The upper conning tower hatch jammed open on a dive. The ship's Navigator, the Captain, and two quartermasters were in the Conning Tower and ordered the lower hatch shut to prevent flooding the rest of the boat. *Tunny* emergency surfaced and sent a rescue team topside to rescue the four trapped men through the upper hatch. The space was flooded completely, leaving the men sucking air in the overhead in the space around the periscopes. Needless to say, the four were happy to see daylight from the open upper hatch and the arrival of the rescue party.[4]

There are as many diving officer stories as there were submarines. During a Submarine School underway training, one of Mr. H's classmates had the dive on a fleet boat. He cleared the bridge, sounded the diving alarm, shot down the hatch into the conning tower, secured the hatch, continued down into the control room; and then to everyone's amusement, turned left and climbed down into the pump room. He looked around and shouted, "Hey, where is everybody?"

Jim LeVangie was conducting his first dive and he knew *Tunny* dove like a rock. He slipped as he headed for the conning tower hatch and all of him slid through the hatch except his left leg. With assistance, he got all of his body through the hatch, pulling on the lanyard for all he was worth with his head on the conning tower deck.

"Last man down, hatch secured, sir," he shouted. Then he looked up and saw the Captain, Doug Stahl, looking down at him from #1 periscope with one hand on the diving alarm ready to emergency surface. "God, he was tall from that position."[5]

Grayback also experienced a hair-raising event. She was on transit to station, on the surface, at darkened ship in rough seas. It was winter, with rough weather and temperatures below freezing, in a howling wind. *Grayback* labored into the seas and solid green water frequented the bridge with deluges of water roaring down the access trunk. The lower hatch was shut to prevent water from pouring into the attack center. Visibility was limited by a blinding snowstorm and blowing salt spray when an unidentified surface contact emerged through the snow squall, close aboard to starboard, likely a Soviet trawler. Following standard procedures to remain undetected, Lieutenant Chuck Wilbur cleared the bridge and hit the diving alarm with appropriate language on the 1MC indicating it was imperative to dive in a hurry. Under the circumstances, it was standard procedure to open the vents on the ballast tanks prior to getting a straight board since *Grayback* dived slowly.

Unknown to anyone, the drain from the access trunk was plugged and for hours, spray and water had poured down the open upper hatch and remained in the trunk with the water level nearing the top of the trunk. As the boat dived, the QMOW un-dogged the lower hatch and attempted to open it. The weight of the water above the hatch prevented the hatch from opening since it opened up and into the trunk. The two lookouts cleared the bridge and jumped through the upper hatch opening. In the trunk was a watertight red light the lookouts saw but didn't realize it was under water. The OOD didn't hear the splashes and yells in the howling wind and leapt through the hatch opening behind the lookouts with the hatch lanyard in his hand. He almost drowned one lookout and drove the other's head halfway up his butt, landing on the two lookouts who clung to the top rung of the trunk ladder in water. Instantly, the three appreciated the problem as they stood neck deep in water on the same rung near the top of the ladder—somehow. Chuck dogged the upper hatch before the last few feet of air in the trunk filled with water.

The Attack Center knew the OOD and lookouts were down since the upper hatch indicator showed shut. A straight board was achieved and the dive continued. The QMOW called for help with the lower hatch while the diving officer struggled with a slightly heavy boat. The COW immediately understood the problem. The chief checked the drain valve open but the pump room bilge was dry. The Auxiliaryman quickly blew high pressure air up the drain line clearing the blockage.

The trunk was drained, the lower hatch opened, and three very wet, cold, shivering, and scared submariners laid below. They became members of the North Pacific Polar Bear Club.[6]

Chapter Four
Life on Patrol

Growler had relieved *Grayback* on the eastern edge of station with *Grayback* ready to sprint for home—a sprint for an SSG was a crawl for most other submarines. On station, *Growler* was an intelligence gathering machine as well as a missile platform. Part of the patrol routine was to monitor Soviet missile operations when such activity took place in her patrol area. Near sunset Wayne asked Bob to take the periscope while he went into sonar. Bob gave the dive to the COB.

"In Control, COB's got the dive." There were neither contacts nor any special orders except to snorkel after dark so Bob took a quick swing of the periscope, "Okay, Wayne, I've got it."

A few seconds later, Wayne called on the 21MC, "Conn, Sonar. Request you come right 30°." Bob altered course without question since it kept them moving further into the patrol area, but he checked.

"Hymie, check this course on our plot." QM2(SS) Robert Hoffman, nicknamed "Hymie," quickly plotted the boat's DR position (dead reckoning) and laid down the new course.

"No problem Mr. H." Hymie then placed the cover back over the ship's position plot. A few minutes later, Wayne came out of Sonar and relieved Bob on the conning stand.

"I've got it, Bob. How's the trim doing?"

"Pretty good. Looks like we may be a little light aft," he responded.

"Very well, I'll watch the dive. Take a look in sonar." Bob walked to starboard and aft into Sonar. Passing through the curtain into the "Sonar Shack," he walked into a black hole absent of sound and light. Slowly his eyes adapted to the darkness and he made out the two sonarmen on watch as they carefully observed the light green sonar scopes. The eerie green light from the CRT scopes flashed white with noise spokes periodically, casting weird silhouettes of the sonarmen who drew yellow marks on the screen with grease pencils.

"Mr. H. Sit down. I want you to listen to something." Bob found a stool behind the sonarmen and Scotty flipped a few switches and the room echoed with the sound of active sonar pinging. Bob jumped. Scotty chuckled and asked Bob what he heard.

"Active sonar pinging on long range. Sounds American, SQS-23 I think, but I never spent much time in sonar on tin cans."

"You're right, sir. It is our own active sonar on surface ships boiling the water with energy looking for submarines."

"What are they doing out here, Scotty?"

"They're not here, sir. If I guess correctly, those tin cans are more than a thousand miles away. We're hearing their noise in a sound duct. Did you check the BT?"[1]

"Yes, it showed a gradient around 120 feet."

"Right again, sir. When conditions are right, we can hear ships from one ocean to another."

"I heard about this in school but never experienced it."

"Watch this, Mr. H." He swung the sonar array toward the landmass and a nearby Soviet harbor. Ship and boat noises boomed out of the sonar speakers.

"It sounds like harbor noise; a lot of ships."

"It sure is. With these conditions, we can hear when every Soviet ship and boat in the harbor starts their engines and track them out of the harbor and follow them on their trip."

"Amazing," Bob murmured.

"Yes, sir, it is. We have specific characteristics on each of the other guy's ships. It's almost like fingerprinting a person. When we hear the contact, we determine the ship and where it is going, which is recorded in our patrol report. We also tape the contacts so they can be analyzed when we get back. If I call you in control and give you a name of the vessel, you can damn well believe I've been able to match all of her signatures to the ship."

"I'm impressed."

"I wanted to show you this so you have a better grasp of what happens in here and understand if I ask for a course, speed, or depth change."

"Thanks, Scotty," said Bob.

"You're certainly welcome, sir, and please come back to see us."

"You can count on it."

Back behind the planesmen, Bob thought about his sonar lesson when Wayne ordered, "Prepare to snorkel, two engines." Activity began throughout the boat.

"From sea, flood auxiliaries two thousand!" barked Bob, as he flooded in water to replace the weight of the water displaced in the snorkel mast and piping once the engines started. The watch standers looked forward to snorkeling since the watch had been dull except for the sonar lesson.

"Make your depth 62', Bob," ordered Wayne.

Bob gave the planesmen the new ordered depth and a down bubble. A down bubble kept the big bow further away from the surface effects and if the boat must go deep in a hurry, the boat only needed to add speed to drive it below.

"Raise the ECM mast."

"Conn, ECM all clear, sir. Nothing but air search radars sir." The moment the ECM mast was raised, the Electronics Technician on watch searched a variety of frequencies, looking for threat radars.

"Very well. Raise the snorkel mast."

Before snorkeling, the watch knew there were no close threatening radars since the Type 8L Periscope ECM antenna had intercepted no signals.

"Commence snorkeling, two engines," ordered Wayne on the 1MC. Two engines rumbled to life and the pressure in the boat dropped as the engines gulped huge volumes of air through the snorkel piping and the boat. A draft throughout the boat moved stagnant air aft to the engine room, taking with it the CO_2, smoke, and a variety of smells and pollutants. The crew inhaled deeply and gratefully smelled the fresh ocean air drawn in from the snorkel system and distributed throughout the boat.

Growler snorkel charged a few hours when Wayne asked Bob to visit ECM. The trim was stable so he slipped around the corner to ECM. ETC(SS) Dick Ekenberg methodically checked frequency bands.

"Hey, Chief, what's up?"

"Hi, Mr. H. Just doing some routine housekeeping and observations at the moment, but the first hour of snorkeling I was busy. Early warning radar is no threat to us but we track their locations since the bad guys have a habit of moving them around. I plot the bearings of each site and record the characteristics of the radars. Like sonar, we keep fingerprints on each of their radars so there is no question about who is radiating. As we move around, I record the details of each radar and soon we have the location of all the radar sites by triangulation as well as their specifics." The entire time on watch was a lesson for Bob.

"Thanks, Chief."

"Conn, Maneuvering. Charge complete. Carrying a zero float. Request permission to secure #1 Main Engine." Wayne called the CO to inform him of the charge completion and get further instructions since the Night Orders weren't out yet.

"Bob, we'll continue snorkeling for the night and transit further up into our patrol area. We'll be running standard speed, one engine."

46

"Okay, Wayne, whenever you're ready."

"All ahead standard." Standard speed on one engine was the maximum speed at periscope depth without causing a severe vibration in the periscopes.

Near the end of the watch, Wayne said, "Bob, care to follow me on my below decks inspection?" It was called a "walk through the boat," which each OOD performed after every watch. It was a cursory check for boat safety. At the end of the "walk through," the officer reported any abnormal conditions to the Captain.

The next night while snorkeling, "Conn, ECM. S-Band contact, signal strength 5, sir. Looks like about 280°," reported Jerry Bowman.

"Secure snorkeling, make your depth 65'. Lower the ECM Mast. Lower the Snorkel Mast." By the time Wayne dialed the CO, he was in Control.

"What's up, Wayne?"

"S-Band radar, Captain, with a signal strength of five bearing 280°."

"Conn, ECM. Last look as the mast went down was a signal strength 5 (maximum strength signal) and increasing. He just started radiating the area, sir. It's airborne surface search, drifting left or astern, antenna scan rate was low so he probably didn't see us."

"Let's come right 90°, slow to one-third, and we'll keep an eye on him as we clear the area."

"Conn, ECM, I've got the radar on the periscope. Request you rotate the periscope through a 360°."

"You've got it, Chief," answered Wayne.

"Wayne, full rudder at one-third speed is giving me trouble. Can you ease the rudder a bit?" Bob asked.[2]

"Sorry, Bob. Ease your rudder to right 15°."

"Conn, ECM. Contact continues to draw left and the signal strength is decreasing. Signal strength 4 now." Don Haines was at his shoulder and taking notes. He was one of the spooks on this patrol.

"Wayne, continue on this course until 0200. Then call me. If everything is quiet, we'll snorkel for the rest of the night. Here are the "Night Orders." The CO left control and returned to the wardroom.

"Wayne, why did the CO come right 90°?"

"I suspect he came right because the target was drawing left and we don't know if the Soviets have MAD gear yet (Magnetic Airborne Detection) but if they do, we came to course north to run parallel to the magnetic lines of force of the earth. MAD gear picks up anything breaking the magnetic lines of force or a magnetic anomaly."

"Oh... okay. That makes sense. Thanks."

George relieved Bob.

"I got it, Bob. Sweet dreams," George yawned.

"Okay, Bob, let's go aft and check out the boat." Thirty minutes later, Wayne walked to the CO's stateroom and reported he was relieved and conditions were normal throughout the boat.

The next day was happy for *Growler* as the crew received the first Familigrams from the Commodore. Every other week or so, wives and loved ones submitted a short message to SubRon One who transmitted the messages to submarines when there was room on the radio broadcast. Twenty-five words or so were permitted, which challenged the wife's intuitiveness. It mattered little what was said as long as the crew knew their families were well and they were loved. This connection to the families back home was originated in Regulus and continued in the Polaris, Poseidon, and Trident Programs.

Growler received a message on 6 May 1962 indicating the U.S. was to detonate a nuclear blast near the Bikini Atoll on Johnson Island. The operation was called "Frigate Bird" and the USS *Ethan Allen* (SSBN-608) was to launch an A-1 Polaris Missile with W-47Y1 warhead. The USS *Carbonero* (SS-337), no stranger to Regulus, and USS *Medragal* (SS-480) were stationed 30 nautical miles from the burst to observe and take photographs.

Growler was ordered to observe the shot from their northern position and record what was observed. The bomb was detonated on Bob's watch and he enjoyed the opportunity to see the blast thousands of miles to the south through the periscope, though he saw little more than a brightened sky, real or imagined. There was no mushroom cloud associated with the nuclear explosion to be seen but the horizon on the correct bearing to Bikini glowed slightly. More important than viewing the glow was monitoring the explosion's effect on the ionosphere and radio communications. A preset series of radio signals were broadcast all over the world and U.S. Navy ships worldwide monitored the signals. *Growler* happened to be the Northwest Pacific Ocean listener. The spooks were busy this night. (Data available on numerous web sites on internet.)

Days later, the CO and XO were called to Radio; the Soviet Pacific Fleet was about to conduct a fleet anti-submarine exercise in *Growler*'s patrol area.

"Geezus! All we need is the entire damned Soviet Fleet joining us for supper," spat Bill.

"Hey, Bill, it'll keep us from getting bored and we're here to gather intelligence. It doesn't get much better than this—to sit right in the middle of the Soviet Fleet and watch them do their stuff," smiled the CO. "XO, assemble the officers. Don't make a big deal of it. I don't want to get the crew nervous."

Bob was asleep when the XO stepped into the room. Don was reading and the XO told both officers to get up for a meeting in the wardroom. Don jumped up but Bob didn't budge.

The XO bent over Bob's right ear and let his full beard brush across Bob's cheek and quietly whispered, "Bobbie Dear. This isn't your wife next to you honey, so would you please awaken and get your ass up? Come on, honey, open your eyes." Bob's face smiled, not the reaction the XO wanted. In a loud raspy whisper, he ordered, "Get your ass out of the bunk!" The meeting began thirty seconds later with all officers in attendance.

The CO slowly finished his coffee and looked each officer in the eye.

"Damn, but if you aren't the ugliest thing I've seen in a while, Bob." It broke the ice, for special meetings were rare and the officers were apprehensive. "Gentlemen, there is going to be a hot time in the old town tonight. The Soviets started a fleet exercise designed to stop U.S. submarine penetration into their local operating areas and their ports. The majority of units home ported in Petropavlovsk are underway and last reported passing Point Shipunskiy. The exercise area, fortunately, is almost identical to our patrol area. Soviet air units will support the exercise. This provides us a wonderful opportunity to learn, and in some cases confirm, Soviet ASW doctrine. Remember, to have an anti-submarine warfare exercise, you must have subs. We must be quiet and on top of any indication of their presence. I'm putting the Top Secret Intelligence folders back out on the Conn so you can refresh your memories on what we may face. Any questions?"

The next day, the Soviets showed up on ECM and sonar. They were to the west with ample indications other units were joining the exercise from the Port of Kamchatka. The patrol area became a beehive of activity with the initial arrival of Soviet destroyers. The thermal gradient was favorable and *Growler* remained clear. However, the Soviet strategy of searching for submarines was quite different from the U.S. Navy. The Soviet destroyers moved from one position to another, then stopped and listened for a while. They didn't charge about the ocean at high speeds nor use active sonar, an immediate identification of a destroyer's position. They employed the passive approach, the same as used by Submariners.

Growler's first encounter with the Soviet Fleet came at 0200 on the second night of the exercise. The watch conducted the usual snorkel charge but the crew was edgy and more cautious than usual.

"Conn, Sonar. Noise spoke bearing roughly 270°. It's a wide spoke so may be multiple targets, sir."

"Sonar, Conn, aye. Any estimate as to range, Huber?" queried Dave.

"Not yet, sir. It would help if we shut down for a few minutes or put the contact further up on the bow, sir."

On the 1JV telephone, "Captain, we have a noise spoke to port. It may be more than one target. No analysis yet. Sonar wants to come left or secure snorkeling to hear better, sir."

"Okay, Dave. Let's play it safe and secure snorkeling." The engines stopped, the circulation fans slowed and it became quiet. Everyone in Control heard the noise emanating from the sonar repeater on the conning stand.

"Conn, Sonar. We have at least three and maybe five surface craft on the port beam; sounds like warships, probably tin cans. Designate the Skunks Alpha through Echo from left to right. I have a good turn count on Bravo of 155 RPM or about 13 to 14 knots. Request you remain on course and speed for a few minutes so I can get a bearing rate."

Bob remembered being a team member. He dressed and went to Control, looked around and noticed the TDC unmanned so he turned it on and set up for a torpedo solution. The CO and XO were in Control listening to the contacts.

"Conn, Sonar. Estimate range to the contacts in excess of 20,000 yards, sir, slight left bearing rate. There are five contacts and Echo may have a CPA close aboard to port sir."

"Good job, Coffman," piped the CO. Tom Coffman was the senior sonarman on watch.

"Thank you, sir. One last item, sir, the CO's name on Echo is Ivan and he's smoking American cigarettes." A grin creased everyone's face realizing that Scotty had joined the 'team'.

"Dave, put up the ECM mast and see if there is anything we can use," said the CO.

Minutes later, "Conn, ECM. No signals above signal strength 1, sir. Usual early warning radar on the beach, one surface search aft of us way out there... oh, oh, just caught a burst of conversation to the west of us, sir and fairly close." The Soviets understood ECM and didn't transmit on radar or sonar but blew it by conversing on the radio.

RM1 Ed Strickler dashed out of Radio and spoke excitedly to the CO. Ed Strickler was one of the "spooks" on board to help gather intelligence. Radio picked up the radio transmission, too, and alerted the CO a Russian vessel was near. The conversation was not understood and did not enlighten *Growler*.

The CO chatted with the XO and Dave, then ordered, "Take her to the layer, George." He then turned to Miller, the AOW, "Put out another 200' of floating wire." *Growler* was carrying an experimental long antenna wire that floated on the surface. It was fed out of a fitting in the stern room and floated to the surface and was supposed to receive radio and Loran-C signals. It was not to be used except as an experiment or a backup to the antennae permanently installed on board. Slowly *Growler* sank, a foot at a time while George slowly pumped out more ballast water to accommodate for hull shrinkage. She settled as if on a soft mattress—they were on the layer.

"We're on the layer now, Dave, depth 141', sir. The BT confirms the layer."

"Good. Maneuvering, Conn, dead slow turns. Sonar, Conn, how's sound conditions?"

"Perfecto, Conn. Just beautiful," replied Coffman.

"Okay, I'm going to come right to open your CPA estimate. I'll try to keep them out of the baffles but if you have trouble hearing, let me know right away."

The boat came right 30° and, "Conn, sonar, the bearing drift has increased to 1.5° left. Range is now about 15,000 (yards), sir." The CO walked forward and the watch settled into a routine with a bit of tenseness. Dave explained a phenomenon called the 'Chinese Effect' to the diving team.

"There is a point when the speed of the submarine slows so much the action of the planes actually reverses. The bow..."

"Conn, Sonar. Contacts are changing course to their left. Speeds are changing, too, probably to maintain station. They have zigged toward."

"Captain to Conn," Dave spoke on the 1MC, not wanting to waste precious time on the sound powered (SP) phone. The CO was in Control before Dave replaced the microphone.

"The tin cans have zigged toward, Captain." The CO nodded and went into sonar.

"Conn, Sonar. These are *Riga* Class destroyers and steadied on new course 080°. Their CPA is directly on top sir!"[3]

"Dave, this is the Captain. Rig for silent running and drop to 200'. Come left with 5° rudder." The order went out immediately via SP telephone to rig for silent running. "Make your depth 200', 5-degrees down bubble, full dive on the bow planes. George, let me give you a little speed to help you get down. Remember, when you come out of a layer, you're likely to drop like a rock. Tell Maneuvering, all ahead one-third, do not cavitate." It was Bob's first experience of breaking through a layer so he watched and listened intently as George slowly fought his way through the layer. As soon as it looked like George was breaking through, he pumped from auxiliaries to sea and by the time he hit 200', the trim was perfect. "Two hundred feet, sir."

"Nice job George." The CO stepped out of Sonar into Control. "This is the Captain, I have the Conn."

"Sir, the ship is rigged for silent running," Dave whispered.

"Very well. Left 10° rudder."

"Conn, sonar, bearing rate is zero on Charlie, range 7,000 yards, sir. Speed is still 14 knots." The CO's strategy was to keep the bow pointed at the closest destroyer, thus presenting the smallest configuration or target for the destroyers. As the ship passed, he turned with the bearing of the destroyer. It also provided sonar's hydrophone array an unimpeded look at the contact.

Everyone in Control heard the unmistakable noise of heavy screw beats over the UQC-1 or Gertrude (underwater telephone). The sonar CRT flashed wildly with bright yellow light. The bow planesman, who wore the sound powered telephone set, reported the range to Charlie was 2,000 yards and closing. The CO turned down the sound and everyone heard the destroyer's screw beats coming through the hull of the boat as if she was heading down the bridge hatch. The diving party was kept busy maintaining depth as the CO increased the rudder to point the target. Later, they chuckled a bit as everyone in Control had looked at the overhead as the destroyer closed and then passed almost directly overhead. Obviously, no one could see it but everyone looked up at the 'swish-ump' noise of the Soviet's screws.

As Skunk Charlie passed overhead, sonar reported the destroyers made another zig, this time to their right. The screen of destroyers wheeled about Alpha, then once on course, resumed speed. Slowly the noise declined and when at 10,000 yards and opening, the crew sighed in relief.

"That was too damned close," George whispered to Dave.

"Yea, but I've seen 'em closer," he responded. Scotty reported Skunk Charlie passed directly overhead.

"How much closer, Dave?" Dave grinned and said, "Watch your depth Mr. Playdon."

"Conn, radio, we've lost communications." Radio had shifted to the new floating wire while they were deep.

"Make your depth 65 feet, George, all ahead standard, do not cavitate," ordered the CO. "Let's get topside and see what's going on."

"Conn, Sonar. Targets zigged again, this time to their right, so they continue to open. Present range is 11,000 yards and opening." Bob looked at the TDC solution and realized he had become so engrossed with the destroyers he forgot to enter the last course change. A lot of help he had been.

Every *Regulus* boat experienced run-ins with units of the Soviet Navy. On the previous patrol, *Grayback* was on station snorkel charging when their sonar detected contacts. They secured snorkeling and discovered three Soviet *Riga* Class destroyers close aboard. *Grayback* rigged for silent running and went deep to avoid detection. For some reason, they descended with a dry snorkel mast. The *Riga*s passed directly overhead when, suddenly, a resounding 'boom' was heard as the relief or seals on the snorkel mast popped. The crew cringed, thinking they were being depth charged. Fortunately, the *Riga*s kept on trucking completely unaware of the boat's presence.[4]

Chapter Five
The Patrol Area Gets Hot

The 2D attack periscope broke the surface and the CO whirled through a complete turn, then slammed the periscope handles up. Down came the periscope with the characteristic 'whisssh' and final dull 'thunk' as it lowered onto the stops at the bottom of the periscope well.

"No contacts visible, looks like a state three sea running from the north with a stiff breeze. Make your depth 63'! Glacy, #2 scope, at the waist!" QM1(SS) Lawrence Glacy was the QOW and had been ordered to raise #2 periscope, which was the Type 8B. Actually, it was a Type 8L since the periscope had been lengthened when the Growler's sail had been extended ten feet in the previous dry docking in Pearl Harbor Naval Shipyard. Waist high meant to bring the periscope up just high enough for the lens to reach the Captain's waist so he can squat to peer through the lens thereby reducing periscope exposure for the initial look-around.

Perry was the DO and reported aboard with Bob. He was an honest to goodness "Ensign Benson."

"Peré (pronounced like P-air), hold me steady. Up scope!" Glacy rammed the hydraulic lever up and then back to neutral. Perfectly, the periscope eyepiece stopped right at the CO's eyes while in the squatting position. The CO rotated 360 degrees in the squatting position reminiscent of a Russian dance style, as he hung onto the handles and ran with legs stretched to the side.

"Two block it, Glacy!" He raised the hydraulic lever again and the periscope rose to the fully raised position. The CO whirled through another complete circle.

"ECM is clean Captain," Chief Ekenberg reported. ETC Ekenberg's tour of duty on Growler was likely to be his last at sea before retiring. His vast knowledge of electronics was the tip of the iceberg when it came to his value to *Growler*. He could have been a COB on another submarine but like most *Regulus* sailors, he loved the rigorous and demanding duty of *Regulus*.

"Put me on the center target, Glacy," the CO ordered.

"Generated bearing is 010° relative, sir," piped Bob from the TDC. Glacy pulled the periscope around to 010° relative.

"If they're out there, they must be at darken ship. I don't see a damned thing. Anything on ECM, Ekie?" ECM was quiet but sonar still held the contacts. "Lower the scope." The CO stepped back and sat on the fold-down seat for a few minutes. He rubbed his chin slowly—he was deep in thought. "Let's come left 30°, Peré. Sonar, this is the Captain. I'm coming left 30°. Take another look at our baffle area. Let's go down to the layer and wait for things to quiet down a bit more, XO. I want to continue on this course for the next four hours to move out of the area. Stay alert for other Soviet Fleet units. Their whole damned Pacific Fleet is out here somewhere. "Peré, take her down to 130 feet."

"Up scope, Glacy."

Suddenly, the 21MC speaker barked on the conning stand, "Captain, strong airborne surface search radar 240° relative. Soviet airborne surface search signal strength 4, sir," barked Ekenberg. Everyone in Control heard the signal coming from the ECM speaker in the base of the 8L periscope. "Ziiik ziig, ziiik ziig."

"Get us down fast, Peré," ordered the CO as he whirled the scope around to the port quarter. Then the scope went under. "Down scope. I didn't see anything of the aircraft. Might be flying darkened but then I think the sky is overcast." The radar Ekenberg detected was common on the Russian Badger and Bison aircraft expected to be involved in the fleet exercise.[1] Were they detected? Chances were *Growler* wasn't detected but was a possibility. A signal strength 4 contact had sufficient power to reach *Growler*, reflect off the periscope, and return to the aircraft but the scope went under following only two sweeps. Only an exceptionally good operator could discern the little blip on the radarscope as a 'sinker' and not sea return.[2]

"Sonar, this is the Captain. How are you tracking the five targets?"

"Pretty good, Captain. As soon as we steady up again, I'll be able to give you a better update. Whoa! I think the five are zigging right now. Yes, they are, sir, they zigged to their left. I have no other contacts, but carpenter fish are acting up near our port baffles."

"Roger, Sonar. We'll be clearing the baffles in a minute. Don, what's the status of the battery?"

"Fair, Captain. The evening watch almost completed a partial charge[3] before the contacts arrived on scene. The can is about 75% full, sir."

"Good. If it's less than that, let's take advantage of the lull to get a few more amps in before sunrise." With a Soviet Exercise being conducted in the area, the higher the state of the battery the better.

"Captain, Wayne is in Maneuvering and says they haven't taken the specific gravities yet but agrees with an estimated 75% can, sir."

"Okay! Stay here until things quiet down and resume the charge at 0200."

"Conn, Radio. We've lost our signal again. When we came up to periscope depth last time, we re-established communications on the whip antenna and then shifted to the floating wire. Now we've lost it again, sir. I think we've lost the floating wire, sir."

"Back up to periscope depth, Don," commanded the CO.

"On my way, Don," piped Perry.

"Miller, pull in the floating wire and give me a report on its condition as soon as you can," ordered Don. EN1(SS) Miller was off in a flash.

"Aye aye, sir," shouted Miller on his way aft.

"Chief Anderson, you have the auxiliary watch until Rintz reports on duty." *Growler* returned to periscope depth and no aircraft was detected on ECM.

"Conn, Radio. Re-established communications on the 8B stub, sir. Request you raise the whip."

"Radio, Conn. That is negative, Radio. Remain on the stub."

"Radio, aye, sir," came a rather disgruntled voice.

"We all have our own little crosses to bear," mumbled Don. Perry gave Don a quizzical look. Don explained, "I'm not really sure why Peré, but putting up the little whip antenna when the scope is up equates to a radar target equal to the area between the two masts. A radar target that size increases our chances of being detected. That's a chance I'll not take as long as Radio can receive our broadcasts on the stub."

The stern room reported retrieving the floating wire. Don was busy moving the periscope but paused a moment to report to the CO that the floating wire was aboard. Then it was back to rotating the periscope with a short pause.

"Sonar, ECM, this is Conn. Report contact status."

"Conn, Sonar. The noise level astern of us is increasing in intensity and I believe we'll see a contact developing out of the noise spoke. The Soviets up front are still loud, clear and opening. I estimate the range now in excess of 30,000 yards. They're changing course on a regular schedule so they should come right in about two minutes, sir."

The watch changed and Bob and Wayne came on watch though they had been up most of the night assisting with the contacts. They relieved the watch and observed the weary duty section head for their bunks. Wayne rotated the periscope and as he slowly moved around the conning stand, he cast a huge shadow from the dim red night-lights. Wayne's huge shoulders and arms were typical of a collegiate swimmer. His being a Stanford graduate was sufficient to gain Bob's respect, but being an All American swimmer elevated his respect to greater heights. Wayne gained the admiration of the crew for his sincere dedication to *Growler* in repaying the Navy for the NROTC Program, which paid for his college tuition. He qualified in Submarines in a minimum time and became the Engineer due to his exceptional knowledge of the boat.

As the boat's Engineer, Wayne was the qualification officer and had a reputation as extremely demanding on qualification candidates before he initialed a crew member's qualification card. He was tougher on officers. He was thorough and made sure every officer knew virtually everything about a system before signing the officer's drawing. Wayne was a quiet and deep person. Bob occasionally thought Wayne not cordial but he never left Bob wanting when it came to studying a boat's system. Wayne listened to qualification questions bantered about during the watch and loved to say, "You're all wrong!"

Rintz and Guy Blades entered Control with the remnants of the floating wire. The watch had changed and Blades relieved Miller in the Stern Room. The bitter end of the wire appeared sliced off by a sharp object such as a ship's propeller blade.

"How close did the target come according to Dave?" His pearly white teeth reflected the red light in a big smile from behind the periscope. Wayne unmasked the port baffle area where a noise spoke had been generating for the past few hours.

"Conn, Sonar. I have a contact coming out of the port baffle with a definite set of high-speed screws, 170 turn count, twin shafts, and five blade screws. Initial classification is a *Kotlin* Class Soviet destroyer. Bearing rate is zero and I do not have a range but seems to be distant. I think we're seeing a companion tin can to the right of the contact but I am not hearing him well. Their speed by turn count is around 18 to 19 knots. Sir, request maintain course and speed for a few so I can get a bearing rate on the targets."

"Designate the target at 170° as Skunk Foxtrot, and the possible as Skunk Golf."

Wayne called the CO and updated the contact situation. The CO directed him to come right across the bearing to Foxtrot sufficient to drastically change the bearing rate as soon as Sonar computed a good bearing rate on the present course. (Bearing Rate = change in bearing per unit of time) "Remember, if you get the bearing rate to change to the opposite direction or significantly in the same direction, we'll have his range nailed," counseled the CO.

Almost immediately, "Conn, Sonar. I have a left bearing rate of 0.6, sir. Recommend coming right at least 60°, sir," Scotty requested. The increased activity brought the CO back into Control, still holding his cold coffee.

"Bob, come right with 10° rudder."

"Sonar, Conn. We're coming right with 10° rudder. Scotty, tell me when you hear the target clearly coming out of the starboard baffle." *Growler* came right 60° and steadied on the new course.

"Conn, Sonar. I've got the contacts loud and clear again, it would appear Skunks Foxtrot and Golf are *Kotlin* destroyers. They are on a course around 060°, speed 18 knots, range around 15,000, sir. CPA is 7,000 yards almost dead astern! No zigs detected yet, sir."

"Thanks, Scotty. Any update on Skunks Alpha through Echo?"

"That's a roger, sir. Still moving away from us. They are actually smaller than destroyers and are sometimes classified as patrol vessels. They are three hundred tons and..."

"Scotty, we read the intelligence reports, too, but thank you."

"Roger, Conn... but I bet you didn't know that Skunk Charlie's Captain has a girl friend in the KGB!"

The CO slowly sipped his cold coffee, then a frown creased his forehead as he raised his head to speak, "Gentlemen, let's review the situation." Another sip of coffee and he lit a cigarette. "We're sitting between five patrol craft with some damned good anti-submarine equipment and at least a couple *Kotlins*. I don't need to remind anyone of their capabilities. We can come left a bit to open the CPA with the *Rigas* but risk the chance of losing contact with the *Kotlins*. Remember this! You always want to know where your enemy is and what he is doing. The move for us right now is to do nothing. We'll remain here for the time being. The *Kotlins* are slowly closing as the *Rigas* open so we will maintain station between the two groups. I don't like sitting here at periscope depth. Get the spare floating wire rigged ASAP. When the floating wire is rigged out, shift communications to the wire, return to the layer, and conserve the battery. We'll clear the area and charge before sunrise. The floor is open for comments." Obviously, the Captain had gained respect for the reliability of the floating wire. Everyone's attention was riveted on the CO and the officers accepted his plan as gospel. It wasn't the reaction he wanted as he tried to promote thought and ideas. "Okay, let's get with it," he snapped. "Mr. H!" barked the Captain.

"Aye, sir," replied a surprised Bob.

"Please tell me what you know about a *Kotlin* destroyer!"

"Aye, aye, Captain. The *Kotlin* Class Destroyer is very similar to our own *Gearing* Class Destroyer, sir, displacing roughly two and a half thousand tons, has twin screws with a shaft horsepower of 80,000, making it a little stronger than our *Gearing*. The *Kotlins* were designed and first assigned duty in the Black and Baltic Seas...."

"Well I'll be damned," stated the CO, "you *have* been reading the intelligence reports and remembering the good stuff. Good. Good. Very good, Bob."

"Thank you, sir," mumbled Bob.

"Thanks... thanks... did I hear you say thanks? Thank you hell, Bob. We just caught you doing your job." The CO looked at a deflated Bob, grinned, patted him on the back, and walked forward to his stateroom.

The watch observed the exchange and smiled for Bob was inflated with his answer only to have the CO puncture his balloon. Bob missed seeing the twinkle in the CO's eyes that reflected his real feelings. The crew loved their CO and was impressed with his demeanor. They never saw their CO anxious nor fearful, as he was a picture of confidence. He knew no fear. His few words with the watch section and the officers replaced apprehension with confidence. Most of all, they watched his eyes for they reflected his mind. When he talked with them, his eyes were intense and clear while his voice remained calm. Everything was okay.

Radio shifted to the wire. Slowly, *Growler* departed the upper reaches of the ocean and sank to the comfortable layer below. She settled on the water strata as the time arrived for Wayne and Bob to be relieved. Wearily, they toured the boat. The below decks inspection completed, both officers literally collapsed into their bunks and fell asleep. They had slept only six hours in the past forty-eight; they were exhausted. Later, the officers were awakened by the sound of snorkeling. They rolled over and fell back to sleep. The CO had called it right again.

It was reveille and the officers awakened for the 08-12 watch. They stumbled into the wardroom at the same time from opposite doors. They sat down and SD1(SS) Bacal and SD3 Cantolas quickly had a mug of fresh hot coffee in their hands. They looked at each other and chuckled.

"Wayne, you are a sorry looking piece of crap."

"You must be looking in a mirror." They both laughed and took a sip of their coffee.

"Wayne, you look wasted. You okay?"

"Yea. Had a problem with #2 engine again last night about an hour after we started snorkeling. Ah, the life of an engineer." They made small talk for a few minutes and ate their breakfast. The XO arrived near the end of the meal with a cheery "morning." He never tired yet was always with the action, day or night, and he wore a smile! How can an XO be happy?

They made a head run, brushed their teeth, and headed for Control. They checked the chart and Wayne whistled lowly, "Wow, the old man really called it right, didn't he?"

"I'll say. That man is unbelievable."

Then Curbow piped up, "He sure did, sir. We haven't had a sonar or ECM contact in four hours."

"That's good. I could use a quiet watch," mumbled Wayne.

They relieved the watch as the battery charge finished. Within minutes, *Growler* was on the layer at minimum turns. It had the makings of a quiet watch, a respite for the majority of the crew. Bob sat on the cushioned bench behind the planesmen and sipped his fourth cup of coffee while enjoying the sounds of whales coming out of the UQC speakers.

Those whales sound pretty close," cracked Rintz from behind the auxiliary manifold, "they didn't name 'em humpbacks for nothin'!"

"I heard someone mention the carpenter fish are really whales," Bob offered.

"Interesting," replied Wayne, "I've heard a lot of postulations about what they may be, but I don't recall anyone suggesting a type of whale."

"Who the hell is interested in what's making the noise, or even heard the noise, except for nuts like us or the Soviets?"

"Don't know, chief, but apparently the White Whale fits most of the characteristics known about the carpenters. They school in huge pods and make a hammering noise when upset or frightened." Bob offered. "That's why it seems every time we hear Carpenter fish, a contact seems to appear out of the midst of the hammering noise."

"You're destroying my vision of this fish with a hammer attached to a fin, Mr. H.," added Curbow. The topic for the watch was whales and sonar sounds.

About 1000, Bill Gunn strode into Control in his pompous and cheery manner.

"No need to fear, your friendly navigator is here."

"What's up, Bill?" queried Wayne.

"Bowditch is my name and navigating is my game," Bill responded. Then he continued, "Men, take me to periscope depth so I can get a fix on something besides Loran-C on the floating wire. I'd like to get a couple visual bearings if the weather is clear and a sun line would do just fine. The Captain said it was okay. I'll be up in the Missile Compartment tinkering with the Loran-C. Call me when you're topside." They added turns to ahead one-third and *Growler* came off the layer reluctantly. She felt at home in the security of the layer. Bob trimmed the boat a bit heavy and up to periscope depth they climbed. Bill was called and he started aft for Control. Wayne put up the 8L periscope and watched the darkness of the Arctic Ocean become lighter as they approached the surface. Quickly he spun the scope through a complete rotation and suddenly lowered the scope. He turned and looked at Bob with a look of disbelief.

What's wrong, Wayne?"

"I don't believe what I just saw," muttered Wayne. The entire watch looked at Wayne whereupon he grumbled, "Pay attention to your jobs men. Don't worry about what I'm seeing."

"Okay, Wayne, now you have everyone's attention, what's happening?"

"Just a minute!" He rubbed his eyes, raised the periscope again and slowly walked around the circle. "Jesus Christ! I don't believe it," he exclaimed. Wayne rarely used the Lord's name in vain. He called forward again to insure the navigator was on his way, looked at Bob and, "Come up here and tell me what you see." Bob jumped up to the conning stand and grabbed the periscope. He did a 360°

turn, whistled to himself and started the second time around slowly.

"I don't believe it," he sung out, "where the hell are we?" He kept the periscope rotating while adjusting the focus as he went around. He stared at landmasses that completely surrounded them. Try as he might, he found no inlet or opening to the sea. According to the chart, they were a long way from any land except an island.

"Hey, guys, what ya got out there?" queried Bill as he stepped through the watertight door.

"You tell us," as Bob relinquished the periscope to the navigator. Bill did a little hippity-hop movement onto the conning stand, then walked the scope in a circle.

"Son-of-a-bitch," Gunn howled as he jumped in horror away from the periscope after a round. For the first time anyone could recall, Bill was without a grin on his face. The entire watch was at their wit's end as to what the officers were looking at.

"Okay, what the hell is up?" barked Chief Stebbins. It was a rare occurrence but the officers ignored the COB.

"I'll ask the CO if we can take a single ping on the fathometer. That should definitely tell us something. I can't believe we are surrounded by land. It has to be an illusion I've never seen before," Bill said calmly.

"Captain in Control," piped Curbow as he rechecked his DR Track on the chart and past fixes. Calmly, the CO walked into Control and studied the worried and anxious faces of his officers.

"Good morning, gentlemen. You look a bit perplexed. What's up?" Three officers talked at once, then Bob and Wayne gave way to Bill. The twinkle in the CO's eyes indicated he had heard the entire problem from the wardroom.

"Captain, take a look through the periscope, sir!" The CO peered into the eyepiece and the skin around his eyes wrinkled at the corners in open laughter. He chuckled after a full rotation.

"COB. They've left you out. Come here and take a little periscope liberty." The old Chief started his round and a grin grew into an audible murmur of mirth.

"Haven't seen anything like this since I was with the Foreign Legion, Captain. The CO lowered the periscope, lectured Wayne on keeping the scope up too long without looking through it, and then explained what the officer's saw.

"If you look on the horizon, you will see land is not on the horizon but a bit above. On a hot day, you will see landmasses or other objects miles away and beyond the horizon because they are refracted by the atmospheric conditions. It is the same as seeing a mirage in a desert."

"We're not landlocked then, sir?" "We are looking at an optical illusion." Collectively, all hands sighed with relief.

Tunny faced a navigation nightmare during an exercise along the Pacific

Northwest of the U.S. in 1958. The boat faced overcast skies and a relentless anti-submarine group, so *Tunny* used the ocean bottom to navigate. Not only were they successful, but advanced a navigation procedure known as "bottom contour advancing," which was to serve the Navy, submarine and surface, for years to come.[4]

Growler returned to the layer in a more relaxed posture.

"I remember one time when we got lost on the first *Barbero* patrol up here," Chief Stebbins spoke and everyone knew it was time for one of his sea stories. "It was in the middle of the typhoon season as I recall," as he made himself comfortable on a bench with his back propped up against the diving manifold. "It was raining harder than an Olongapo gully washer in the Philippines. Day and night it rained and the CO got close to the mainland a few times to make sure it wasn't another forty days and nights of rain. Hadn't had a fix in seventeen days due to the overcast. This was back in the old days, when there wasn't any fancy Loran-C. Shit, the best we had was Loran-A!"

In the opposite corner of Control was heard a mumbled, "God, I thought he'd tell us *Barbero* had sails."

Unruffled, Stebbins continued, "Not a single fix for two and a half weeks. No one had the slightest idea what the Kamchatka Current was doing during the typhoon season, so it was almost impossible to plot a reasonable DR (Dead Reckoning Position). The seas were so rough our gyro tumbled and then we didn't know which way we were going for a day or two. If we woulda had to shoot, we would have to get a radar fix first and you all knows what that means," and he paused a moment. He got the desired result from a first patrol seaman.

"Geez, Chief, what woulda happened?"

"Well, I'll tell ya, son. After the first couple of sweeps of the radar, the Russkies woulda knowd we were here by our radar radiating. Within minutes, their aircraft would be all over our ass as we sat on the surface trying to launch those two birds."

"So how did you ever find out where you were, chief?"

"Well, young fella, a few weeks later it turned warm and calm as hell but we didn't see no land. So we surfaced and saw this island with all these bare breasted women running around on the beach. We found Fiji and by the time we had liberty and made it back to Pearl, I got orders to *Growler*."

"You kidding me, Chief?" asked another kid.

"Yeah, kid, a little near the end. Actually the navigator, had a nickname of Noah, and I worked out the best position we could figure. When we were finally able to get a fix, I really hate to brag, we were right on the money and only off by a few feet!"

"Hey, chief, I can top that one," hooted Rintz.

"Rintz, go down and make sure the pump room is dry!"

Chief Stebbins was a talented QM and Assistant Navigator to Joe Ekelund on *Growler's* first patrol. Typical of most submariners, they sought to improve everything. Together, they rediscovered and refined a procedure of periscope navigation using the built-in stadimeter on the scope described in "Submarine Navigation," a chapter in the bible for navigation, by Dutton. They were able to achieve rough positions by using the bearings and the passive range from the stadimeter. Their position was as accurate as the Japanese charts, the latest known survey of the area—at least for the Free World. Later, the Sperry Mk III Periscope Sextant was developed, but did not work well.[5] Submariners used the Contour Advancing Method of determining ship's position for years, but the method requires the use of the fathometer, which was detectable.

Submarine navigation, without the input of modern day inertial and satellite positioning, was particularly hazardous and difficult in a submerged submarine. *Halibut* was enroute to a SEATO demonstration in the South China Sea and was running deep and at full power. STS2(SS) James Pope was on watch in sonar and was conducting an active SQS-4 search as ordered. He noticed the bottom bounce from the sea bottom was slowly indicating shoaling water. A report to Conn resulted in a comment that they were in deep water and there was nothing to worry about. A request to turn on the fathometer was declined. As the active sonar showed shallowing water, Pope requested Conn inform the Captain of his report. That got attention and the fathometer was immediately turned on. The Captain was called to Conn and stopped in Sonar on his way.

"What's going on, Pope?"

"Captain, I think we better slow this son-of-a-bitch down because we're heading for a cliff."

"All stop!" shouted the captain. He then looked at the fathometer that confirmed the bottom was coming up and fast. The depth was ordered reduced in one-hundred foot increments, yet the bottom still raced toward them.

"All Back Emergency," ordered the captain. *Halibut* was at 125-foot depth and slowly backed away from an uncharted submerged mountain. Puckered butts finally relaxed and after the trip, the official report recorded the uncharted mountain. The Oceanographic Survey Office recommended the mountain be named "Pope's Peak."[6]

Growler monitored radio broadcasts from the beach as the Radiomen, spooks, and Electronic Technicians taped communications between Soviet Fleet units. The fleet exercise continued but the center of interest for the Soviet Fleet became distant from *Growler's* position. *Growler* carefully tracked the contacts detected and monitored the exercise until it ended and the sea became devoid of military vessels. Life returned to boring and the CO conducted drills again to keep the crew on the edge.

Bob took advantage of the slack period to work on qualifying. To learn and be tested by his shipmates became a challenge and a source of entertainment. During day watches, when the boat was deep on the thermal layer, Wayne permitted Bob to continue work on his qualifications. When Bob became super saturated with information, he often took a break and went to sonar to listen and learn. The patrol was during the summer, so sonar kept busy tracking fleet and maritime units traversing from and to Murmansk along the northern route after the ice broke and permitted sailing relatively ice free.

Of all the noises heard, the most frightening was ice. Ice floes rubbed against each other, or icebergs broke free and crushed against ice masses, creating loud groans and moans. Unfortunately, ice made strange noises but also damaged equipment. *Growler* lost a periscope on an earlier patrol.[7]

One of the major categories in the qualification process was learning the weapons carried on board the submarines. The torpedomen kept the unqualified men notified when they conducted work, fire control checks, or maintenance on the fish so they could observe or get hands-on experience.

Bob was engineer on two destroyers and developed a fondness for the men and equipment that made ships run. To him, the torpedo couldn't be fired if the submarine didn't get to the firing point and if power to shoot the torpedo was absent. The "snipes" (engineers) sensed his love of engineering and offered him every opportunity to learn, handle, and master equipment. He did not mind dirty hands or oil in his hair, but losing a uniform to battery acid was a bit much.

A basic lesson a newcomer learns is how to operate the head (toilet). Even though the new crew member operated the heads during Submarine School, accidents occurred. All the refuse on a submarine goes to a sanitary tank. Routinely, the contents of the sanitary tanks are blown overboard when full, or during the mid-watch, with high-pressure air. If the submarine is submerged and deep, a significant air pressure is required to push the contents out of the tank. Prior to blowing the tanks, the inlet valves to the tanks from commodes, sinks, scuttlebutts (drinking fountains), etc., are shut and a sign placed on the door of the heads and valves warning of the forthcoming event. On a rare occasion, the signs were overlooked or a sign not posted and the man received a shock of his life. To flush the commode, a large lever was pushed forward placing the operator spread-eagled directly over the commode. As a ball valve rotated to the open condition, the unfortunate sailor's deposit was returned to his face and chest followed by other contents in the sanitary tank. The sound of the "monster crap can" alerted the crew of the event, but one glance at the offender told the story. The offender was nicknamed the "speckled trout." Standard Navy toilet paper received a strength test on the victim's face, which became speckled with assorted material. Hair was swept back, as in the old ducktail haircut, and the individual's smell was atrocious. The most prone to receive this treatment were the spooks in their first week on board and on their first submarine. They hadn't attended Submarine School, and often weren't instructed on the head's use by the crew—sometimes, deliberately. Regardless, no one was happy with the smell that overwhelmed the charcoal air filters.

When Bob was on the *Becuna* for his First Class Midshipman Cruise, sanitary tanks were blown one afternoon as the boat's cook was preparing the evening meal. His drain stop from the sink in the galley had been overlooked when preparing to blow the tanks, as had the scuttlebutt (drinking fountain) in the Crew's Mess. The mess cook bent over to take a drink just as the blow began and received a horrendous dose of crap in the face while the cook, peeling potatoes in the sink, wallowed in sanitary tank flotsam. The galley took on the smell of a *benjo* ditch (sewage trenches used in some third-world Asian countries), the mess cook threw up, and the cook rinsed off the potatoes and put them in his pot. Fortunately, someone caught the cook and his potatoes in time and he was relieved of his duties for a week to clean the Engine Room bilges.

Familigrams arrived and Bob's read, "IN NAVY HOUSING, FORD ARRIVED AND VW ACCEPTED. MAKING MANY FRIENDS IN NAVY HOUSING. MIKE IS FINE. MISS AND LOVE YOU." It was a brilliant job of condensing all the important things.

Chapter Six
Completing Patrol One

Following the Soviet Exercise, life returned to normal although it was summer and fishermen were out in force and sea states increased. An Akai tape recorder in the wardroom and three tapes were available for the officer's listening pleasure. Every time one of the ex-*Growler* officers hear Peter, Paul, and Mary, the Smothers Brothers, or the Kingston Trio, their minds revert to the tiny wardroom with brown Naugahyde. It was their dining room, study, reading room, recreational room and almost always, one of the three tapes played.

With summer came the birth of the storm season. A typhoon spun out of the South China Sea and reached the patrol station as a tropical storm. *Growler* was clobbered by the storm and life was miserable for a few days. The ocean water became isothermal (uniform water temperatures to great depths) as the heavy seas mixed the ocean to a depth of a couple hundred feet. The advantage of the thermal layer disappeared, the sound ducting, and ability to hide from searching sonars vanished.

Snorkeling or maintaining periscope depth was a challenge of mammoth proportions. It was virtually impossible to run with or against the seas for the bow was quickly sucked up to the surface or rammed to great depths by the weight of the waves. So *Growler* remained in the trough and rolled like a beached whale. Everything not tied down or secured tumbled to the deck. For hours, the boat was filled with sounds of "things" hitting the deck, followed by a flurry of unmentionable language. The longer *Growler* got beat up, the more tired the men became and soon the crew was a testy group. One could not walk down a passageway without being slammed against a bulkhead or worse. The crew member hung onto his bunk for dear life and when he fell asleep and relaxed, all but the most seasoned sailor found himself airborne following a large roll. A coffee cup could not be set down or a plate let go. Even sitting in the head, one desperately hung on for fear of sliding off the seat in any direction.

"Sonar, Conn. Make a sweep around for any contacts!" A few minutes later, the sonar check was complete.

"Conn, sonar. Completed sweep for contacts, sir. We have no contacts at this time but sea noise is extremely loud. I can even hear the wind blowing up there, sir." They must charge batteries so they commenced in the trough.

"Commence snorkeling!" The head valve cycled open and shut, even with the head valve out of the water. The wind swept waves blew sheets of water across the surface in such quantity the electrodes on the head valve shut the valve due to heavy spray. The charge began with two engines.

"I'm going to need some more speed, Wayne!" called Bob.

"Roger, all ahead two-thirds," answered Wayne.

"Full dive on the bow planes, Underwood."

"Aye, sir, but it doesn't seem to help much, Mr. H."

"Give me seven degrees dive on the stern planes, Bean." The depth kept decreasing as Bob tempered his orders to the planes to prevent catching the rise with large dive angles and then plunge headlong below snorkel depth and flame out.

"Broaching, sir, sorry."

"Okay, Bob, try to get her back down. Want more speed?"

"Not yet, let me try." *Growler* was at 45 feet and broached on the surface when a huge wave broke across the sail with a loud bang and roar as the ship heeled hard to starboard. *Growler* shook it off as she fought to gain an even keel.

"I'll take a standard bell, Wayne."

"You got it. All ahead standard!"

"Alright, we've got her now, two-thirds please, Wayne. Clarabell, take the dive off the bow planes!" "Five rise on the bow planes. Come on guys, catch her! A little less rise on the stern planes, Bean. Good." "Sixty-five feet, sir, and still going down, sir." The head valve shut and the vacuum built in the boat. "I'm not going to catch it, Wayne!"

"Secure snorkeling, secure snorkeling." Although they were in the trough, *Growler* yawed and pitched in the huge seas, with her screws nearing the surface a couple of times and sending tremors through the hull. Even stowed equipment found its way to the deck and the crew picked up injuries varying from bruises to a broken arm. The crew's eardrums took a beating from the pressure fluctuations.

"Captain in Control," shouted Hoffman.

"Hasn't let up any, huh, Wayne?"

"No, sir. It's a bitch up there. I think the seas are running about 20' with a few sets at 30', sir and a mixed sea is beginning. The wind appears to be from astern, from what I can see of the smoke and spray around the head valve."

"Okay, Wayne, let's try it with just one engine. That should give Bob a little more time to recover."

"Maneuvering, Conn. Secure # 3 engine." The watch set up to snorkel charge again, but with only one engine.

"Commence snorkeling, one engine." # 1 engine rolled over, kicked in, and roared as Maneuvering got the engine on line and restarted the battery charge. With only one engine running, the vacuum increase with the head valve shut was much slower and gave the diving team more time to recover. But Bob and the planesmen continued to struggle with depth control. Their valiant effort lasted about fifteen minutes before *Growler* headed down again.

"Secure snorkeling."

"Well, I've seen enough," said the CO. "Only an idiot would be out on a night like this on the sea or in the air. Let's broach. Keep the vents on the main ballast tanks open and be ready to head down at a moment's notice. We do have the floating wire in, don't we?"

"Yes, sir, Captain. We took it in prior to coming to periscope depth."

"Good. Let's snorkel on two engines. See if we can remain relatively stable at one-third speed so we can jam the battery." The battery charge was restarted and the boat maintained a 45 foot depth with relative ease, but the rolls were intolerable and the boat came close to tumbling the gyroscope. The CO ordered coming into the seas, which reduced the rolling, but the boat pitched heavily in the huge seas. However, the pitching was mild compared to the discomfort of the heavy rolls. Wayne slowed the boat to ahead dead slow, which barely kept steerage in the seas, but it kept the stern from coming out of the water. Had the screws cleared the water, the electric motors, without a load, could run away and cause damage, even self-destruction.

ECM was the center of attention as *Growler* wallowed on the ocean surface with the sail and large bow out of the water and her decks awash. The CO's assumption was valid. There were no idiots at sea or in the air—at least there were no radars detected or sonar contacts. Only the familiar land based air search radars were up and only half of them were active.

Late in the watch, a huge wave hit the boat with a roar and crash. *Growler* staggered in her gait and then it was quiet for a few moments. A second large wave crashed down on her deck and this time it was accompanied by the sound of ripping and screaming metal.

"What the hell was that?" the CO asked. His question was met with stony silence and scared looks.

"I'm not sure, Captain, but we must have hit something topside, maybe some debris," Wayne answered.

"Have all compartments check for damage or anything unusual and report immediately. I'll be in radio for a few minutes." Wayne passed the word and waited for the responses.

"Wayne, I'd like to go into sonar for a moment and see what they think," Bob whispered.

"Make it so, Bob. COB take the dive—be it as it may."

Bob staggered into sonar and looked at the scopes and printout; every scope and recorder was cluttered like chaff on radar.

"Hey, Scotty, what do you think the big noise was," Bob asked.

"Hi, Mr. H. Well, sir, we didn't hit anything motorized. Even though it's noisy as hell out there, I would've heard an engine close aboard. There are all sorts of things floating around in the ocean. It could've been a tree or remains of some craft—who knows, sir. It sounded metallic, though, and there was a ripping sound. After the ripping sounds, I heard fluttering off to port, then nothing."

"Do you think some of our superstructure or sail ripped off. The sound was preceded by a huge wave crashing on deck and we were broached?" Bob queried.

"I doubt it would be part of the sail. That thing is solid steel but all the superstructure is fairly light aluminum and we've already lost some of the fairings around the hangars a patrol or two ago."

"Thanks. I think we've got the answer."

A large piece of superstructure was literally ripped from the boat aft of the sail. Luckily, it did not damage any vent valves or engine ports topside. As the piece moved aft, it might have sliced the floating wire had it been out.

Growler fought the seas until the battery was charged. Sheer exhaustion permitted the crew to fall into a fitful sleep as they clung to their bunks. Around 0400, Bob awakened with a start. Something was wrong... or different. It was quiet and the boat was not rolling. *Growler* had gone deep for the day. Later, *Growler* was at periscope depth. It was a quiet and beautiful day, with clear skies and a flattening sea. A slight chop ran topside and it was Bob's turn with Matilda. The periscope lens was splashing in and out of the water. He came around from the starboard beam, the scope went under and then cleared as Bob happened to look straight ahead.

The sun went out and he stared directly at a huge and frightening face; two badly bloodshot eyes with brown veins, a huge, bulbous nose pressed up to the periscope. Bob jumped back with a shout, "Holy shit!"

Everyone in Control jumped and wondered what was wrong. Wayne bounded up onto the conning stand. "What's wrong?" Bob didn't believe what he saw and his answer was to grab the scope and take another look.

"There's nothing there," he yelled then swung the scope around to look aft. Then he saw it. "I have the ugliest looking thing I've ever laid eyes on out here since I last looked at you, Wayne. Its got huge teeth and glaring eyes and I have no idea how big he really is." Everyone in Control gathered around the conning stand, including the CO, who heard the shout. No one breathed, and all stood

The commissioning crew, "plank owners" of USS *Growler* (SSG-577). Commissioning CO Lieutenant Commander Charles Priest, Jr., is second from right.

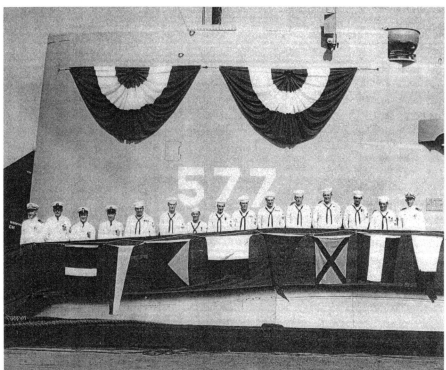

Growler Commissioning Operations Department: L-R: Lt(jg) Duke, QMC Stebbins, RMC Mikula, ETC Higgins, QM2 Meyers, RM2 Hein, RM2 Klappholz, SO1 Whiteman, ET1 Flarherty, ET1 Marcautonio, ET3 Atwood, SO2 Lund, QM2 Marullo, RM1 Powers, LT Ekelund.

COMMISSIONING PARTY
GUIDED MISSILE SUBMARINE

GROWLER

U.S.S.
GROWLER

TELO UTOR
PEREGRINABOR

SSG 577

27 AUGUST 1958

VFW HALL.
DEER STREET
PORTSMOUTH, N. H.

Commissioning Party Program cover.

The original wardroom. Front: Lt Lawrence A Scott, Lt Herbert Tibbets, Lt(jg) Robert Duke, and Lt(jg) James Murphy. Standing: LCdr Charles Priest, jr., CO, LCdr John C. Burkhart, XO, Lt Joseph Ekelund, Lt Robert Kutzleb.

Author at #2 periscope as Navigator (Gold), USS *James K. Polk* (SSBN-645), in 1966.

Right: Cook Duane "Hotdog" Heatwole ladling a refreshing concoction, with George West looking on.

Top: Part of missile crew with red bird in the starboard hanger.
Bottom: Note the fairing on the starboard hanger. Both fairings were later lost in heavy seas in the North Pacific and Bering Sea.

Above: The submarine head and source of many embarrassing moments for the unqualified. *Growler*'s CPO head, 2000.

Top: Ship's party following Patrol #2. L-R, Captain and Mrs Crawford, Marie O'Day, and Barbara Sampson. (Photo by Don Burrell)
Bottom: Rear Admiral Ekelund in center, with Lieutenant Robert Hoffman to his right, circa 1972.

Top: Gilmore Park, named in memory of Howard Gilmore, the first commander of the World War II *Growler* (SS-215), who received a posthumous Medal of Honor for his actions during her third war patrol.

Left Center: North Pacific Yacht Club patch.

Right Center: Crew member in maneuvering room.

Bottom: Captain Robert Crawford congratulating SM1(SS) Don Burrell on promotion.

Two *Growler*s coming down the ways. There have been four U.S. Navy vessels named *Growler*. The first two were sloops commissioned during the War of 1812. The last two were submarines.

Top: *Growler* (SSG-577) is launched at Portsmouth Naval Shipyard on 5 April 1958.

Bottom: *Growler* (SS-215) is launched at the Electric Boat Company (now the Electric Boat Division of General Dynamics) yard in Groton, Conn, on 22 November 1941. U.S. Navy Photograph. Photo by William Hagedorn, crew member of the SS-215 prior to her sinking.

top: After portion of sail during fueling operations (note Bravo flag) at Pier 9, Pearl Harbor, with Escape Tower to the left rear.

Left: Lieutenant Herb Tibbetts.

Bill Gunn's Battle Flag for *Growler*, designed and made in Yokosuka, Japan, April 1962 by the Diamond Patch Company. Inference made to Regulus' single crew, called the Black and Blue Crew, compared to the Polaris Blue and Gold Crews. Hawaii was home port and the torpedo recalls an errant torpedo that almost went up the generating plant's outflow pipe at Barber's Point. The *Growler*'s name in Japanese. Yen = money reflects the experience of the exchange of yen for dollars. The Albatross, called a "gooney bird" on Midway. The Regulus missile shows a hash mark for each patrol to that time. The totem pole is Adak's symbol, frequently stolen by submarines. Since the design and sewing of the flag, the Navy SeaBees moved into Adak and added a "Bee" atop the pole.

Right: A quick gulp of fuel at Midway Island, enroute Patrol Number 6. QM1(SS) Robert Hoffman, and EN1(SS) Herman Naciemento.

Top: Stern Room, where a zerk fitting let loose and looked like massive flooding.

Bottom: Christmas cake, 1962.

transfixed, with eyes glued on Bob. Everyone's eyes were saying, "What the hell are you looking at?"

"I am looking at a full grown Walrus who, a few moments ago, had the audacity to look down the scope at me. No big deal. I just pissed all over myself!" The men roared in laughter, much of it in relief, for Bob had scared the hell out of them. "Drinks all around, chief. I'm buying the coffee." The crew grinned and relaxed. They were still up tight after the beating from the weather.

Then Wayne piped in with a big smile on his face, "Keep dancing, Bob. I can't top that show."

Above Bob was an elaborate packing gland that kept the salt water in the ocean and not on his head. Some slack was left in the packing and a bit of dripping was normal. The caps Bill purchased came in handy for they soaked up water and hydraulic oil that fell on the officer's head. The U.S. cap's visor was too long for the eyeball to reach the eyepiece unless the cap was tilted back on the head or the cap worn backwards. With water shortage problems, one did not need to add oil and salt water to his scalp.

Growler's two distillers produced fresh water for ship's use but not enough for showers. After weeks without a shower, some of the crew members washed their privates in the engine room, using the warm saltwater engine overboard discharge. They tried it only once; it felt good for a moment or two—then the salt dried...!

Both stills rusted through the center uptake tube and both failed at the same time. When this occurred, the crew feared they would never shower again. Ingenuity took center stage and the engineers found the standard Carnation Milk can fit perfectly as a replacement for the uptake tube. Although it rusted through after a few weeks, they were in business and made sufficient water to survive—and there were plenty of Carnation Milk cans.

Every CO is concerned with equipment out of commission, but no captain was more involved than Captain Christian on *Tunny*. A standing order was that every piece of equipment or item on board, broken or impaired, be reported to the CO immediately. The rule resulted in a humorous exchange of reports and questions while *Tunny* was on the surface one day:

"Chief, the cook reports the C41 is out of commission." A sequence of reports began and acknowledgements from the cook, Control, Bridge, to the CO. The CO asked what a C41 was and the sequence repeated in reverse. The CO finally found the toothpick dispenser was down. Minutes passed, then the voice of the CO on the 21MC, "Dive the boat."

The intensity of reports on OOC equipment slackened dramatically for the rest of the patrol.[1]

A couple months had passed since *Growler* departed port and the last shower—in fact, it was seven weeks. The CO granted a frugal submarine shower; a squirt of water to get wet; a soap down, followed by a brief rinse. The crew took showers while snorkel charging. The COB monitored enlisted showers aft and the XO insured no boat officer overstayed his time in the shower. The officer's shower was tall enough to stand in, but 2.5 feet on a side. The crew's shower held 3 men and was open on the head side. The XO announced officers would take showers in reverse order of seniority. The junior officers thought it odd but were to quickly see its wisdom. When the XO and COB administered showers, the event was serious.

George was the first officer into the shower as cold air whistled through the passageways. The boat knew when George turned on the water for it was followed by a wild whoop and holler with some other words thrown in. The message: the water was ice cold. By the time the XO and CO got in, the water was warm. It took a long time for hot water to reach the shower head when so little water was used and the officer's shower was three compartments away from the heater.

Submariners are known for pranks and showers provided an opportunity for fun. The XO was to be "gotten" during his shower. The XO got into the shower and wet down.

The OOD told "Maneuvering, Conn. We're shutting the Snorkel Head Valve. Notify Conn if you have a problem." The two engines on the charge sucked air rapidly from the boat. As the vacuum neared shut down on the engines, the low pressure in the boat sucked the contents of the sanitary tanks upward through the open drain line and the XO stood ankle deep in human and other waste. He jumped out of the shower with towel around his waist and howled in anger.

"God damn it, who has the dive. Dumb SOB is going to stand dive watches for the rest of his life. Get up and open the head valve!" He stood directly in front of the WT door to the Missile Compartment and yelled aft toward Control. The word reached Control; the XO reacted as expected and stood in the middle of the passageway yelling.

"Maneuvering, Conn. We're opening the Snorkel Head Valve." Ice cold air flooded the boat and whistled through the forward battery's narrow passageway. The force of the air returning into the boat blew the XO's towel from his middle and into the next compartment.

"Thank you to the SOB that has the dive," screamed the XO.

The CO stuck his head out of his stateroom and yelled at the XO, "Get your ass back in the shower XO and clean the shit off your feet!" The boat rocked with laughter. The XO came out a few minutes later with a big grin on his bearded face. He was had; he knew it, and agreed it was a great joke. The entire crew was in on the joke and had secured all the other drains to the sanitary tanks, thus the only open drain was the officer's shower.

A few more scares, many more contacts, and it was time for *Growler* to be relieved on station. The crew's thoughts turned to home, wives, sweethearts, and children. Their thoughts were always with them, but tucked in the rear of their minds so they didn't dwell upon them and sadden at the separation. Pictures came out and the topic of conversation centered on homecoming. They reached the first stage of "Channel Fever."

Tunny and *Barbero* relieved *Growler* and without a word between the submarines, *Growler* was relieved and started her homeward journey. It was *Tunny*'s sixth trip to the area. The CO ordered *Growler* to 300 feet and changed course eastward. The transit began to Adak Island in the Aleutian Island Chain. They cruised at two-thirds for four hours until the boat cleared the patrol area.

"Wayne, come to periscope depth and begin the snorkel transit home," said Captain Don. "Come left to course 080°. Sonar, Conn. I am coming left to clear the baffles. Get a good look around and then we'll head topside for our snorkel transit."

"All clear, Conn. I do have a noise spoke ahead of us. Might be a fisherman," reported Sonar.

"Make your depth 100 feet, Bob. Slow to all ahead one-third. Sonar, I'm clearing the baffles to starboard this time. Take another listen."

"Roger, sir. It still looks clear except the noise ahead of us is now astern and is a trawler, sir."

"Captain's in Control," piped Curbow.

"I'll take her up, Wayne."

"Aye, Sir. Captain has the Conn."

"All ahead two-thirds, make your depth 65 feet." There was a Russian trawler astern of them a few hundred yards and showing her stern. The CO took the boat down to 100 feet for fifteen minutes, and returned to periscope depth. "I'll be damned," said the CO, "the trawler's still with us and showing us her heels. Well, hell, take her back down to 100' and come left to course north." Down they went, turned to port, and ran another 15–20 minutes. *Growler* returned to periscope depth.

"I'll be damned again," said the CO. "It appears we have become a very large fish in this fellow's net and are dragging him around. Guess he doesn't want to save himself by cutting his net loose.[2] Well, we can't stay in the net and there's only one way out. He may have reported his situation already. All ahead standard, make your depth 500 feet." Back into the depths and fifteen minutes went by before they returned to periscope depth. There was no repeat to the CO's irritation. The trawler was gone. They hoped his stubbornness didn't interfere with cutting the net loose and saving his life. Minutes later they were snorkeling and homeward bound.[3]

The transit to Adak took a few days. The island was home to a Naval Air Station with a couple squadrons of P2V aircraft, whose entire purpose in life was to find submarines. The new P3A aircraft were arriving in the fleet, but had not

71

replaced the P2Vs on Adak. The aircraft hoped to interdict, or at least detect, Soviet submarines deployed from the Soviet Union, from Petropavlovsk on the Kamchatka Peninsula or Valdivostok, who moved across the Northern Pacific to their patrol stations off the Western United States. The detection of a Soviet submarine started a reaction of events intended to harass and hinder the effectiveness of the submarine. The Soviets deployed guided missile submarines off the coast of the United States for similar reasons the Regulus boats deployed to the Western Pacific.

Adak became important in 1942 when 4,500 Allied troops landed and built an airstrip to fight the Japanese on Attu and Kiska Islands. It was turned over to American control and eventually ended up a Navy Air Base in 1950. It closed 31 March 1997, as a BRACK closure.[4]

The men's thoughts were divided between families and fresh food to come aboard in Adak. They had survived three months without anything fresh—milk was #1 on the most missed food list, closely followed by fresh fruit and vegetables. The food was not bad—far from it, as lobster and steak graced the menu weekly. The cooks and stewards demonstrated great ingenuity in the preparation of palatable dishes from canned and frozen goods, especially with the likes of "Ma" Irwin and "Hotdog" Heatwole. Many thought of a cold beer, or maybe more than one. The second phase of channel fever arrived.

Growler secured snorkeling a few times during the transit to go deep and avoid the probing American airborne APS-20 surface search radar carried by the P2V aircraft. They successfully avoided detection and lost little time in resuming the transit. The crew took on the personality of two different people. They were moody and spent time by themselves, reflecting perhaps in their own minds, on thoughts of home and memories of past returns. On the other hand, they were excited, speaking at length and detail of their love adventures on the beach and how this return promised even better.

Bob observed something new. As he moved through the boat, he noticed men knot tying or net making. At first, Bob let it pass, not wanting to make an ass of himself by asking what the sailors were doing. Finally, his inquiring mind had to know and he asked Chief Mike Powell, a Torpedoman Chief what he was making.

"Hey, Chief, how goes it?"

"Hey there, Mr. H, just fine, thank you. What's up?"

"Well, chief, I'm curious. Over the past couple days I've watched you and a number of men making something with white line?" (a small rope)

"Well, sir, ever been to Adak?"

"No, chief, I haven't."

"Well, sir, the island's waters teem with Alaska King Crab. You had Alaska King Crab, sir?"

"I've eaten crab, but don't know if was Alaska King Crab."

"Well, sir, you woulda known it if you had ate it, believe me."

"Pretty good, uh?"

"The best, especially when it's fresh. Da crabs swim on the surface and come right alongside the boat. All you have ta do is reach over and scoop dem babies outa da water and plop'em in a kettle of boiling water." Bob was suspicious and wondered if he was getting his leg pulled. It wouldn't be the first time.

"So you're making scoop nets to catch crabs in, uh, chief?"

"You got it, Mr. H."

Bob looked at the Aleutian Islands through the periscope. Attu Island had peaks covered in snow that glistened in the sun and his mind returned to a Naval Academy classroom. He recalled studying the battles with the Japanese in the Aleutians during World War II. The boat slipped to the north side of the Aleutian chain near Rat Island in the hope air coverage would lessen on the Bering Sea side of the islands. Then the islands looked like silhouettes as the sun was low on the horizon on the opposite side of the islands. He was entertained by thousands of colorful Puffins, appearing so stuffed with food they became airborne only with the greatest of effort.[5]

Bill moved the navigation plot into Control to provide close support to the OOD. Saturday night they made landfall on Adak Island. *Growler* cruised along the northern edge of the island and then turned south toward the harbor. Bill convinced the Captain it would be fun to arrive unannounced and undetected on a sunny Sunday morning and just surprise the hell out of the airedales. It became the plan. The battery was charged and they would take on water, fuel, and stores the next day, so the CO decided to go deep and wait for first light to enter port. It was showers all around and a game of hearts in the wardroom. It was Saturday Night and they were alive. The major question in the wardroom—what time was it? There was the International Dateline, Alaskan Time, Daylight Savings Time, and *Growler* had yet to arrive in Adak with the right time. At 0600 *Growler* time, they returned to periscope depth off the harbor entrance and looked around. The day's flight sorties had departed or had yet to depart, as there were no radar contacts on ECM. It was clear, blue skies, and sunny but looked like a late winter afternoon back in the Midwest. It looked cold!

Growler moved past Kuluk Shoal Light and into Kuluk Bay with no sign of activity.

"Conn, Navigator. Recommend coming right to 220, sir." Bill got a fix from Zeto Point to the north, Pit Rock to the south, and a tangent into Scabbard Bay. He also had a couple of radio towers to the west. *Growler* slowly came right into the harbor and made her way toward the fueling dock inside Sweepers Cove. Not a soul was evident on the fuel pier and swinging the scope to the right, one merchant ship was in port—good, for it meant fresh food—and a couple Navy YTM tugboats were tied up at a small floating pier to starboard.

Bill planned the arrival. Officers and chiefs wore Japanese caps and the crew went topside out of uniform. They wore jeans and old foul weather gear. Most of the men grew enormous beards and long hair—Admiral Zumwalt would have been proud. The CO had the Conn and made a long, swooping turn from the south and came north to parallel the fuel pier.

As *Growler* came alongside the fueling berth and about fifty yards off the pier, she battle surfaced.[6] The hatches popped open and the scroungy crew appeared forward and aft, bearded and wearing red stars on their caps. *Growler* was covered in algae and slime, with a huge bow like nothing known in the American Fleet; there were no numbers or national ensign flying, and a gapping hole was in her superstructure where the storm had ripped off the decking.

An old retired chief in the fuel office awakened and stumbled out to the pier, rubbing his eyes in disbelief. He moved faster and ran back to the shack and moments later, another old chief came out. One of them yelled, "Ahoy there, who are you?"

Bill awaited the question on the sail with the CO. With megaphone to his mouth, he answered in a flurry of Russian. The two chiefs ran for the shack and hit the alarm. (It was 1962; the height of the Cold war.) "Whoop, Whoop, Whoop" screamed across the serenity of the Aleutian island.

A truckload of Marines arrived, followed closely by the Commanding Officer and the OOD (Officer of the Day). By the time the vehicles reached the pier, Don had maneuvered *Growler* sideways alongside the pier. The old chiefs refused to come out, so the *Growler* crew jumped onto the pier to take the lines and secure them to the pier.

The Commanding Officer of the base strode up to the boat and asked angrily, "Who the hell are you?"

"Good morning, Captain," answered Captain Don, "USS *Grayback* returning from patrol sir."[7]

"What can I do for you, Captain?"

"We need fuel, stores, fresh water, and liberty, sir," answered the CO.

"Very well, Captain. Have your Supply Officer come ashore and we'll accommodate you. By the way, I would appreciate it if you would fly the American Ensign, sir."

"Right away, Captain!"

"Anything else I can do for you, Captain?" asked the Base Commander.

"Yes, sir," replied the CO, "can we get the clubs opened?"

The Commanding Officer of the Base looked at his watch and replied, "But Captain, it's only 0900!" Now they knew the time.

"I appreciate that, sir, but we've been out for a long time and sure could use a few cool ones, sir."

"I'll see what I can do, sir. Meanwhile, my OOD will give you a set of our Rules and Regulations, which, by the way, spell out the proper procedure for entering port!"

"Much obliged, sir." With that, the Base Commander returned to the Chapel, the OOD ordered the clubs open, and supply personnel took off with fists full of requisitions. The rest of the crew went about their duties.

The noise that frightened everyone during the big storm was obvious. A huge section of aluminum superstructure had ripped off the main deck above the watertight hull and aft of the sail. It made line handling on the starboard side precarious. There was little room to walk aft of the sail except on the remaining frames. They also found the port bow plane broken at the knuckle and disconnected from the operating shaft. Apparently, the action of the starboard plane alone permitted them to operate normally. *Growler* looked like she had been through a war.

Liberty would wait for Bob, who was on duty. It wasn't bad news, for he wouldn't have the duty for the first few days in Pearl. He monitored the preparations to fuel and Wayne walked him through the fuel lineup. The senior engineering chief, ENC(SS) Schooley, was also on duty, so the fuel operation was in good hands. Fueling began and Wayne went ashore, assured all was well.

Members of the duty section, not standing watch, fueling, or taking on stores, took out the crab nets and began netting the Alaskan King Crab. After dark, the crabs appeared by the dozens and the cook, Ma Irwin, had kettles of boiling water and seasoning below. He made a sauce, melted butter and the feast began. What couldn't be eaten was frozen for the rest of the crew. Chief Terry returned with stores and the first item to come aboard was cases of frozen Alaskan King Crab meat. It cost only $0.15 a pound from the cannery on Adak, but it lacked the flavor of the freshly caught crab.

Grayback's first Captain, Hugh Nott, purchased a huge box of frozen crab for a special party he was planning later back in Pearl Harbor. Upon return from the boat's first patrol the crab was forgotten with most thoughts concentrating on families. The crab remained in the freezer for over a month when it was finally time for Captain Nott to utilize the crab for his party. Just about simultaneously, the boat's softball team threw a party after a game and celebrated a win with Alaskan King Crab. No one knows for sure what was substituted at Nott's dinner for the crab.

The engineers fueled and supply personnel took on stores. For the moment, Bob was in charge of the submarine in almost a foreign country. He was nervous. He began a below decks inspection a few minutes after liberty call sounded. As he passed through the after battery, he heard a disturbance topside and investigated. The topside watch had tied a line (rope) around the chest of a very drunk and boisterous shipmate.

"My God, Meyer's been on liberty for less than half an hour."

"It's okay Mr. H, Dick just had too much too fast. These young kids forget they've been without booze for months and it hits 'em hard and fast. He had qualified on patrol and drank for his dolphins. He probably chugged a quart of whiskey or somethin'," said the topside watch.[8] (The practice ceased on *Growler* by order of the CO). The POW (Petty Officer of Watch) came up the ladder and between the three men, they lowered their shipmate down the hatch into the crew's mess. Meanwhile, in the forward torpedo room, Heatwole was being lowered down a similar hatch. They both had finished drinking for their dolphins.

"How many of our crew went over today to drink for their dolphins Brown?" Bob asked.

"Six I think, sir."

"Oh, great," murmured Bob. It didn't take long for the four to show up. With the newly qualified stowed away safely, Bob felt his problems for the day were over. As the day wore on, the crew dribbled back, each with a different story of his great adventures ashore.

"There's one tree they call the Adak Forest," reported one of the sailors. "The Exchange has a sale on fur Eskimo parkas in progress—great for Hawaii!" After nightfall, Bob went below for seconds on the crab when another racket started topside. He climbed up the ladder in time to greet ten of the crew returning in a stolen truck carrying a log.

"What are you guys up to?" Bob queried.

"Hey there, Mr. H, look what we found." In the dim light he looked at a totem pole.

"Damn it guys, you can't steal the island's landmark"

"You can bet your sweet bipee we can, sir."

"Well take your sweet bipee and this totem pole back where you found it!"

"Aye, sir, but Commander Gunn told us to take it to the boat, remove the wings, and stow it in a tube." Bob heard stories on patrol about the totem pole and the tricks submariners played in the past but... oh, well.

"Okay, if Mr. Gunn said to do it, I'm not one to contradict a Commander's orders. Okay, then, get it down below fast and get the truck out of here too."[9]

About 2200, the CO returned with the officers. As they walked up the gangway, a car pulled up and the XO jumped out with that big smile.

"I got hold of tomorrow's flight plan so we'll know who is flying where and when."

"Ah ha. Well done, XO, very well done." The next morning when they headed south, they would know where the pesky P2Vs were and be able to disappear well before being detected. "How's the fueling going, Bob?" asked the CO.

"Pretty good, Captain. Only have #4 Fuel Ballast Tank left to go."

"Good. I'm hitting the rack. When the fueling is complete and things stowed, set the Maneuvering Watch and wake me."

George Playdon and Dave Butler had returned with a nurse from the hospital. They had promised to show her the boat. They stopped for a cup of coffee in the Wardroom and during the conversations, heard about Hotdog. Devilishly, they escorted the nurse into the Forward Torpedo Room where Hotdog was sound asleep—or very out of it. With a little prompting, the nurse leaned over Hotdog's bunk and prepared to give him a kiss. Hotdog came out of his rack, fists flying and ready to do battle with anyone attempting to kiss him. You never bring a woman into a submarine berthing area, especially after liberty.[10]

The engineers finished fueling at midnight and as the crew removed the hose from the boat, Bob noticed a Navy truck hurrying down the hill toward the pier. The truck came to a screeching stop by the gangway and a super-hyper airdale lieutenant commander with "OOD" on his sleeve ran up the gangway yelling, "Okay, where the hell is the totem pole?"

"I beg your pardon, Commander?"

"I said, mister, where the hell is the totem pole?"

"Excuse me, sir, but you forgot to request permission to come aboard!"

"Say what, Lieutenant?"

"You're on a United States warship, Commander. You're supposed to salute the watch and request permission to come aboard."

"I'm supposed to salute a seaman?"

"That's the name of the tune, Commander."

"Bull shiiit! I want to see the Captain and right now. Do you read me, mister?"

"Yes, sir, I hear you but don't see you since you really aren't here for you never received permission to be here, sir!" Bob glanced at Petty Officer Larry Gleason and knew he must stop playing with the airdale soon for his topside watch was about to explode in laughter. Gleason had to admit, Bob had balls.

"Sir, would you please put out your butt?"

"What... what did you say, mister?"

"Your cigarette butt, sir. The smoking lamp is out."

"Oh," and he threw his cigarette over the side. He didn't know whether to get angry or die of frustration. "Mister. I am here to retrieve a large totem pole your crew stole from the base."

"A totem pole, sir. Isn't that your base symbol, a totem pole?"

"Yes, damn it. Where is your Captain. I want to talk to him."

"He's asleep down below, sir."

"Well wake him. I have to talk to him right now."

"No way, sir. No one wakes up our Captain without authority, no one, no way."

"Well then I'll wake him. Where do I go?"

"Right down that hole over there, sir."

"Thanks."

"You're welcome, sir. By the way, if you hear a klaxon sound, we'll be diving under, sir." There was no way the pilot was going to go below with that thought in mind. Bob finally relented and took him to meet the CO. The CO was enjoying a deep sleep. It was the first time in months he had no worry.

"Excuse me, sir, this is the base OOD who is looking for a lost totem pole sir."

"Totem pole," said the captain, "How'd it get lost?"

"We believe your crew stole it, Captain, and we want it back now!"

"I don't know anything about your lost totem pole..."

"But, sir, I'm sure its on board this submarine, sir," the OOD interrupted. The CO sat up, turned on his bunk light, looked at the OOD, turned off the bunk light, and laid back down.

"Bob, take him through the boat until he is satisfied his lost piece of wood isn't here, then kick Chief Sitting Bull off the ship!" They found no totem pole, nor even the slightest trace of one, so Bob saw the cocky airdale off the ship, made a quick check of the boat below decks, and stationed the Maneuvering Watch.

Growler made a typical submarine impression on Adak, which seemed so ripe to attract the mischievous talents of the crews. There are numerous Adak totem pole stories and it is difficult to ascertain which are true. *Grayback* claims to be the first boat to steal the pole but was caught after the fact and returned the pole prior to leaving port. *Barbero* did steal the pole and managed to leave port with it, but by the time they returned to Pearl, the theft reached type commander level. The pole was off loaded under the cover of darkness and delivered to the XO's house, Gene Wells. Weeks later, Gene threw a party at his house and set up the totem pole as the center of interest. The CO, Lieutenant Commander Mueller, found little joy in the sight and immediately sent it to Adak.[11]

A patrol or two later, *Barbero* stopped at Adak enroute to station and the officers vented their fun on one of their own at the O' Club. The club was a tiny place, a Quonset hut converted into a bar, and the officers indulged. A lieutenant (jg) went a bit overboard and passed out. He appeared in bad shape, so the officers carried him to the dispensary to make sure he was okay. The chief corpsman assured the officers he would be fine after he slept it off. Then mischief entered and the officers convinced the chief to place the lieutenant (jg) in a full cast on each leg. Following the plaster job, the officers carried the lieutenant (jg) back and placed him in his bunk. The next morning, he awakened at sea with a headache and baffled by the sight of his legs. The officers explained he followed a lady to Navy housing only to have her husband return. He had hurtled out a bedroom window on the second floor and broke both legs. It was a great joke yet the wardroom carried it further. They didn't tell him the real story and he suffered through six weeks of hobbling around the submarine. When his casts were removed, his legs were so white and wrinkled, he couldn't tell his legs were never broken. He moved cautiously as his legs strengthened. The officers never told him what happened and to this day, his medical record indicates two legs were broken.[12] In reality, there were no promiscuous ladies at Adak.

The Duty Chief had trouble getting the crew up and the new "qualifies" never did answer the bell. Bob had trouble with the officers who were not eager to get up.

"Go to the bridge, Bob, and get things started. I'll be up shortly," the CO told him. The engines were running, but the pilot and tugboats didn't show up. Bob called the CO and told him the Maneuvering Watch was set and ready to get underway.

"Fine. Bob, get the boat underway," ordered the CO.

"Excuse me sir, did you just tell me to get the boat underway?"

"Get the crap out of your ears, Bob. Yes, get the ship out of here. You remember how we came in don't you?"

"Yes sir."

"Well, go out the same way but don't submerge." Bob was scared but it dawned on him he knew how to drive ships. A submarine couldn't be much different.[13]

The wind and cold rain howled down the mountains but Bob was too busy to feel the cold.

"Single all lines." He had to twist the boat around without tugs and against the wind; that wouldn't be easy. He had done it on destroyers many times but they had 60,000 shaft horsepower compared to under 3,000 SHP for *Growler*. "Maneuvering, Bridge, answer all bells."

Bob felt a decent Evinrude outboard motor would give him more power but *Growler* swung out as the boat shuddered from the power twist. Off the pier came *Growler* and slowly backed away from the arc of pier lights and was cast in a shadow of darkness. Her bow came through the wind as if she knew she was homeward bound. He required recommendations from the navigator for courses.

"Bridge, this is Glacy. sir. The Navigator isn't here."

"Boy, when he told me to take it out by myself he meant it," Bob mumbled to himself. "Quartermaster, Bridge. Do you have a navigation plot going?"

"Yes, sir, and we're right on. Recommend coming left to course 060°, sir."

"Damn, Glacy. I never thought I'd love the sound of your voice." So they stood out to sea, past Pit Rocks Light and toward the open sea. Soon the boat heaved and gently rolled under a good sea. A feeling of relief and satisfaction crossed Bob as he watched the last Adak buoy pass astern. "Control, Bridge. Secure the Maneuvering Watch, set the regular underway watch." "What section is up next, chief?"

"Control, aye, sir. You're next on watch." There was a long silence and Bob wearily replied, "Bridge, aye, chief. Thanks a lot! Please send up hot coffee and my mittens." Suddenly,

"This is the Captain, I have the Conn, Bob. Your relief is on the way. Nice job." Bob heard laughing in the background. The officers had been on station including the CO. They wanted to see if Bob could handle the situation and were ready to step in if he headed for trouble. Bob's left leg got longer... again.

One of the responsibilities officers faced on the last leg of the patrol was to become gentlemen again. Most of them used four letter words liberally when they spoke. The solution was "Couth Week." Every profane or otherwise offensive word or gesture carried a cash penalty when used. The money went into a pot traditionally used to fund the first wardroom party after returning to Pearl. The wives were always curious to know the biggest contributors and for the past three patrols, the title went to Bill hands down. Bill was determined not to be the loser again. The first few days, he taped his mouth shut with masking tape so he couldn't swear.

The remainder of the trip went without incident as they dived at the first indication of approaching aircraft. A few days out of Adak, *Growler* was on the surface at best speed for home plate.

South of the Aleutian Island chain, the ocean current turned almost 180 degrees. The current swept north along the Asian landmass, then was turned eastward by the Aleutian Islands, and eventually headed south along Alaska and Canada. Along with the current floated Japanese fishing balls that had broken loose from nets over the years. *Growler* was ahead of schedule, so sightings of fishing balls resulted in man-overboard drills for the officers. The duty section went topside to recover the glass balls for the OOD or whomever he declared owner of the ball. It was fun and many balls were gathered and the entire crew eventually ended up with at least one glass fishing ball. What mattered was the experience the officer's received maneuvering the submarine. It was also a time to cross train the engineering ratings that came forward and took part in dives, surfaces, and boat's maneuvers.

Growler surfaced on Saturday morning well within the submarine local operating areas of Hawaii. It was now permissible to be detected. The crew went topside to enjoy the fresh air and place a little color on their white bodies. Sunburns came fast and the algae on the boat baked white under the hot Hawaiian sun.

That evening the crew listened to radio stations on Oahu and reminisced about Japanese pilots who listened to the same stations twenty years earlier. No one slept as "Channel Fever" peaked.

The crew enjoyed the last night of the patrol, including the wardroom. They played "Oh, Shit," watched movies, and while Captain Don was laughing loudly about something, Bill asked what they should do with the totem pole.

"What!!!"

"Sir, I just asked what you want done with the totem pole."

"We have Adak's totem pole?"

"Ah, er, yes, sir."

"Where the hell is it?" No one said Bill lacked guts.

"I'll tell you when you put a dime in the pot sir."

"For what?"

"For the H word sir."

"Damn."

"Make that two dimes, sir."

"Okay, here's a quarter. Keep the change. Now where is it."

"Tube #3 sir."

The wardroom was stony silent. Everyone's eyes were on the CO. He sat with jaw muscles working and stared at each of his officers. Bob couldn't look him in the eye. Then suddenly, he jumped up, "I love it!"

Sunday morning, they neared Papa Hotel (PH-Pearl Harbor's sea buoy) and everyone took a shower and donned their tropical white long uniforms for entering port. Everyone was smiles and happiness. Bill was fine free for "Couth Week," which ended when the ship tied up. As they showered and dressed, some officers moved into the wardroom to afford their roommates room to dress in the staterooms. *Growler* rolled gently in the sea and Bill stepped out of his stateroom to give the XO room to dress. In skivvies, with whites in hand, the boat rolled heavily to starboard. Bill lurched into the wardroom, grabbed the table in front of him to prevent slamming into it. The momentum and sudden stop caused his manlihood to fall out of his boxer shorts and land on the wardroom table. Laughter bellowed from the wardroom and he was fined $25.00 for displaying himself in public. He was the loser again.

Growler's topside looked a disaster. Only the *Grayback* had looked worse when she lost every bit of superstructure aft of the sail. The boat was white after the algae baked in the sun, except where dead algae had peeled off, revealing the original black vinyl paint. Someone thought it clever to paint black machine gun bullet holes across the sail as if they had been strafed and so it was done.

Growler rounded "PH" and the Maneuvering Watch was stationed. Entering port after a patrol, the Conn was always in the hands of the CO or XO. Bob was topside and sighted the Admiral's barge (boat for a flag officer) standing out to meet *Growler*. It was a routine practiced by submariners and no reason for concern. The Admiral would board, congratulate the Captain for a successful patrol and then the two officers would swap stories and lies until the boat tied up.

"Commander, Submarine Force Pacific arriving," bellowed the 1MC speakers as Admiral Clarey clambered aboard. Captain Don climbed down to greet the Admiral as he stepped aboard. The usual smile was not on the Admiral's face. In its stead was a frown and look of horror.

"Good morning, Admiral."

"Good morning, Don. How was the patrol?" responded the Admiral curtly.

"Admiral, the patrol went well. I think you will be pleased after you read our patrol report."

"Well, Don, I'd be one hell of a lot more pleased if you weren't carrying the totem pole from Adak and by god, get those machine gun holes covered up on your sail right now!"

"I'll get to it right now skipper," yelled XO Bob, who headed down the ladder for the main deck.

"Totem pole Admiral? What totem pole are you speaking of sir?" answered the CO.

"Damn it, Don! Do you or don't you have Adak's totem pole?"

"I cannot tell a lie admiral... we do." There was a pause for a moment, then the admiral grinned,

"Alrighta! Good. Damn good. Well done. It's time we got a shot in against those fly boys again, Don."

"Thank you, sir."

"Of course, you understand, you must immediately send the totem pole back, along with a letter of apology."

"I understand, Admiral."

Growler berthed at Pier Sierra Nine (S-9) with tugboats shooting water into the air and the band playing loudly. The usual banners and welcome home signs were everywhere as the families welcomed the crew back home. Dave was on the forecastle (pronounced folk sail) and his fiancée was on the pier. She called out,

"I love you, David." Then the entire crew topside quipped back in unison,

"We love you, David." Dave turned red. The crew remembered Dave had qualified in submarines just prior to the last trip but had not received his customary "heave-ho" over the side. The crew grabbed him, took his cap and wallet, and unceremoniously, tossed him over the side. They helped him up the side of the boat and as he stood soaking wet waving at his bride to be, he realized his whites had become completely transparent. He turned brighter red.

Homecomings were great events and participated in by all hands with a great deal of gusto and enthusiasm. *Barbero* returned home from a patrol with a new navigator who reported aboard between back-to-back patrols, so none of the crew knew his wife. The submarine berthed and he surrendered the periscope to the crew in the Conning Tower for periscope liberty. The men took turns looking through the scope for their loved ones.

One crew peered through the periscope and hollered, "Hey, there's a good looking broad out there in a purple dress. Boy, I tell you what I'd do with her for a night!" The single men were rather descriptive about any skirts observed that included the lady in purple.

The chatter continued for ten minutes among the single sailors when the navigator took the periscope back and announced, "The lady in purple is my wife!" The Conning Tower became quiet and when the navigator looked up, it was empty.[14]

Growler received the ComSubPac Unit Commendation for both her Regulus patrols.

Not all mischief and fun took place in Adak. Early in *Halibut*'s life, she was docked in Wellington, New Zealand on what was deemed to be a shakedown cruise. A local television station asked for permission to hold a live fashion show topside utilizing some of the crew for a background. Permission was granted and models came aboard to change clothes for the show and sale. For some reason, the TV show had a mascot that was a beautiful and large white cockatoo in a cage. The show went on as scheduled and went well until it was time to close the show. The show always ended with a close up shot by the camera of the bird. The producer asked MM2(SS) Bob Hurley to pick up the cage and carry it towards the camera. The wind was blowing a stiff breeze on the waterfront and it was difficult to hear. Bob thought he said to pick up the model. He walked up behind a model, grabbed her, kicking and screaming, and dragged her toward the camera. She presented a much better closing than the cockatoo.[15]

Chapter Seven
Home at Last and More Practice

The tensions, angers, and anxieties of a five-month patrol melted away in the warm and smooth body that so gracefully and willingly surrendered to his every move. The long patrol disappeared into a memory bank containing remains of duty to country.

"You can't believe how many times I dreamed of this moment," they whispered simultaneously. They went to Bellows Air Force Base on a perfect day in Hawaii and Bob couldn't wait to get into the warm aquamarine waters; but then it was a perfect day for them no matter what the weather. By nightfall, his white body was burned to a bright red. He didn't need a sunburn for his homecoming night but eventually he went to sleep. Only moments elapsed when he awakened with a start as the beach cottage bounced and vibrated. The night air was filled with the roar of engines and clanking steel treads. The mechanical noises were joined by the shouts, yells, and grunts of hundreds of men.

"What the hell is going on? Do they have earthquakes in Hawaii?" Bob raced to the bedroom window. It was still dark but someone was awake and moving. Seeing little, he dashed to the front door of the cottage that faced the beach and ocean. He tripped over his own underwear enroute to the door, "Holy shit! We're either on Iwo Jima or John Wayne is making another movie." The entire beach was filled with Marines storming ashore with tanks and LCTs. The tanks and carriers passed down either side of the cottage as did the Marines. As the battle dressed Marines passed by the cottage, they looked up and whistled and cheered.

"What's going on Honey?" asked his wife who stood next to him in a teddy. One glance at her and Bob understood the whistles.

"Looks like some kind of amphibious landing exercise and the Marines have landed. You better get inside before the Marines decide to attack you and forget the beach."

"It's a good thing they don't have women marines or they would be whistling at you," his wife replied. Bob looked down and, "Oh, boy!" The elastic band on his shorts had rubbed his sunburn so he removed them when he went to bed. His face turned redder than his back.

They enjoyed a week in the sun, the warm water, and being in each other's arms. Bellows was a recreational area for all of the Armed Forces, hosted by the Air Force. The little wooden cottage was on the water's edge of the white sand beach just north of Kanehoe. The weather was perfect and they enjoyed it almost as much as each other. They ate and sang, swam and enjoyed the week under the sun and moon.

The next thing the crew accomplished was offloading torpedo and missile warheads. The second week back in Pearl, on Monday morning, they went to the Naval Ammunition Depot in West Loch. The first trip to West Loch was a historic event for the new crew members. The channel to West Loch was off the Pearl Harbor main channel and contained remains from the "Day of Infamy." They passed skeletons of LSTs (Landing Ship Tank) and remnants of the pier where the ammunition ship *Pyro* exploded. The scars of Pearl Harbor were evident everywhere. When the crew wasn't looking at the ruins, they watched hammerhead sharks. They proliferated in West Loch, which some claimed to be a primary breeding area.

Growler pulled alongside the old wood wharf and the skipper of the Ammunition Station came out to greet them. He exchanged pleasantries and documents with Don for the missiles and warheads. The ammo depot was a picture from a World War II history book and a weapons facility during the war. The ammunition bunkers were covered in jungle growth and the air filled with the sound of birds and the musty smell of a rain forest.

When the boat entered the channel to West Loch, it was akin to entering a world not of their time but of years past. Outside sound vanished and the channel was covered in a canopy of tree limbs and vines. The water was a muddy brown and quiet as a puddle of oil. Few men knew of another World War II connection and the old ammo bunkers at West Loch.

One hundred miles north of Iwo Jima and 500 miles south of Tokyo is a small volcanic island called Chi Chi Jima. Early in the war, the Japanese wrested the island from a handful of natives and set about the work of building a large ammunition supply depot. The ten square mile island was captured by the United States and came under U.S. control in 1945. It became a Naval Facility in 1952. In one of the old cave bunkers, the Japanese lined the cave with a copper sheath to halt water seepage into the cave. The Navy kept some nuclear warheads for the Regulus in the cave. Not far from the island, a young George Bush was shot down. Today, Chi Chi Jima is a huge tourist facility.

West Loch was the new crew members' first opportunity to watch *Growler's* huge hangar doors open and the missiles ram out unto the launcher. *Growler* set a modified Battle Stations Missile and crew members that handled missiles and missile systems were on station. The men read and spoke from a Nuclear Weapons Check Off Sheet. Nothing on a nuclear warhead or system was touched without strictly following a prescribed procedure.

The locking rings on the hangars rotated to the open position, similar to a torpedo tube, and the enormous doors lifted open. The missile launcher shifted to a point directly behind the starboard hangar. A piece of rail slid into place so the missile could be rammed out of the hangar and onto the launcher. A crane gently lifted the missile off the launcher after disconnection from the rail and set it in a dolly on the pier.

The four tactical "blue bird" missiles were replaced by two exercise missiles. The real or tactical missiles were painted blue and the exercise missiles red. The exercise missiles were equipped with wheels for landing and were reusable. *Growler* was to launch two exercise missiles during a training period preparatory to the next patrol.

When all the missiles were transferred, the Mk 14 war shot torpedoes were off loaded. They were the heart of the World War II torpedo threat after the detonator problems were solved. They were reliable and used primarily against surface ships. The Mk 16 torpedoes were offloaded next, which were also steam-propulsion, but oxygen was provided by a substance called Navol. Using Navol *vice* a large air flask gave the designers room to add more explosives in the warhead and the MK 16 carried a huge wallop. Navol was relatively unstable and required constant monitoring for it could become explosive. Once the Navol became unstable, it produced oxygen and heat in an exponential curve leading to an explosion. Next the Mk 37s were off loaded, which were the primary anti-submarine torpedoes.

The Maneuvering Watch was stationed and *Growler* headed back to S-9 at the Sub Base. Bob was permitted to drive the boat back and it was enjoyable. He headed out of West Loch and steered the winding channel back to the main Pearl Harbor Channel, which was like taking an "E" ticket ride at Disneyland. Tall trees and palms hung out over the water as they were surrounded by a rain forest ecosystem. The crew enjoyed the ride as well and sat on deck with a cup of coffee and a cigarette taking in the serenity of the channel.

"Bridge, Radio. U.S.S. *Kitty Hawk* standing into port sir. She reported passing "PH."

Before he figured out the answer himself, Bill called, "Bridge, Navigator. At this speed, we should enter the main channel about a mile ahead of the *Kitty Hawk.*"

"Navigator, bridge, aye. Thank you, sir," Bob replied.

"Thank you, sir? Oh you are so welcome, Sir Mr. H." It was a slam at more than a simple acknowledgment and using the word "sir." A grin crossed Bob's face and he looked at the CO, who busily wiped a smile from his lips.

Bill Gunn thoroughly enjoyed laughing and funny remarks. A common remark of his was, "You do nice work for a hairlip!" It was actually a compliment and wasn't considered inappropriate at the time. He usually reserved the comment for navigation work of the quartermasters.

Growler moved past Ford Island ahead of the *Kitty Hawk* without a nudge in the stern by the carrier.

"Pearl Harbor Control with their challenge, sir," reported Glacy.

"Send, *request permission to enter port,* quartermaster," Bob ordered. The signal light chattered with the typical clack, clack, clickety clank clanking sound as the message went out to the Control Tower and acknowledgement of the reply,

"Permission granted *Growler.*"

Growler passed the carriers berthed at Ford island, hung a right and passed the destroyers and cruisers plus the shipyard to starboard. A hard left sent the *Growler* into the Sub Base basin. The next morning, exercise torpedoes were loaded. They also were to be fired during the training prior to deployment.

In the Regulus Program, officer and enlisted often changed duty stations to billets within the Regulus program. This was logical since there was little expertise in Regulus outside the program and it took time to train new men.

The engineers went to work following the stand-down. There were many equipments to be repaired and a main engine to be overhauled. They worked every day, all day, and well into the night to finish their maintenance and repair. Meanwhile, the weapons area prepared for refresher training and the at-sea exercises with missiles and torpedoes. The CO sent Bob and Perry to the torpedo shop with the torpedomen to get hands-on experience in making torpedoes ready to be fired.

More times than not, the Regulus boats ended up in the shipyard following a patrol for major repairs. Shipyards posed a challenge to submariners to get as much work accomplished as possible for the buck and to see how much could be "borrowed."

Grayback had the master midnight requisitioner in MM1(SS) Valpoon. He was a Kinaki, or native Hawaiian, who fit in perfectly with the shipyard workers. He wore bib overalls and an appropriate colored hard hat to match the shop he entered. He walked freely through the entire complex and shops of interest, helping himself to whatever material or equipment he required. On one such expedition, he not only borrowed a significant amount of goods but also "borrowed" a truck to haul his load back to *Grayback.* Following a number of nights of requisitioning, his work was noticed and the Naval Intelligence Service was called in to find the thief. They quickly traced the thefts to Valpoon and *Grayback.* The material was returned and Valpoon reprimanded—but not seriously since his efforts transferred ownership from one naval unit to another—not a penny for himself.

GMU-10 (Guided Missile Unit 10) held schools on the Regulus and Bob spent a week learning the system from the real experts. The timing was perfect for it filled in remaining blanks in his Qualification Notebook and his personal knowledge of the missiles. A part of the Officer's Qualification was a notebook each officer wrote, which required drawings of the ship's systems and answers to a series of questions considered pertinent to the qualification process and the officer's individual submarine. The main categories of the questions were in shipboard systems and tactics, including missiles. MT1(SS) William Karr was his favorite instructor. Karr made the move from Puerto Rico to Pearl Harbor on *Growler* a few years earlier.

A requirement for graduation from Submarine School was successfully completing an escape from the fifty-foot level in the Escape Training Tank. Although it was so entertaining and fun, most submariners volunteered and made the escape from the one hundred-foot depth as well. The required "blow and go" was a source of many a story of near successes and near disastrous but funny after all was well. The de-paint job of this tower has been discussed but the other tower, in New London, Connecticut, is the other. Many years ago, the facility burned to the ground—melted is more accurate. It has been alleged by an undisclosed wife of COMSUBLANT in Norfolk, that "Only a bunch of submarine sailors (expletive) could burn down a steel tank filled with salt water."[1]

Two weeks after *Growler's* return, the officers and wives held their first party. Don Breeding held the party at his home on Ewa Beach. It was a typical *Growler* wardroom party with 100% participation except the duty officer. Everyone wanted to talk to everyone, so they sat in a circle in the living room and talked and told stories. Bob hadn't talked with the wives since they greeted him in Honolulu a half year earlier.

"My goodness, Bob, you have added a bit of color since returning a couple weeks ago. You're looking very well."

"Thank you, Billie (Henderson). Looks like you and the Captain have seen a little time outside yourselves."

"Well, while you were at Bellows, we enjoyed Barbers Point." Then came the big question.

"Okay, who was the big loser on this patrol? Bill won't tell me so I suppose it was him again," howled Gerri Gunn.

"Let me tell the story," broke in Wayne. "I've got to tell it. Ladies, this year we witnessed the biggest turnaround the *Growler* ever witnessed in Couth Week." There was a chorus of "yahs!" from the officers as they urged Wayne on with his story among multitudes of laughter and chuckles. "Well, Bill didn't want to be the big loser again so... and then just as we were about to enter port, he stepped into the wardroom and *voila*, the smallest little thing you every did see fell out of his shorts and onto the wardroom table."

Tears rolled out of everyone's eyes in uproarious laughter when Bill's wife said, "Little thing, that's Bill!"

The group quieted and split into smaller group conversations as the wives wanted to know everything that happened on patrol and the officers wanted to hear the latest happenings in Pearl Harbor and about their friends. There were no games or entertainment, just a group of couples who shared so much. Bob was amazed and pleased with the warmth and camaraderie shown by everyone. In minutes, they became a member of a close and wonderful community. When they finally got up to leave, Bob's sides were racked with pain from constant laughing for hours on end.

The following Monday *Growler* departed for sea to conduct underway training which concluded with the launching of a training missile. The submarine launched from a location off Kaena Point on the west side of Oahu to a target point that was a large rock just north of Kaui. Chase aircraft followed the missile and took control of it if anything went wrong. The submarine simulated ending the missile's flight over the target and the spot of flight termination was triangulated to determine the accuracy of the shot. A guidance officer on *Growler* guided the missile left or right and down, ordered as "Check One, Two, and Three." There was no ability to increase the missile's altitude after the initial ordered altitude was achieved. The flight was terminated by simulating 110% power and the missile going into a terminal dive with the order "Check Four." Then the chase aircraft took control of the missile and landed it on a small airstrip on the west side of Kaui Island known as Barking Sands.

On the Sunday night prior to getting underway, the Squadron Commodore ran into an Annapolis classmate who was the skipper of the new super aircraft carrier, USS *Constellation* (CVA-64). One thing led to another and soon a bet solidified. The Commodore bet his Regulus Missile could penetrate the carrier screen and simulate destroying the carrier.

"Commodore, are you trying to tell me your Regulus can penetrate a carrier screen, avoid the CAP aircraft, and get through to my carrier?"

"You can bet your butt on that, Captain and if you like, I'll even land that little bird right on your flight deck!"

"Bull. My flyers will have the bird turned into falling debris 30 miles away from the carrier."

"Well, Captain, talk is cheap. Put your wallet where your mouth is!"

"Damn it, cover this hundred bucks, Commodore, or are you still chicken?"

"Chicken! You're covered and add another hundred."[2] As *Constellation* stood out to sea the next day, the Commodore called the Captain to insure he had sufficient materials to patch the soon to be hole in his flight deck.

"Commodore, I've got more material on board this carrier than all the submarines in the Pacific can carry."

"I can't argue that but after today you'll have more holes in your hull than all the submarines in the Pacific!" Cooler heads prevailed and *Growler* would fly Regulus down the side of the carrier about a mile off the beam rather than overhead. *Growler* followed the Monday exodus out of Pearl, headed west, submerged, turned north and traveled up the west side of Oahu until she reached the launch site off Kaena Point. New crew members were excited, including Bob, as they were about to witness their first Regulus launch.

Growler went to Battle Stations Missile and battle surfaced. The CO assigned Bob as DO for the exercise so he went to the bridge. Bob had reread the Battle Bill so he knew what to do but wasn't prepared for what happened. Missile communications was on the 32MC powered by 12 volts DC. Bob put on his headset and listened. His guidance from the CO was to keep quiet except when spoken to or if he saw a safety hazard.

"Bridge, Missile Control. Request permission to open hangar door #1." Bob looked over the sail and saw nothing in the way of the starboard door so he answered,

"Missile Control, Permission granted to open hangar door #1." The hangar door raised until it was upright above the hangar opening. The launcher moved behind the starboard hangar. MT1(SS) Warren Streeter flipped a section of bridging track into place.

"Bridge, Missile Control. Request permission to ram missile onto the launcher." MT2 Jerry Bruno walked out of the hangar with remote control in hand ready for orders.

"Missile Control, Bridge. Permission granted to ram missile onto launcher." Whenever nuclear power or nuclear weapons are handled, the entire procedure is spelled out on check-off sheets that are conscientiously followed. There was no room for error when dealing with nuclear power or weapons.

"Request permission to pressurize missile fuel system." MT3(SS) William Neff checked the bridging track lowered to the stow position; checked for stray RF energy around the igniters to the boosters; and when satisfied, withdrew to the missile hangar.

"Request permission to start up missile on the launcher." Bob called Control to insure a green light indicated the hangar door secured and checked the main deck around the missile.

"Permission granted to start up missile." The jet engine reached a pitched whine and Bob was grateful he wore a headset.

Bob realized why no one argued about going to the bridge for a view seat. The launcher was repositioned to centerline and elevated to ordered launch angle. The launcher used to be able to swing side to side but was changed during the overhaul with the sail heightening. The bow had to be within 60° of missile course. The Regulus II Missile System permitted the boat to remain on course and point the launcher but the Regulus II was never deployed.

The deck around the launcher was a scant two feet above the sea, and waves rolled across the deck beneath the missile. The jet exhaust hit the sea and vaporized the water. The hot vapors rose up through the inside of the sail and, in minutes, Bob was soaking wet in salty vapor. He was in a salt water sauna as the headset shorted between his ears. It was only 12 VDC but not comfortable.

"Bridge, this is the Captain. Clear the bridge and lay below!" Bob cleared the bridge happily. The boat was ready to launch. The launch sequence started with the ignition of two JATO boosters that lifted the missile off the launcher and up to a speed where the jet engines sustained the missile in flight. (JATO means Jet Assisted Take Off) The JATO bottles consumed so much oxygen, suffocation resulted if anyone remained topside.

"Missile away, missile away," came across the 1MC. A gigantic whoosh followed as the JATO bottles ignited. The missile took off and *Growler* staggered a bit. Bob was in the bridge access trunk securing the upper hatch when the missile was launched. The unexpected roar rattled him as he clung to the ladder. Bob thought the missile was to be launched after the bridge trunk was secured. The CO watched the missile leave the launcher and its initial flight through the periscope. When the boosters were expended, they dropped off the missile, as were the "slippers" or brackets that kept the missile on the launcher rails. When he saw this, he reported,

"Clean bird." The flight problem fell to the chase aircraft for safety and the guidance officer for accuracy. Bob went to his Battle Station Missile position in the wardroom where he donned a headset and monitored the same circuits as Dave, the guidance officer. He listened to missile traffic and helped George plot the missile course on the DRT in the wardroom table. Dave checked out his radar commands to the missile and reported,

"All functions satisfactory on the bird, sir." The F-8U Crusader chase aircraft flew with the missile. Dave brought the missile around to the west and flew the missile directly to the target. If the plot was an indication of accuracy, the missile was on target and headed for a hit if Dave "dumped" it correctly. "Stand by to dump missile," Dave passed on to the aircraft and tracking facilities on Kauai. "Check Four, now, now, now," Dave ordered.

"*Growler*, this is Chase Two. Looks like a perfect shot." The accuracy of the missile was determined by the tracking facility and chase aircraft.

Now the Commodore's bet came into play. The chase aircraft did not take control and Dave steered the missile south toward the task force. Regulus was a strategic weapon and had never been used tactically by a submarine. The missile was tracked by the BPQ-2 radar active emission from the submarine guided by the Trounce 1A Guidance System. On the tail of the Regulus missile was a directional antenna and transponder that boosted the submarines radar echo back to the submarine. Pulses sent by the radar made it move right, left, and down. The antenna was directional so an enemy could not jam the missile from forward of the beam. No one had tried to control the missile with an aspect forward of the beam.

Following the simulated dump, Dave gave it a series of predetermined left turn orders and brought its course to south toward the *Constellation* task group. The missile received Dave's orders cleanly as it flew away. Dave calculated the number of hard and soft turn commands perfectly as the missile headed directly for *Constellation*.[3] The exercise criteria assumed *Growler*, in a war scenario, would either detect the task group or receive usable intelligence of the group's location.

George shifted plotting paper and plotted *Constellation* as the target and drew a rectangle with a large "64" to simulate the flight deck. Bob heard pilot chatter in his right headset. Earlier, Dave ordered Radio to patch CAP Control (aircraft radio frequency) into one ear and the 32MC in the other. The carrier detected the incoming missile and launched a strike group to back up CAP. *Growler* was at periscope depth but had no radar that could look over the island so they relied on the mouths of the pilots for guidance and received it.

Regulus pooped along at its casual 500 knots or less when the CAP fighter aircraft vectored in to intercept. The aircraft overflew the missile, missed seeing it once, was finessed by Dave's drastic course and altitude changes, and the pilot's chatter on the radio circuit provided *Growler* with a wealth of information to successfully simulate hitting the target.

The CO called the Commodore in Pearl.

"Sir, *Constellation* is missing the big six four."

"Well done, *Growler*. You and your crew will kindly assist me to enjoy the skipper's loss. Upon return to port, the officers held their own mini celebration in the "Clean Sweep" Room at the Sub Base Officer's Club. The Commodore did not renege on his promise and a few weeks later, the O'Club held a popular event. Coincident with a large Hawaiian Luau Party, *Growler* was feted by the Commodore.[4]

Near the end of the party, the attendees were treated to authentic Hawaiian dancing. At the conclusion of the dancing, they asked for volunteers to learn the hula dance. A roar came from the *Growler* officers for their new navigator, Horace Leavitt, to go on stage and make an ass of himself. Horace was a wonderful Naval Officer, smart as a pin, and had a wonderful sense of humor, but a hula dancer he was not. The tall 6' 4" lanky man flapped his arms and jerked at the hips as the wardroom wept tears of laughter. Nancy Leavitt required help as she fell out of her chair laughing. The wardroom laughed with Horace who laughed more than any of the audience.

Perry and Bob decided it was the ideal time to take advantage of Horace. Horace owned a tiny Italian Siata car. Everyone wondered how he got his legs into the thing. Perry and Bob pushed the car from the parking lot to the Post Office. There were ten cement steps up to a landing in front of the Post Office door. The twosome found volunteers enroute and with the added help, picked up the little car and placed it in front of the entrance doors. On Monday, Horace mustered a working party from the crew to rescue his car amid stifled chuckles.

Synonymous with submarines were torpedoes. Bob and Perry, with the help of the TMs, prepared a torpedo to be fired in an exercise. Part of the officer's qualification practical factors was firing a torpedo. Sub School taught the torpedo, but this time TMC(SS) Mike Powell made the officers do each step in preparing a torpedo to fire. The checkouts were completed and the torpedoes loaded aboard with other exercise fish. The officers couldn't wait for their chance to fire their "own" torpedo.

Growler went to sea to hone her skills at firing torpedoes with USS *Florikan* as their surface target. *Florikan* was a submarine rescue vessel (ASR). As they stood out to sea, Perry and Bob's minds concentrated on torpedo tactics. A few hours later she made the first dive preparatory to beginning the torpedo exercises.

Wayne, Bob's mentor if you will, casually walked up to Bob and said, "Bob, I'd like you to have this. I'm in the service to repay the Navy for my scholarship at Stanford. You're going to be a career officer and this will mean more to you than it ever will to me." That said, he handed him a small black book entitled, "A Submarine Officer's Torpedo Record."

"Thank you, Wayne. This means a lot to me."

"You're welcome, Bob. Put it to good use."

"I hope to. Thank you."

The operating area was off Barber Point NAS, with a large oil refinery neighboring the base. The area was along the 50 fathom curve and very isothermal, meaning there were no layers within the boat's operating depth.

"Man Battle Stations Torpedo," blared the 1MC and the boat shifted into a war and shoot mode. The only voices heard were newcomers trying to find their battle stations.

"That's why we have exercises," mumbled the old timers. The first torpedo run was conducted by *Growler*'s torpedo fire control and torpedo team. The CO made the approach and nailed the *Florikan* with a MK 14 amidships. The torpedo running depth was always set well below the depth of the target's keel to avoid actually hitting the target. After the shot, *Growler* surfaced to help look for the exercise torpedo.

"Navigator, Bridge, give me a course to follow the torpedo track."

"Navigator aye, recommend coming right to course 350°, sir," called out Horace.

"Bridge, Radio, *Florikan* reports the run as a direct hit."

"Of course," replied the CO on the bridge, "I shot it!"

"Bridge, Radio. The torpedo chaser reports he has the torpedo in sight and will take it aboard. Recommends we continue with our next exercise when ready and he'll follow."

"Bridge aye. We'll dive in five. Inform Mr. H the next torpedo approach is his."

Bob's hands were cold and clammy but he was ready. A few minutes later, the boat dived and then, "Man Battle Station Torpedo." The CO called Bob to the Conn and gave him the scenario.

"We are in a patrol area off the coast of Russia and expect to encounter Soviet destroyer and destroyer escorts types. Their primary mission is looking for American submarines, which they know are in the area. It can be expected the destroyer types will practice evasive steering but with the intent of catching *Growler* and sinking her. Our mission, hunt and destroy all enemy vessels. Do you understand the situation Bob?"

"Yes, sir."

"Very well then, you have the Conn."

"This is Mr. H and I have the Conn."

The exercise began and it seemed that just seconds went by before it was over. Captain Don dutifully made the first entry into Bob's log. The entry was constructive, commenting on Bob's style and approach method, but in the bottom right corner, he wrote "HIT." Bob almost had to have his ears moved back so he could grin wider.

The next run was by Lieutenant Commander Eugene Wells in the midst of his Qualification for Command schedule. He was appraised of the same scenario and the exercise again initiated.

"Conn, Sonar. I have a contact. Bearing 265°, fast turn count, sir. Sounds like a Soviet destroyer, sir." Sonar played the game to add reality to the drill.

"Very well. Designate contact as Skunk Alpha. Lieutenant Commander Wells went through a similar exercise, including a last second change of course by the target. He took a deep breath at the moment of truth and knew he had the target dead to rights. "Up scope for final bearing and shoot!" The scope leaped upward and QM1 Taylor put him right on the money. "Damn, target zigged, target has zigged to his port. Down scope"

"Sonar confirms target has zigged away, sir."

"Roger. That's great because it opens his firing angle for me. Bearing... Mark!

Range... Mark! Down scope. Set Port angle 50. Shoot!" *Growler* vibrated a bit as the torpedo left the tube.

"Conn, Forward Torpedo Room. #4 tube fired electrically. Torpedo running hot, straight, and in low speed, sir."

"Low speed!" Gene cried into the 21 MC. "All torpedoes are set at Hi Speed unless otherwise directed, isn't that correct?"

"Yes, sir."

"Conn, Radio. *Florikan* reports torpedo passed 100 yards astern, sir."

"Very well," he answered and then set up for another shot. Gene wanted the torpedo to be a hit. They went through the exercise and fired a second torpedo that was a hit. Radio reported,

"*Florikan* reports first torpedo ran up on the beach at Barbers Point 10 feet east of the refinery cooling water outlet."

"Very well," Gene answered.

When the data was in, Gene had a near perfect solution on his first shot and a hit on the second. Later, when the torpedo was recovered, the TMs established the torpedo had not malfunctioned but was inadvertently set on Lo Speed. They also found the stretch of beach hit by the torpedo was frequented by ladies who wanted a tan with no sun lines. When the torpedo ran up on the beach, the ladies frantically exited leaving most of their tops and bottoms behind. The end result was the oil refinery stitched onto the ship's flag.[5]

The torpedo shot was the apex of peacetime torpedo statistics until a few years later when Lieutenant George Henson fired a Mk 16 torpedo at a PCE (Escort Patrol Craft) which was the target. The torpedo ran erratically and porpoised along the surface, striking the PCE amidships at the water line instead of passing below the target. The torpedo passed through the hull and out the other side, sinking the PCE. The submarine picked up all of the PCE's crew. George established himself as the leader of tonnage sunk during peace time of his own Navy.[6]

Grayback also enjoyed a torpedo target story. In 1961, the USS *Epperson* (DD-719) was her target. Despite observing the wake of the torpedoes pass directly under the destroyer's hull, the destroyer repeatedly reported the torpedo runs as misses. *Grayback* reported the next torpedo porpoised and struck the *Epperson* aft of the stacks at the water line, hitting a rib and placed a 3 foot wide dent in her hull. That torpedo run was evaluated as a "hit!"[7]

Years later, Bob was on the *Catfish* in a fleet exercise and was being held down by a HUK group (Hunter Killer Group). The destroyers and helicopters followed the *Catfish*'s every which way she turned and the helicopters dropped a series of explosive grenades above the submarine and the attack was evaluated a "near miss" despite insulation raining down throughout the boat. When *Catfish* surfaced, two of the bomb remnants were wedged between the wooden slats on her main deck.

Chapter Eight
Off and At 'Em Again

As *Growler* passed the Control Tower at Ford Island,
"Pearl Harbor Control this is *Growler*, over."
"This is Pearl Harbor Control."

"Pearl Harbor Control, request permission to proceed to sea for local operations."

"This is Pearl Harbor Control. Permission granted to proceed to sea *Growler*. Be advised *Hancock* is ahead of you and *King* astern."

"Roger, Pearl Harbor Control." The CO waved at the tower as they steamed by and received a wave in return from behind the tinted glass window.

Growler's numbers weren't painted on the sail but pasted on with masking tape to appear like numbers and her name no longer appeared on either side of the Turtle Back.[1] She was underway for her 6th deterrent patrol. One look at the sobbing wives and crying children on the pier when *Growler* departed was indicative of the submarine's destination.

Bill Gunn was missed, although the crew was proud of his billet as Executive Officer on *Grayback*. The new Navigator was Horace Leavitt and he loved the new Lorans and SINS (ships inertial navigation system) that were aboard as a prototype. The crew felt he was an excellent officer and navigator but would never replace Bill as the Couth Week winner; and they were correct.

Within a half hour, *Growler* was rolling in a slight swell and turned west toward the setting sun. They were to stop at Midway Island to top off fuel and food. Most of the crew had never been to Midway. New crew members included a senior Chief Radioman (master chiefs hadn't been invented yet). He qualified during World War II and was assigned to *Growler* for the patrol. He'd been on COMSUB-PAC's Staff for years and needed sea time or loss of submarine pay.

The CO planned the transit on the surface so they rolled and pitched a bit.

Within five minutes of clearing Pearl, the "old sea dog" was seasick. Most submariners remained at sea for most of their careers while the unfortunates who suffer seasickness do not remain in the Navy. The old chief went to his bunk and didn't move. It wasn't long before the entire crew knew he was sick. No one found his sickness humorous but felt sorry and blessed it wasn't them. HMC(SS) Herb Edwards helped but his efforts were in vain. Within a day, he was so weak, he was unable to get out of his bunk, even to the head. He tried soda crackers and broth but it didn't help.

The old chief dehydrated and one wondered how he was virtually the senior chief in the Pacific Submarine Force and became disabled within five minutes of being at sea. The crew learned later the chief might have died had it not been for HMC Edwards, who was credited with saving his life. The CO submerged and snorkel transited making it smoother. The seas never were rougher than a state 2 or 3 (waves a few feet high known generally as a chop) during the entire three-day trip. When *Growler* reached Midway, the chief was carried off the boat in a stretcher and research into his background uncovered he had managed to avoid sea duty his entire career. He knew submarines and radio but couldn't go to sea. *Growler* was short an RMC for the duration of the patrol.

Theoretically, Regulus boats were allowed about 110% of manning level. This included young sailors who were getting submarine experience prior to going to nuclear power school (E-3 ratings with an NEC of 9901).[2] Unfortunately, the majority of the men assigned to *Growler* that didn't stand watches or deploy were ball players for COMSUBPAC; a situation not looked on favorably by Submariners.

The channel was cut out of a coral reef into Midway's harbor. The water was so clear the coral looked inches from the hull, and as beautiful as it appeared it was sharp and deadly. It was a beautiful sight with the tropical fish, the white coral surrounded by the crystal clear blue waters, the white sandy beaches, while the remains of the Battle of Midway stood rusted but awesome. *Growler* berthed and readied to fuel and take on stores. Midway was a Naval Air Station filled with fliers so the wardroom went to the O' Club for a cool one after lunch when the aviators were back at work.

The club was uninhabited, so the officers made themselves at home. They drank cold Millers, shot a little pool, and played liar's dice. By 1600, the aviators shuffled back into the Club. Near dark, with the number of aviators to submariners increasing, the submariners decided to part company and tour the island. Aviators and submariners have the greatest respect for each other professionally but in a club environment, bad things did happen.

They felt good and a walk was the reasonable thing to undertake. They walked a main street; there were only two main roads they knew about, and passed the

Waves Barracks. They knew better than to mess with the ladies but they focused on bicycles in front of the barracks. The officers discussed the situation for a few minutes and decided to borrow the bicycles for an hour or so while they toured the island. Two wheels were easier than two feet. They started a tour of the island that isn't a long trip.

They passed a softball field where the locals played a destroyer in port. The officers stopped to watch the game and catch a beer. Midway was big on softball and one of few entertainments they participated in actively with fleet units. The game was broadcast on local radio. The officers chuckled as the game stopped every inning or so to get "Gooney Birds" or Albatross off the playing field. One of locals told them many stories about the birds that were so interesting and amusing including the transfer of the Albatross off Midway Island to Eastern Island so they wouldn't hamper air operations. The birds were back within a few days.

They finished their beers and continued on their trek, eventually arriving at the end of a runway. They didn't see any aircraft so they pedaled along the landing strips and ran into a large group of Gooney Birds. They were fun to chase off the airstrip. They were careful to remain clear of the large beaks that could snap a small stick or a finger. The game was so much fun, they didn't notice the Shore Patrol trucks slowly creeping toward them. Their attention was diverted for a moment when Perry Benson missed a Gooney bird and pedaled off the runway into the brush. That was the moment the Shore Patrol needed as they closed in on the officers, lights blinking and siren blaring. For a few moments, the scene was reminiscent of the Key Stone Cops as the bicycles deftly kept clear of the jeeps but finally succumbed to the endurance of the gasoline engine. They placed the bikes and themselves in the back of the trucks just as Perry wandered out of the brush.

"Hey, wait for me." The officers motioned him to stay away but he cycled madly after the trucks on this bicycle with a square front wheel—all the way to the Shore Patrol Station. The young Ensign on duty was flustered with an entire wardroom on hand so he sent them back to the *Growler* with instructions to remain on board until the submarine departed. Wayne Mehl had to sign for all the officers and promise to keep them aboard.

They returned to *Growler* and laid below for coffee, but Horace disappeared into the darkness and went ashore. He returned a few minutes later with a Gooney Bird wrapped in a blanket. He said,

"Where's the COB?"

"The COB's sitting on the throne," answered George—he was in the little cubicle too small for one to turn around—he was using the bathroom!

"Let's get 'im." They filed out and followed him forward to the double head in the Forward Torpedo Room.

Horace knocked on the door of the Chief's Head, "COB, are you in there?"

"Yes, sir, I'll be right out, Mr. Leavitt."

"No big rush COB. I just picked up the latest copy of Playboy, and thought you'd like to take a look at it."

"Great, sir. Just a second." The officers watched the "occupied" sign change to "unoccupied." The door opened a crack and the COB's hand reached out.

"Here, Chief," Horace said as he pulled the door open, threw the Gooney Bird into the head and slammed the door shut. The words that followed from the COB are not printable as he faced the oversized goose with beak snapping while sitting with his pants around his ankles. Amazingly, the sheet metal surrounding the commode remained intact as the bird and the COB engaged in mortal combat. Every yell by the COB was followed by the rasping noise of the Albatross, punctuated by the "clicks" of his bill. The COB managed to save all his private parts.

TMC(SS) Mike Powell was sound asleep in his bunk. He was to become the next COB and slept in the nude. When the COB managed to exit the head intact, the officers repossessed the gooney bird. It took little imagination to guess what happened next. The upper bunk amidships in the "Goat Locker" exploded into a battleground as the chief and the Goonie Bird fought for dominance in the small space behind the rose-colored bunk curtains. The bird won the fight as the chief flew out of the upper bunk with the bird's beak still snapping. The bird then tore up the chief's pillow and left a deposit in the middle of his blanket. The officers retrieved the bird, fed him some donuts and let him go. The officers returned to the wardroom and wondered if the bird's mate believed why he got home late. The look in the eyes of Chief Powell and his flexed muscles wasn't lost in the glances from the officers. The COB to be was never tampered with again. The chiefs got even!

While the officers were making mischief, the crew was not idle. A number of men found a huge gooney bird egg and slipped it under the CO's pillow.[3] It is unknown what happened to the egg, for the CO didn't mention it, and some believe SD1(SS) Casuto Bacal enjoyed a giant *balot*, a Philippine delicacy. FT2(SS) John Anderson and CS1(SS) Duane "Hotdog" Heatwole never were caught slipping the egg into the skipper's stateroom. Meanwhile, Phil "Killer" Coyle saw little of the frolicking at Midway Island since he was the Fuel King and spent the entire time on the island fueling the submarine.

Grayback had a similar experience with the Gooney Birds. Bill Gunn, now the Executive Officer, returned from the O' Club and hopped into his bunk and flipped the blanket up with his feet. In so doing, he clobbered an albatross in the head residing at the foot of his bunk. Round one was underway. Bill got a sheet between he and the bird but could not get out of his bunk without exposing himself to the snapping beak. It was a stalemate as Bill barely kept his vitals from the bird's beak. By remaining quiet, Bill got the huge bird to relax and go to sleep. The duty electrician walked down the passageway checking the ventilation lineup during a battery charge in progress. A venturi in Bill's stateroom brought the EM into his stateroom.

Bill sighed with relief and ordered EM2(SS) Jones in his best command voice, "Jones, get this god damned bird out of here." Jones turned his flashlight on the bunk and quickly assessed the situation.

"Mr. Gunn, sir, I may not be too smart but I'm sure as hell not going to grab that bird!" With that terse statement, he departed leaving Bill alone with the bird. A similar event had taken place a couple patrols prior when the officers placed a huge albatross on Jim Murphy's bunk while he was asleep. Imagine, if you will, the ensuing battle between a huge 250 pound man and a bird with an eight foot wing span in a bunk barely large enough for one to roll over. The bird was finally removed but not until after it shredded Murphy's sheets and eliminated it's waste a number of times.[4]

With fueling complete and stores stowed, they were back at sea by sunrise. Passing Frigate Point to starboard, *Growler* swung northward and about midday, pulled the plug on an ECM contact. They snorkeled for a few days while the CO conducted his typical drills. At nightfall, the boat often surfaced to make better speed. If the boat was still on the surface at dawn, the OOD could always count on a fresh cup of coffee from the stewards, who loved coming topside to gather flying fish lying on deck. They cleaned and cooked the fish with rice. It was a routine activity when transiting between Midway and Peal Harbor.[5]

The transit proved uneventful but they witnessed another marine scene no one had seen before. One afternoon, Bob noticed a Portuguese Man of War (toxic jelly fish) in the water through the periscope; and then another, then many, then millions. *Growler* transited through poisonous jellyfish for miles. They were small, with a purplish sail between two and three inches in length. They hoped surfacing was not in the CO's plans.

At a point beyond the range of both United States and Soviet land based aircraft, the CO used the opportunity to run on the surface for a few days. Sonar was limited due to surface noise, so the watch kept an extra keen eye on ECM. Bob was the OOD one beautiful evening—a night anyone would enjoy. The weather was cool as they moved north on a crystal clear night. Keeping an attentive eye on the horizon and sky for contacts was an effort with a brilliant display of aurora borealis (northern lights) in the sky. It was a show rivaling modern laser shows. The lights were gorgeous and then, "Mr. H, there is something weird on our periscope, sir."

"What's weird Bruno?" asked Bob as he turned and looked at the periscopes. "Where... what are you looking at?" Bob said. Jerry Bruno was a tall and handsome young Missile Technician who often was in Bob's foursome on the golf course. Bob usually marveled at the distance Bruno could hit the ball, usually he drove well over 300 yards.

"At the very top sir, right there on the antenna." Saint Elmo's Fire had formed on the tip of the 8L Periscope antenna. Bob explained the phenomenon as the eerie green glow crept slowly down the scope. Before long it covered the entire scope and started spreading across the other masts and the top of the sail. Bob reached out and wiped a piece of the glowing matter off the top of the sail and showed it to his lookouts.

"Is it hot Mr. H? Won't it hurt you?"

"Not at all. Its just a small electric discharge very similar to the bioluminescence you see in the water. Look behind us in the wake. See how it sparkles with a multitude of flashing lights. It's caused by small little animals like plankton being agitated and giving off a small discharge of electricity. I think it's very similar to the lightning bug in that respect." It was the largest display of Saint Elmo's Fire he had seen.

Suddenly, "Torpedo, sir, torpedo. Starboard beam, sir... sir!" Bob leaped to the starboard bridge step and looked to starboard.

"...ooooh shit!" Two torpedoes were headed directly for them with a line of bubbles straight as a ruler headed for amidships. Bob reached for the collision alarm, there was no time to explain and the alarm might get some watertight doors shut and hull fittings secured in time. As his hand reached the knurled knob, "Its a porpoise, sir!" A quick glance over his shoulder confirmed the observation.

"Damn it, Gleason! Don't scare me that way," Bob yelled and realized his knees were locked in place. The bioluminescence left trails of two dolphins as they swam to play in the ship's wake.

"Sorry for yelling at you," he told his starboard lookout, "you did your job but scared the hell out of me."

"It's okay, Mr. H. It scared the hell out of me, too. I think I'd like a relief to go to the head, sir."

Years earlier, *Halibut*'s OOD, Lieutenant Bill Gunn, was on the bridge and decided to clean the lens on the periscopes. He called below to the Attack Center to lower the periscope into the sail or house them so he could reach the lens,

"House Number One Scope!"

The AOW, a burly Chester Bienkowski, responded, "It's fine, sir."

Growler approached station and fell into her regular patrol routine. Bob felt he never left station. The time in Pearl was a short dream. He just picked up where he left off before the dream. The crew veterans were immediately back on patrol routine.

A common prank that never seems to grow old was pulled on a new Ensign reporting aboard *Barbero*. The newly commissioned officer had been a heavyweight wrestler in college and everyone in the crew told him he was in deep crap because he could easily gain weight on patrol. The young officer struggled with workouts daily, but the crew carefully removed a tiny piece of his webbed belt every week. He noticed the change but when he weighed himself, the diving officer would put a slight angle on the boat that made the scales read high. The skipper didn't know of the prank and just felt he had some lousy diving officers. As it turned out, he managed to keep his weight down.[6]

The final leg of the transit was constant snorkeling and the atmospheric pressure in their little world constantly changed, with resultant sinuses that bled profusely for some. The crew ate APCs (aspirin) like popcorn to stem the headaches, usually in vain.

It was the middle of the 1962–63 winter and the temperature turned cold. This time, Bob brought plenty of old but warm clothes. He wrapped all his clothes in plastic to keep out the smell of diesel oil and other obnoxious smells.

The first days out of Pearl were depressing as the crew despaired at the separation from loved ones. Then everyone shook it off and lightened up for the transit. Joke playing was at its best except for the homeward transit. In officer's country in the middle stateroom were Bob, Don, and Perry. The bunks were three high with Perry in the bottom bunk, Don in the middle, and Bob on top. Don snored but never believed it, even after listening to recordings. Perry and Bob decided to get even for the annoyance.

Don stood the evening watch and was extremely scheduled. When relieved of watch at midnight, he toured the boat and reported to the CO at 0020; he drank a glass of milk in the wardroom; made a head call; and went to bed. He read himself to sleep and, almost like a clock, he awakened at 0115 to make one last head call, probably to deposit the glass of milk, then returned to sleep through the rest of the night. Perry and Bob planned to take advantage of the routine.

Don came off watch, made his tour, drank his milk, went to the head, and settled down with a book. When asleep, Perry and Bob taped a piece of clear plastic Plexiglas across the front of his bunk. He wouldn't suffocate since there was a vent duct in his headboard. Don was encompassed by Bob's bunk on the top, Perry's bunk below, and the hull to port, cabinets, and the piece of plastic to starboard. Quietly, the two went back to their bunks.

At 0115, Don stirred and made his move to get up for a head call. The stateroom was pitch black. As he tried to roll out of his bunk, he was stopped by the plastic—suddenly, he went crazy. He struggled and screamed, thrashed, and banged in every direction until he fought his way out of the plastic. He was terrified as Perry and Bob pretended to sleep. Later, Perry and Bob looked in his bunk to see what he was reading; *The Premature Burial*, by Edgar Allen Poe! He did get even .[7]

Growler arrived on station and relieved *Grayback*. This time, *Growler* came in the northeast corner and *Grayback* went out the southwest corner. *Grayback* had never visited a foreign port and had received permission to depart station and go to Okinawa for a rest and recreation. Bob chuckled when he heard and was asked what was wrong.

He said, "You guys obviously have not been to Okinawa. Naha is a nice town but there isn't much else on the island except White Beach in Buckner Bay. That's where the Marines landed in World War II, under the guns of the Japanese. There are a few villages we called one, two, and three because no one could pronounce their names. They're set up to entertain the G.I.; the Marines and SeaBees stationed there. It's not great liberty nor shopping except in Naha." Regardless, *Grayback* went — to Naha.

Midway in *Grayback*'s patrol, an unusual occurrence took place, so discreet in nature the most experienced submariners aboard failed to recognize the problem. Somehow, the stern planes came loose from the operating shaft on station. When *Grayback* surfaced, the problem was not noticed, as the planes trailed along behind the boat. She transited to Naha, taking about a week. *Grayback* entered port and proceeded down the channel at Naha. The port pilot's boat stopped directly in front of *Grayback* and forced her to stop. Her bow fell off toward a quay wall so the CO backed on the starboard engine to hold his head in the channel. The starboard shaft backed followed by a large bang astern and the submarine shuddered. Immediately, Maneuvering reported a fire and inability to answer bells.

Bill Gunn immediately went aft to Maneuvering. The fire was out, but a series of fireballs sparked in the cubicle, and the starboard motor and #3 generator were blown. The starboard stern plane had flipped forward with the wash of the backing bell, caught the starboard propeller, and snapped the shaft off at the strut. With no load on the motor and generator, the motor ran away and the engine shut down on high RPMs. Once alongside their berth, divers confirmed the damage to the starboard shaft and screw and found the port stern plane missing. An astern bell on station would have been disastrous. The *Grayback* departed for the Philippines for repairs with an ASR escort. Subic Bay was the closest dry docking facility.

An early task assigned *Growler* was to observe a Russian missile splash down off the east coast of the Soviet Union. The area was similar to the Eastern Test Range at Cape Canaveral or the Pacific Missile Test Range at Point Mugu. No launch observation took place but it was a big day for radio and ECM monitoring orders and telemetry for the splash down. Roll after roll of recording tape and periscope camera film was expended.

Growler experienced another nuclear blast, Perry Benson style. Early one morning, Pere' Benson was on the periscope when he saw something to the west off the coast of Kamchatka. He carefully scanned the area for a few minutes as daylight slowly arrived. Satisfied there was nothing, he continued his periscope sweep.

As he continued toward the east, he suddenly yelled, "Nuclear blast, man the photo team." *Growler* went to Battle Stations Camera. The CO was on the conning stand in his shorts to observe Perry's finding, as was the XO. The other scope went up and cameras clicked away. Perry was shooting pictures when Control heard Perry say, "Ahh shit. Its nothing but a sunrise!"

It was winter and the route between Murmansk and Kamchatka was sealed shut by the ice. As a result, *Growler*'s intelligence effort eased until the summer warmth again opened the ice to transiting ships. The main effort was constrained to waters off the east coast and adjoining landmasses. *Growler* continued her dual mission of a strategic deterrent weapon and intelligence collector. Even in the wardroom, no one knew exactly what was going on except the CO and XO. However, it was exciting to know they were doing such constructive and positive work for freedom and democracy. During the patrol period, USNS *Dutton* and USNS *Bowditch* (research vessels) sailed the Northern Pacific under the pretense of surveying, but actually laid cable and hydrophones for a SOSUS system, a passive listening system on the ocean floor.

The patrol supported the theory submarine life on a patrol was 99% boredom and 1% stark terror. Terror showed its face. It was mid-afternoon as Bob passed through Control when the wail of the collision alarm scared him and everyone else. He heard a report, "Flooding in the Stern Room." The boat became an instant bundle of activity.

"On my way!" Bob yelled as he ran aft.

Fighting through shut watertight (WT) doors and crew members securing openings to other compartments or to sea, he worked aft. The Conn prepared to surface and shut ballast tank vents while the AOW stood by the air manifold with hands on the high pressure blow valves. Bob flew through the Engine Room as the watch stood by to start the engines and pressurize the Stern Room if needed. Each space can pressurize the compartment from either within or from the adjoining compartment. The valves are located just above the WT door leading and coming from each compartment. Bob reached the Stern Room that housed Maneuvering and the After Torpedo Room. He looked through the deadlight (small porthole in each WT door) and saw no flooding. No water was above the deck level. Water in Maneuvering was potentially disastrous but the entire crew responded perfectly to minimize any danger or damage. Maneuvering let him through the WT door into Maneuvering where the ship's electrical power was controlled. An ordinary door separated the two spaces within the compartment as a noise barrier for twelve men who slept in the space. No pressure change was discerned as he went through the WT door so he knew the flooding could not be severe.

Bob threw the door open and nearly went into shock. A solid wall of water headed directly forward and toward him.

"Stop the source and confine the flooding." The non-WT door was useless in preventing flooding to Maneuvering. He had to secure the source—but first he had to find it.

"Where the hell is the watch?" he yelled scanning the area then plunged into the wall of water. He passed through the water in a microsecond and the picture became clear. A grease fitting (zerk) blew out of #6 Torpedo Tube. A stream of water the size of a pencil blew from the torpedo tube inner door locking ring zerk fitting. The boat's depth placed sufficient pressure behind the opening for the narrow stream of water to hit a beam on the overhead where it spread out in a fine spray across the entire width of the compartment giving the appearance of a huge wall of water. The TM on watch placed a spare zerk fitting in the hole. Bob grabbed the 21MC microphone.

"Conn, Stern Room. This is Mr. H. We do not have flooding, I repeat there is no flooding. #6 tube blew a zerk fitting. No assistance required."

"Captain aye, thank you Bob, keep me advised," came a relieved voice.

"All secure Sir."

"Thanks, Williams, good work. Please report conditions normal." The men exercised the tube as part of their Preventative Maintenance Program. The torpedo was removed, the tube flooded, and the outer door opened. All equipment was exercised periodically to insure they performed as designed when called upon. Less than a hundred gallons of salt water entered the boat, most of it was in the bilge. Then Bob felt that familiar feeling; both legs were locked.

During the patrol, Bob stood the 0400 to 0800 and 1600 to 2000 watch. One benefit of the watch was the morning baking in the galley. One morning, *Growler* was snorkel charging in rough seas with an Arctic winter storm topside. The seas ran 10–15 feet and increasing as depth control became a challenge. "Hotdog" was baking six birthday cakes for the crew. He baked real Angel Food Cakes vice the usual flat pan cakes. He placed six cakes in the oven. The cakes were in the phase when cakes rise to their full height when the snorkel head valve closed. Bob was the Diving Officer and desperately fought to return to snorkel depth gradually and avoid broaching. The vacuum sucked the cakes in the oven to record heights. The vacuum wasn't bad for humans but was a disaster for cakes. Bob got the boat up, the head valve opened, the pressure in the boat suddenly increased to normal, and the cakes flattened in the bottom of the pans akin to pancakes.

A bellow came out of the galley followed by crashing pots and pans. The entire crew awakened as Bob awaited a tongue-lashing. Bob caught the wrath of Cain as the cook bounded into Control looking for the DO.

"Damn it, who is the amateur on the dive," he barked. "Oh, its you, Mr. H. I expected better from you, sir."

"Sorry, Hotdog. I couldn't prevent it," Bob apologized.

"Help it! Help it! Look at this mess," as he threw the pans of cakes at his feet.

"They do look pretty bad, more like pancakes," Bob admitted.

"Pancakes, I'll give you pancakes alright. You like my donuts don't you, Mr. H?"

"They're the best."

"Well, sir, guess how I'll make the holes in yours from now on?" He stomped out of Control and into the galley. He didn't hold a grudge but Bob passed on donuts for the next few mornings.

On *Grayback's* 6th patrol, the blowing seas froze on the snorkel head valve seat and eventually prevented the valve from seating. She took on water from spray but when below snorkel depth, instead of pulling a vacuum, water poured into the Engine Room causing severe control problems and flooded out the centerline generator. Quick action by the crew and Captain Ekelund prevented a disaster. The electricians spent the remainder of the patrol washing and drying out the generator—an operation *Growler* was to experience shortly.[8]

On Christmas, few men wanted to think about it or celebrate. Don Breeding, the boat's layman, held church services for everyone in the crew's mess. Eighty-five men in a steel tube far from home and family provided a background for Don's Christmas service that was exceptionally touching. He gave a sermon on God and goodness that transcended all religions and then read from the Bible. Regardless of religion, race, color, creed, and political persuasion, the crew heralded the birth of Christ and thanked God for keeping them safe. God also got a number of requests to continue his good work.

Unbeknownst to the crew, the wives had been busy during the past inport period. While the crew was on local ops, the wives put together a large box for Christmas. They found small Christmas trees of wire and green plastic that could be bent and flattened. That was quite a feat in September on Oahu. They fashioned ornaments for the tree; each ornament held a picture of the wife, loved one and/or their children. The officer's and crew's trees remained as table centerpieces for the remainder of the patrol.

Everyone received presents, including the bachelors. There were no large or expensive items but thoughtful gifts. Each item was shown to the rest of the men so everyone had an opportunity to comment. Many of the presents were funny, intended to make Christmas a little happier. Dave's fiancee gave Dave nontransparent under shorts, even when wet. Everyone got a stick of deodorant. Many men received audio tapes that were priceless. To top the day, everyone received a Christmas familigram. The CO permitted the main brace to be moderately spliced for everyone not on watch in the form of a very weak eggnog drink.

A year earlier, *Tunny* returned from patrol to Adak on New Years Day. The base was closed down so Captain Doug Stahl found the club manager and purchased beer for his crew to modestly celebrate the New Year. The beer was kept on the pier and the crew was permitted on the pier to partake of the brew. The crisis was to consume the beer before it froze.[9]

The cooks prepared a feast to remember; no turkey logs for this meal. Cooks "Ma" Irwin and Whittington combined with Hotdog's baking to provide a banquet that was the real thing with all the trimmings. The CO ordered the boat deep so all hands could enjoy and savor their Christmas dinner. For a few hours, the men of *Growler* forgot the patrol while the duty section remained alert. During the end of the 20–24 watch that Christmas Eve Night, a poem was written in the Quartermaster's Notebook as the first entry for Christmas Day. It was likely authored by either Don Curbow or Hymie Hoffman:

Near the end of the watch on December 24th
Dave shut down snorkeling for a contact to the north.
Captain Don looked at the light… it was a bright star,
"the Star of Bethlehem, follow it no matter how far."

The snorkeling resumed and the big log read herewith,
"Underway in accordance with CSP on the 25th."
Then Chief Samuels declared the charge complete,
The engines shutdown and watch ready to eat.

Section 2 relieved a tired mid-watch who felt blest
To struggle fore and aft in search of food and rest.
Some of the exhausted men passed on breakfast,
Saving stomachs for Ma Irwin's meal for enthusiasts.

The sound powered telephone circuit 1JV did ring
Word was passed, Christmas Services by Breeding.
Services on the mess decks, Catholic or Jew,
Technicians and bookworms to brutes with tattoo.

Men read from the Bible, testaments new and old,
And sang Christmas carols of modern and retold.
Don spoke of God and the world at peace,
And how our work was akin to a task by Hercules.

*(Then it was silent and the men filled with prayer
they thanked Him for keeping them safe and asked
Him to continue His good work)
And He looked down upon the gathered men and,*

"*God bless you Growler, Grayback, Tunny, Halibut, and Barbero; for you have more
work to do.*"

Christmas in 1961 for the *Tunny* was no fun either besides the sorrow of missing the holidays with one's family. The seas had been raging for a week on either side of Christmas with wave heights estimated much greater than forty feet. When they snorkel charged, her depth ranged between the surface and 90-feet depth. The Enginemen were exhausted from the sheer physical labor of opening and shutting valves as the boat flamed out and then tried again. The cooks tried to bake apple pies for the holiday but the fillings just ended up decorating the inside of the oven, literally exploding during partial vacuums. The officers had purchased a miniature Christmas tree to hang from the overhead in the Wardroom. They had to remove the tree, because the constant swaying of the tree made some of the officers seasick. When it was time for the banquet the boat went to 200-foot depth for a few hours, yet still rolled a few degrees. When they returned to periscope depth, *Tunny* experienced a crashing wave on the deck that removed several sections of the superstructure, as on *Growler*. One can only imagine the heroism of the crew members that had to climb topside and cut the dangling pieces of superstructure to free the boat. Luckily, no topside valves or piping were damaged. Then a nut fell free inside the TDC (Torpedo Data Computer) into the gear train, stripping many gears. If the day wasn't bad enough, late in the evening, Captain Doug Stahl received a message that his baby son had died.[10]

Prior to relief on station, "Conn, sonar. Noise spoke has turned into a contact, designating Skunk Foxtrot. It's a warship sir, destroyer type; a *Riga* Class Soviet destroyer, sir. Bearing drift is zero with an inclination to the left, sir." They were at periscope depth and the CO came into Control and took the Conn.

"This is Mr. Mehl. The Captain has the Conn." A *Riga* destroyer is a small ship, around 1,200 tons, but did carry torpedoes and depth charges as anti-submarine weapons. A rough sea ran with 5–7 foot waves. The CO decided to use the destroyer as a torpedo target to get some practice for his fire control party.

"Battle Stations Torpedo," boomed over the 1MC. The CO was thinking ahead to the next patrol and putting together a fire control team with crew members that would make the next trip. Bob was on the conning stand with the CO when the events began. The CO made a periscope approach, since they coped well with the seas and did not close the target except to see the top of the mast. Then he made his first mistake of the patrol. He asked Bob to assist him on the periscope. He was to raise and lower the scope, place the scope on TDC generated bearings, and read the stadimeter range and bearings when called upon. The fire control party generated a good solution when the CO decided to take another look.

"Bring the scope to waist level, Bob." The hydraulic lever that controlled the periscope was very small on *Growler.* "Raise the scope another foot, Bob." The CO squatted, drooped over the handles looking through the eyepiece when Bob pushed the lever to the "raise" position. The periscope shot upward and the bearing ring on the bottom of the scope smacked the CO on the chin. "Damn it, Bob!" The periscope came up too far so Bob pulled the lever carefully to the lower position. The periscope raced downward and the yoke clobbered the CO atop the head on its way down. Stunned by the blow the CO clung desperately to the periscope handles. Seeing he had gone too far, Bob moved the lever to neutral but in fact, it was to the "raise" position. The CO still clinging to the handles with head bowed when the scope moved upward again, received another shot to the jaw. He staggered backwards, eyes glazed and, "Make your depth 200'. I can't take any more of this." The Captain slowly walked back to the wardroom, took two aspirin and asked for an ice pack. Quartermasters "Hymie Hoffman and Don Curbow stood behind the chart desk, bodies shuttering in contained laughter.

"That's what the captain gets for letting an officer do a quartermaster's job." Bob steered clear of the CO for the next few days.[11]

Chapter Nine
Another Ride Home

Day after gray day slowly passed and soon it was time to think of home. Bob finished his qualification notebook and continued studying. He decided to make his move for the dolphins. Near the end of a watch Bob asked Wayne, "Wayne, I'm ready to begin the qualification process. Will you take me through the boat as Qualification Officer?"

"Gesus, Bob, this is only your second patrol. You've got lots of time before you have to begin this process. You sure you want to give it a try?"

"I feel ready, but there's only one way to find out, Wayne. Take me through the boat and give me your best shot!"

"You wise ass, I will filet your butt. By the time I get done with you it will be more like dragging your ass through the boat than walking you through." After watch, the two headed aft and the inquisition began.

"Hey, Mr. H is doing his walk through right now!" Many of the crew followed along to watch, listen, and learn. It wasn't unusual for crew members to follow a walk-through for enlisted or officer, but this was Mr. H and Wayne Mehl going head to head. About forty men, comprised of petty officers and non-rated, qualified and unqualified, followed the officers for they knew it was to be one hell of match. A Submariner never stops learning, regardless of qualification status, and the walk had the makings of an enlightening venture. Neither Wayne nor Bob noticed them for both were totally engrossed in the challenge.

The officers began in the Engine Room, the heart of the Trim and Drain System. Step by step and system by system, they methodically crawled through the boat.

"Ever been back down here, Bob?" asked Wayne from behind #2 High Pressure Air Compressor.

"Hell, yes. Those are my oily finger prints right there above the deck plate."

The two were in a personal challenge. Time flew and six hours later, Wayne said, "Okay, I'm pleasantly surprised, Bob. Let's get some sleep. We go back on watch in two hours and need to get a little shuteye."

"Thanks for your time, Wayne. You opened my eyes to a lot of things. Can I tell the CO I'm ready?"

"Hell, yes, I'll give him my recommendation."

"Thanks for your help, Wayne, and especially tonight."

"You're welcome, Bob. Just don't forget you've been in my section for these two patrols. You had a good teacher."

"I can't argue that point." The CO was in his stateroom reading while it was quiet and relaxed throughout the boat. Bob knocked on his stateroom bulkhead.

"Come in."

"Good afternoon, Captain."

"How goes it, Bob? Something I can do for you?"

"Yes, sir, I would like to submit my Notebook, sir. It's finished, though I know there is always room to improve." Bob took pride in his notebook and used skills learned as a draftsman to make his drawings. It was a piece of art. "Captain, I think I have satisfactorily completed all the requirements for the notebook and completed all the required practical factors. I would appreciate it if you would review my notebook. If the book is satisfactory, I request to be tested for qualification, sir."

"Bob, I've watched you work on this notebook. I think you spent way too much time on the neatness and prettiness of the book rather than learning the boat. However, I will review your notebook and let you know within the next few days what I think."

"Thank you, Captain."

"Don't thank me yet, Bob. Thank me if I approve your notebook." Bob spent an inordinate amount of time on the book but he wanted it to be the very best. He wanted to be proud of the book. Bob had taken the CO's and Wayne's advice to learn each system so thoroughly, any question or problem in a system would promote an automatic and correct answer. He played devil's advocate with himself as he manufactured situations and problems in the various systems, and then wrestled for solutions. In his walk with Wayne, he found he did not know the systems so well he could envision every possible circumstance. Wayne threw scenarios at him he never considered.

The next few days, Bob went about his work nervously and whenever he saw the CO, he searched his eyes for some sign of approval or disapproval of the notebook. The CO had Bob on the edge and enjoyed watching him cope with the problem. An officer, especially a submarine officer, must be patient. He also must handle stress and the present condition was just a touch of stress. Bob was haunted by memories of battering the skipper with the periscope. He knew the CO was bigger than to hold a grudge but Bob had not acted qualified on that day.

One afternoon, Bob reviewed the message board in the wardroom when the CO walked in for coffee. He poured a cup and sat down. He looked up, met Bob's eyes, and permitted a crease of a smile on the right corner of his mouth and,

"Okay, Bob, you ready?"

"Damned right, sir!"

"Your notebook is a piece of art and I enjoyed your answers. I found a few things you need to research further but the notebook is quite satisfactory... good in fact... not bad at all."

"Thank you, sir. I'm happy you enjoyed it, sir."

"Don't patronize me Bob. It is time to find out if you remember what you drew." With that remark, he rolled out a long piece of graph paper on the wardroom table. He sketched the top view and side view of *Growler*.

"My drawing isn't as fancy as yours, but what I'm looking for is facts. I want you to draw all the tanks on the boat—ballast tanks, fuel oil ballast tanks, fuel tanks, water tanks, lube oil tanks, trim tanks, sanitary tanks etc.—and label each tank with its capacity in gallons and weight. Then I want you to draw every piping system in the boat and show all the valves, valve actuators, type of valve, connections to tanks and other systems, and location of valves. This should include the various air systems with regulators, fresh water, salt water, hydraulic, trim and drain system, Freon, lube oil, ventilation systems, waste water, etc. Then put in electrical systems, including the generators, batteries, motors, transformers, AC/DC interfaces, breakers, fuzes, and major equipment they supply. If you have any questions, I'll be in my stateroom. It is now 1330. You have until 1830 to complete your work. Got it?"

"Yes, sir."

"Okay, then, on with it and good luck." It was a tall order. He recalled Plebe Year and the things he had to memorize. Being able to stow and recall from memory was about to be tested again and he felt thankful for his Academy training. He drew in a deep breath, said a short prayer, and dug in. Quickly, he was in a world of his own as he mentally regurgitated pipes and turned valves. At 1500, the stewards set up the afternoon rations. Don and George wandered in for their rations before going on watch. They looked at Bob's work.

Don mumbled, "Looks familiar to me, Bob. How's it going roomie?"

"Pretty good, Don, except I'm getting writer's cramp."

"Good, you can hack it. Hang in there!"

"Thanks, but get your soup off of my drawing. Hey, you're dripping soup on my drawing!"

"Ease up, Bob. This drawing isn't for your notebook."

Radioman Klappholtz arrived looking for the CO. He looked down at the drawing and, "Holy shit, Mr. H. Good luck with the drawing."

"Yeah, hang in there, tiger," piped George.

"Thanks, George, I'm trying." After Don and George left, Dave and Perry came in after watch. Dave smiled in a knowing way, remembering the day not so long ago for him.

Perry looked at the sheet of paper and, "Hell, this is worse than the final exam at sub school." Bob finished the chore, drew a deep breath, and returned to the drawing. He would check what he drew and wrote.

"That's it, Bob. Stop, roll up the paper, and bring it to my stateroom."

"Aye, Captain. When is the drawing going to be reviewed, sir?"

"You've got the next watch, don't you?"

"Yes, sir."

"Then we'll check it out while you're on watch this evening. Won't be a card game tonight. That should please the officers." A twitch of a grin returned to his lips.

The stewards set up for the evening meal and steaks were the main course since it was Saturday. A few minutes later, Wayne and Bob were in Control and involved in relieving the watch, which was snorkel charging. As they settled into the routine, the XO came out to relieve Wayne. Wayne joined the qualified officers in the wardroom to review Bob's drawing; the CO, Don, Dave, the COB, Wayne, and George.

"Bob! Get your mind back on the trim of the boat."

"Aye, aye, sir," he responded knowing the XO was right. His body was in Control but his mind was with his drawing. About 2300, Wayne returned, relieved the XO of the Conn, and resumed his watch. After the XO walked forward, Bob looked at Wayne for an indicator of how he fared. Wayne wore his poker face and said nothing. The battery charge was completed and the boat continued snorkeling to save the battery. Not a single contact appeared and while the watch struggled with their eyelids, Bob worried about his test.

The watch was relieved and Wayne asked Bob to make the below decks inspection. Bob went through the motions of the inspection, looked at everything, but his mind remained in the wardroom. He completed his inspection and sat down in the wardroom, looked at the CO and reported, "Toured the boat, Captain, and conditions are normal, sir!"

"Are you certain, Bob?" asked the CO.

"To the best of my knowledge, Sir!"

"Well, Bob, your knowledge of the boat has gathered some respect. We went over your drawing for a few hours, and I admit, we were impressed. You did miss one rather vital valve in your life. Would you care to hazard a guess?"

"No, sir! I've thought about what I might have missed for the past four hours and haven't come up with anything."

The officers chuckled a bit. Obviously, they knew. They played with Bob for a while and teased him into guessing the answer. Finally, the CO came forth with a large: "Ahem. Bob, you forgot the stop valve for the drain to your own sink!" The announcement was followed by a roar of laughter, then "Bob, you passed my test. In fact you did very well indeed. Congratulations!"

"Thank you, Captain. Thank you very much."

"You're welcome, Bob, but now is not the time to cut yourself slack. I've watched you for two patrols and I think I know you well enough to know what makes you tick. You tick like a Submariner must and I will be proud to recommend you for qualification to the DivCom."

"Thank you again, sir." Tears of gratitude began to well in Bob's eyes and a large lump was in his throat. He looked away so no one would notice.

"Don't thank me, Bob. You earned your way to this point and you will have to earn it all the way to the golden dolphins. You still have a rough road ahead of you. I'm not sure which boat the DivCom will assign you for underway and the inport testing. But whatever the boat, it will be tough because you know *Growler* that is like no other submarine. We're in a three boat cycle right now without *Grayback* in the circuit. That means you will have your inport examination on *Halibut* and maybe even your underway. Whatever the boat, you must stay on the edge and be ready to perform at your very best."

"Aye, aye, sir. I will not stop studying and practicing. I would like to say one thing, sir. I could never have accomplished this qualification to date without the help of all the crew and officers. They were great sir."

"Don't patronize us, Bob."

"Well I love it and all the people in it." Bob burst with pride so he stepped outside the wardroom and let out an enormous "Yahoo." The chiefs in the "Goat Locker" jumped and even the crew in the After Battery was awakened. Sonar reported a large disturbance close aboard and, "Hey, I'm trying to get some shut eye here, Bob, how about stifling yourself, boot," came from his roomie. There was banging on the bulkhead between Chief's Quarters and Officer's Quarters and some words yelled not for print.

Then *Growler* was bound for Adak. The transit was incident free and they arrived at the Naval Air Station in the middle of the week. One thing didn't change; *Growler* had the wrong time. They approached the port at periscope depth, then surfaced prior to entering port after receiving permission to enter port. They did arrive undetected and asked the clubs to be opened though it was

1000. This time, Bob did not have the duty so he took the opportunity to venture forth.

The same Commanding Officer was dockside, but wore a smile and was happy to see _Growler_. The CO and the Base Commander exchanged pleasantries for a while as the Supply Officer, George Playton, and most of the departmental supply petty officers discussed _Growler_'s needs with their counterparts.

The Officer's Club was a simple place consisting of a bar and a couple pool tables. The bulkheads were covered with pictures and plaques left by ships and aircraft units who visited. As Bob drank his first beer and savored the taste, he searched the walls for _Growler_'s plaque. A club is required to display any plaque presented. Don mentioned the fact to Wayne and Dave who in turn asked the bartender,

"Hey, barkeep! Where's _Growler_'s plaque?" The bartender was embarrassed.

"It's under the farthest pool table." Wayne and Dave got down on all fours, then laid on their backs. There, in all its glory, the representative of the ship was screwed into the bottom of the pool table—right alongside the plaque from _Grayback_! It was difficult to get respect from the airdales.

Near noon, most of the crew descended upon the Navy Exchange to stock up on the necessities of life. They filled up with needed toilet articles and ventured into a gracious souvenir outlay. Shopping complete, most of the officers returned to the ship for evening meal and to check on a few pieces of business. When Bob finished the evening meal it was late, but the chiefs invited him to join them at the CPO Club for a few cool ones. Bob's limited experience in the Navy taught him such invitations usually meant a full evening of good fellowship and a bit of over-doing the brew. They used a pickup truck and headed for the CPO Club. They passed a "round-about" or circle in the road, and Bob noticed sentries posted around the totem pole. Little did he know, the sentries would soon be duct-taped to the barriers and the totem pole removed again. The previous _Grayback_ run, the base had guarded the totem pole with guard dogs only to have them feast on wonderful steaks from the _Grayback_'s mess and the totem pole removed again. This time, the boat was caught and ordered to return and restore the totem pole. The wings had been removed to ease movement. The boat requested tools to repair the pole and received a hammer and some nails. When the submarine sailed, it was noted the wings weren't on the eagle but on one of the ugly heads. There are so many totem pole stories, it is difficult to keep them separate and accurate; some of the stories are likely true and others a bit stretched.

The Chief's Club was also a Quonset hut with a few additions. He shivered as they crossed the parking lot to the entrance as the cold Alaska wind cut through his A-1 jacket. Inside, it was hot and boisterous. He caught good natured flak from the airdale chiefs, no different than any chief's club; he was warmly welcomed.

Bob's money was no good, despite his best efforts, so he contributed to a special fund for purchasing, planting, and raising the second tree on the island. He held his own at the pool table, lost his butt at darts, and got it back arm wrestling. That surprised a few chiefs. They were smart enough not to play liars dice and shook him down at Acey-Duecy.

Bob looked at his watch. It was past midnight so he took leave of the club. *Growler* was getting underway the next morning before first light. The chiefs offered him a lift but he declined, realizing they were having too much fun, and besides, he needed the walk in the cold air. He managed to buy a round on his way out and then slipped out the door. Damned but the air felt good and it had warmed up a bit. He hurtled down the mountainside, going both downhill and downwind. He found the traffic circle so he knew he was on the correct path but was feeling too good to take much note of the totem pole guards duct taped to the barricade poles..

The transit back to Pearl Harbor was a routine cruise and the weather was rough. Bob had consumed more to drink than he should have at the CPO Club and got a little cocky about being ready to qualify. The chiefs were about to deflate his ego dramatically.

Bob, like most of the crew, was still on a daily schedule that included taking his daily constitutional every morning after breakfast. The chiefs knew his routine since they shared adjoining heads. One day they decided to get him. The torpedomen had removed the torpedoes from the tubes for checkouts preparatory to returning the fish at Pearl. All four torpedo tubes forward were empty. The chiefs, with the CO's approval, waited for Bob to do his thing. The boat was on the surface in heavy seas and Bob was on the throne, holding on. Suddenly, the collision alarm sounded, whoop, whoop, whoop, signaling the TMs to fire water slugs out all forward tubes simultaneously. At the sound of the alarm, Bob reached for the toilet paper; then he felt the shock from four tubes firing water slugs. The boat shook violently, convincing Bob they had collided with something. He dropped the paper and burst out of the head, heading aft with his trousers at half-mast. He burst into Control, falling through the WT door, then stood up. He looked at the entire crew enjoying a belly whooper. His face turned purple-red with embarrassment and then he sat back down and laughed at himself. He was a sight and the crew got him.

They baked under the Hawaiian sun for the day before entering port on Sunday morning. The hull was covered in algae baked white again and since they were ahead of schedule, the CO held swim call.

Chapter Ten
Home Again and Qualification

Growler eased down the west side of Oahu in the late Saturday afternoon sun. The crew was topside again, sunning and enjoying the fresh air. Their thoughts were on the return and seeing their families. Someone on the launcher yelled and pointed west. Their eyes turned to starboard and witnessed a great sight in nature. As far as the eye could see, Bottle-nosed Dolphins jumped from the water, doing flips, spins, and twists. No one had seen a sight like it before and no explanation was forthcoming why the dolphins acted in such a manner. A mating ritual possibly, but no one knew for sure. There were dolphins by the thousands, if not tens of thousands. It was beautiful, and with the setting sun as a background, a magnificent sight.

Growler was at "PH" at 0700 on Sunday and the admiral's barge stood out to meet them. As ComSubPac drew closer, everyone noticed he wore a large smile on his face. He scrambled aboard and returned Captain Don's salute.

"Welcome back, Captain. It's nice to see you without bullet holes."

"Thank you, Admiral Clarey. Welcome aboard. Care to join me on the bridge, sir?" The ride to Pier S-9 ended with the band on the pier covered by cheering wives and children. Goose bumps and smiles came to everyone's face and even a tear rolled here and there as the Navy Band struck up, *Anchors Aweigh*. All the grief and despair without loved ones, pain, fear, and tough times disappeared. Everyone had someone special waiting for them. It was a fun homecoming and the fathers marveled at how their children had grown.

Growler returned 11 February 1963, receiving the ComSubPac Unit Commendation and CincPacFlt's Citation for the crew.[1] For Regulus boats, the awards were typical.

It was unexplainable, but Bob decided to take his dirty laundry with him when he left the ship. Laundry was a chore for any day except homecoming day.

The laundry sack almost walked itself off the gangway as it represented months of accumulated dirty clothing. It was not... repeat, not the thing to do if one was looking forward to a romantic homecoming.

Bob returned to Bellows, carefully avoiding sunburn... and left the laundry bag untouched at home. John Wayne didn't exercise, and later in the week many friends came out again to visit. It was fun in the sun and relaxing to party, but the entire time a voice in the back of Bob's head kept reminding him of the impending qualification gantlet. He felt guilty not studying for his pending qualifications. Swiftly the week ended and it was time for the business of running a submarine. The laundry incident could have been worse... his wife became pregnant with their second child on the pure white sands of Kanehoe Bay.

Growler went into the post arrival routine of off-loading war shots and loading out with exercise missiles and torpedoes. The CO recommended Bob for qualification to the Commodore who in turn arranged his In-Port Qualification review on board USS *Halibut* (SSGN-587) only a day away. Regulus submariners enjoyed remaining within the Regulus Family even for qualification. Bob was relieved, for he felt prepared and didn't want to delay the inquisition. He scarcely had time to be nervous.

Bob arrived on board *Halibut* precisely at 1000 and requested permission to see the Commanding Officer. The topside watch escorted him down to the CO's stateroom where he received a warm welcome.

"Welcome aboard *Halibut*, Bob."

"Good morning, Captain Mangold," Bob replied as he worried about his cold and clammy hand.

They exchanged talk about experiences on patrol, and then the Captain introduced him to his department heads. They were to interview him for the remainder of the day. The CO said, "Bob, the XO is going to give you a quick tour of *Halibut* before the questions begin. This will give you time to relax and offer you the opportunity to see the differences in our two boats. This may help you with some of your answers for you'll be able to explain why your procedures differ from ours. Good luck, son."

"Thank you, sir."

Bob was astonished at *Halibut's* single hangar size that held five Regulus missiles.

"You can play basketball in here," he said. Before the questions began, it was lunchtime and he felt more comfortable.

At 1700, he completed the questioning and returned to see the Captain.

"Bob, this is a fine notebook. You must be very proud."

"Thank you, sir, I am."

"My officers tell me you are well versed in *Growler* and submarines in general. I happen to agree with them." He then signed his name indicating a satisfactory completion of the "In Port" qualification. "Congratulations, Bob, well done."

"Thank you Captain, and thanks to your officers for their kindness and hospitality. I was scared as hell when I arrived this morning but I enjoyed the time aboard."

"That's kind of you, Bob, but we are no different than any other submarine. We're all the same family. Good luck to you."

With the words echoing in his ears, Bob departed and didn't feel the ground beneath his feet he was so high on happiness and relief. He couldn't wait to tell his wife and the CO. Now it would be the DivCom's turn to pick a boat for his underway test. No one knew which boat would be selected since *Tunny* and *Barbero* were on station and *Grayback* was in Subic Bay with *Halibut* scheduled to deploy shortly. Unbeknownst to Bob, the DivCom and CO agreed the *Growler*'s annual ORI (Operational Readiness Test) was to be his underway test.[2] Later, Bob was overwhelmed when he heard the CO had such faith in his ability to rely on him for such an important inspection that directly reflected the CO's ability to maintain submarine readiness.

His wife jumped for joy and they danced around the room a few times and she insisted he tell her about his time on the *Halibut*. On *Growler* the next morning, Captain Don smiled broadly and shook Bob's hand.

"That a boy, tiger, keep up the good work."

A few nights later Bob was on duty and conducted a Section Maneuvering Watch drill. The drill was designed to maintain an individual watch section's preparedness to get the submarine underway in an emergency situation using only duty personnel. An exercise was standard procedure every evening before movie call. Bob was displeased with the drill, so he kept the section on station and walked through the entire operation. That done, he called for another Section Maneuvering Watch five minutes later after the watch settled into the crew's mess for the nightly movie. The crew left no doubt in Bob's mind how they felt, but the crew reacted well and the Maneuvering Watch was manned in less than three minutes. Bob gave them a little speech about Pearl Harbor and how three minutes might not have been fast enough. Then they settled down to watch the movie.

Bob conducted a below decks inspection at 0400 and went topside to log his inspection, then went back to his bunk for a few hours of sleep.

"Submarine Division Eleven, arriving," roared the 1MC speaker. Bob bolted upright in his bunk and banged his head on the hull.

"What the hell is Lou Neeb doing here at this hour," Bob mumbled as he glanced at his watch. "It isn't 0600 yet." Bob stumbled topside in uniform but carried his shoes. "Good morning Commodore."

"Good morning, Bob, a Top Secret Operation Immediate message for you." He handed Bob the message and he quickly scanned it. He didn't get past the first line before he knew it was a drill. It read, "relationships between the United States and the Soviet Union have deteriorated for the past few days..." It explained *Growler* was to get underway immediately. "Do you understand the message Bob?"

"Yes, sir."

"Very well. There will be no one permitted on or off the boat from now on or any communications with members of the crew not actually on watch. Get the *Growler* underway, Mister."

"Aye, sir. May I call my Captain, sir?"

"That is negative."

Bob turned to his topside watch and ordered, "Station the Section Maneuvering Watch, section three."

"Come on, guys, remember what we did last night," he whispered as he headed for the bridge. The Commodore followed him. All the communication systems, including the sound powered phone set, were still on the bridge from the previous night's drill—that saved time.

On deck a crew member swore. "Damn, Mr. H doesn't give up, does he? And I thought he was going to be okay."

Bob smiled to himself and then the departments started reporting. As soon as Engineering was manned and ready, he ordered, "Light off and warm up three engines, Maneuvering." The wonderful sound of the engines running was music to his ears. Then the last report came in from Weapons.

"Sir, *Growler* Maneuvering Watch is set, three main engines are warming up, and all lines are singled, sir." The Commodore reached in his pocket, and pulled out a stopwatch.

"Son, you just broke the record. *Growler* was ready to get underway in one minute and 43 seconds."

"Good, sir... good for the crew." Bob felt stupid. What kind of response was that?

"Bob, secure the Maneuvering Watch. As you may have figured, this is an ORI and you have started out in spectacular form. You may tell your crew."

"Thank you, sir." He picked up the mike and said, "Secure the Section Maneuvering Watch. Well done, men. We stationed the watch in one minute and 43 seconds. This is the start of our ORI. You may return to your bunks until reveille. We will be getting underway at 0800. Good job."

"You may call Don Henderson now, Bob."

Bob climbed down to the quarterdeck and called the CO.

"Sorry to wake you, Captain, but Commodore Neeb is aboard and we started the ORI."

"Okay, Bob. What has taken place?"

"I stationed the section maneuvering watch, sir and got ready to get underway."

"Well?"

"Well, what, sir?"

"How did you do for Christ's sake." Bob couldn't pass up pulling his Captain's leg.

"Ah... pretty good, I guess, Captain."

"What the hell does 'pretty good I guess' mean?"

"We just broke the record for quickness in being ready to get underway sir."

"Bob, are you shitting me?"

"No, I am not. We're getting underway at 0800, sir."

"I'll be right there." Click.

"How's Don?"

"Fine, Commodore. He's on his way down, sir."

"You tell him he'd have to remain on the pier until 0800?"

"Never had a chance, sir." Bob entertained the Commodore for an hour and a half while they awaited 0800. The phone rang and the Topside Watch reported the CO was topside and not pleased at remaining on the pier."

"Tell Captain Henderson to join us for coffee in the wardroom," ordered the Commodore.

At 0745, the Commodore ordered Bob to station the Section Maneuvering Watch while he spoke to the other two sections of the crew who were mustered at quarters on the pier.

"You are to go aboard, but not interfere with the duty section unless there is a safety violation or harm could come to the crew or boat. Any unnecessary assistance will fail *Growler* in this exercise. The duty section will get the boat underway and dive it without assistance."

The rest of the crew went aboard, stowed their gear and stood aside as Section Three did their thing.

"Okay, Bob, get us underway."

"Aye, aye, sir," as he looked at his CO. Captain Don gave him a smile and a nod that said, "Go get 'em, tiger."

"Single all lines. Take in all lines except #2." Bob took a deep breath and said, "Starboard back one-third." As *Growler* gathered sternway, "Take in #2 line." The stern swung clear of the pier, "All back one-third."

Out of the corner of Bob's eye, he saw a flashing light on *Tang* at S-8, or the opposite side of the pier from *Growler*. It was QM1(SS) Glacy who had transferred to *Tang* a couple weeks earlier. He made the past three patrols on *Growler* and was very helpful to Bob during his days working on qualifications. He was sending a message. Dozens of things were going through Bob's mind and paramount at the moment was taking *Growler* to sea. He waved back to Glacy with a big smile and his fingers crossed.

"Port engine stop. Port engine ahead two thirds, shift your rudder to right full." He started his twist to starboard after clearing the pier.

"Bob, what was the message from *Tang*?" Commodore Neeb asked.

"I'll find out, sir."

"Oh shit, I blew it!" Bob thought to himself. He should have been alert to something like this. The DivCom knew they were former shipmates and expected Bob's reaction. Bob thought Glacy was shooting the bull with some of his former shipmates, often the case between Signalmen and Quartermasters. Bob's duty QM, Hoffman, was navigating below in Control. It was up to him to catch the message.

He swung the signal light out in front of him and sent, "Bravo Tango."

His old shipmate flashed back to him, "G-O-O-D space L-U-C-K space M-R space H. Bravo Tango." Bob waved back. It was so obvious.

"All stop. Rudder amidship." "All ahead one-third, steer course..." They were on their way out of Pearl Harbor. "Commodore, the message from the *Tang* was..."

"I know Bob. My sentiments also." He caught the "BT" from Pearl Harbor Control and got permission to depart port for local operating areas.

As they cleared "PH," Bob asked, "Commodore, request permission to secure the Maneuvering Watch, sir?"

"That you may, Bob. Set your regular underway watch."

QM1(SS) Hoffman did a fine job of keeping him informed. His work and plot were graded by the Commodore's Staff and received a perfect score. That surprised no one, for Hoffman was a great quartermaster and navigator, as were all the QMs. *Growler* headed for the assigned local operating area as the watch changed.

Bob retained the Conn on the bridge. When *Growler* arrived in the area, the Commodore ordered, "Bob, clear the bridge of all personnel except your watch."

Bob turned to tell the CO and XO to lay below, but they heard the order and were on their way below. Captain Don squeezed his arm and a word was never uttered. He had wished him well.

"Request permission to lay below, sir," shouted the CO.

"Permission granted, Captain." Quickly the bridge was emptied except for Bob and one lookout. *Damn, sure got lonely*, Bob thought. There was little time to ponder his loneliness as the 21MC crackled, "Mr. H., this is Commodore Neeb in Control. Send your lookout below. When ready, you will dive the boat and handle all stations yourself. No one will assist you unless you make a mistake or the safety of the boat is jeopardized. Do you understand me?" Diving a submarine by one-self is not that difficult for any one Qualified in Submarines, officers or enlisted. Everyone who wore the Dolphins had demonstrated his ability to conduct each separate step during the qualification process. The key was to keep one's head and not rush. This was not required of any enlisted man, and few officers, but this was an ORI.

"Understood, Commodore. Captain, did you copy that order?"

"I did, Bob. Follow the Commodore's instructions."

"Aye, aye, Captain. I missed the report if there was one. Is the boat rigged for dive and checked, sir?"

"You just won a prize with that question. The answer is, yes. The ship is rigged and checked for dive, Bob. They withheld the report." Bob envisioned the CO grinning as his junior officer wore his thinking cap.

"Clear the bridge, clear the bridge," Bob yelled to no one. It was time for a deep breath. "Dive the boat by myself. I'd heard of it before but thought it was bull or drinking talk," Bob mused. He knew he could do it but he had to keep his wits about him. He could not afford to panic or get excited. He grabbed the knurled knob of the Diving Alarm, AaaaUuga, AaaaUuga.

"Dive, Dive," he shouted into the 1MC even though no action would be taken. He flew off the bridge and swung down on the upper hatch lanyard. "Whoa. Wait a minute," he told himself. "I'm not being timed. I've got to be accurate. Slow down and think each step through," he whispered to himself. He shut the upper hatch, slid down the ladder to the lower hatch and shut it.

As he hit the Control Room deck, he checked for a straight board (Christmas Tree on older boats) to insure it indicated both hatches shut. The hatches showed two green lines on the board. Now the work began. He ran back to the Engine Room—gratefully only one engine was running. "Whoa again!" he whispered. "Have to shift the load from the generator to the battery before shutting down the engine," he talked to himself for he almost shut down #2 engine.

Bob ducked through the WT door into Maneuvering and felt a sigh of relief from EN1(SS) Don Goldberry when he caught himself. He stepped to the cubicle where EM1(SS) Ed Bell watched his every move. Behind him was a staff chief who observed him, licking the tip of his pencil. Why is it inspectors or graders always licked the tip of their pencils?

"I'll tell you what to do with that pencil chief!" Bob muttered. It was time for another deep breath and then carefully, he removed the electrical load from the diesel-generator set and shifted it to the battery. There were no sparks or fire-balls. He had shifted propulsion successfully. He did, however, leave a few drops of sweat on the Maneuvering Panel.

"I'm ahead one-third, on the battery. Next is to secure the engine and shut the main induction valve," and he walked into the Engine Room. He secured the engine, swung on the induction valve and with effort, shut it. He should have another green light on the straight board. He ran forward again to check. He received a slight slap on the butt from EN1(SS) Don Bosetti for luck—an unheard of move outside the Submarine Force. Actually, Bob and Don were from the same small town in Wisconsin; Beloit and the home of Fairbanks, Morse & Company who made the main engines.

As Bob passed through the Crew's Mess heading forward, he looked at the crew members eating early lunch before the next watch. He was heartened as he heard words of encouragement from his shipmates. The crew was behind him.

Then HM1(SS) Herb Edwards said, "No race today, Mr. H. Slow down." He was right and slowed to a deliberate walk. He ducked into Control and looked at the board... "Good, I've got a straight board. Now what. Get the bow planes rigged out and the stern planes off the block."

Bob checked the hydraulic valves open to the planes and put a little dive on the stern planes. Deliberately and calmly he walked aft to the Stern Room. He pulled the block clear of the stern planes. Next he went forward to the Forward Torpedo Room to rig out the bow planes.

Oh oh. They're already rigged out. What's the catch? he thought. The mechanical indicators showed the bow planes rigged out... and, yes, they were locked. He double-checked the hydraulic valves to the bow plane operating mechanism and they were open. "Hydraulic pressure is okay." Satisfied all was proper forward, he moved aft to Control. Everything was relatively simple and he could use a checklist for any operation if in doubt. He returned to Control to dive *Growler*.

Bob stepped into Control and to the conning stand. Was there anything left to do outside of Control? His answer was negative. He jumped onto the conning stand and looked out #2 periscope to check the bow planes rigged out. They were. He started for the diving manifold and the ballast tank vent valve actuators. "Ah ha!" he muttered out loud, he remembered, "Shift the planes and rudder to one station." It was time for another deep breath. Reaching below the backs of the seats, he shifted all rudder and plane control to the starboard seat. He glanced around Control and was encouraged by the looks in the CO's and XO's eyes.

He moved to the manifold and caught Mike Powell's, the COB, eye with a glance. A thumb pointed up and his confidence skyrocketed. The time was now. He opened the vents on the forward ballast tank group and heard the roar of tanks venting, then the after group and... and, yes, the depth gauge moved. They were submerging!

With vents open, Bob jumped on the conning stand and gently pushed the Commodore away from #2 periscope. Yes, the depth gauge wasn't lying. They were submerging. With a skip and a hop, he landed in the bow planes man seat and placed 10° dive on both planes and left rudder to get back on course. As the boat reached periscope depth, he realized he was heavy aft. He was headed for the trim manifold when the Commodore said, "That's enough, Bob. Well done, son."

"Whew, thank you, sir."[3]

"Let's go get a cup of coffee."

"Sounds fine to me, Commodore."

The remainder of the day, Bob was an accident waiting to happen. Wherever he walked, a simulated casualty occurred and he found himself in the midst of battling the casualty, helping with repairs or whatever. They simulated flooding in the Torpedo Room, flooding through the GDU (Garbage Disposal Unit) in the After Battery, a runaway Mk 16 torpedo (NAVOL), loss of stern plane hydraulics, etc. The crew was so reactive and fast, Bob, in reality, only had to fall in with the repairs already being conducted by the crew.

Finally, the ORI was completed and *Growler* headed back to Pearl. Bob was tired, but *Growler* passed the inspection. The final few drills were conducted without Bob's involvement, so that he could eat and rest a bit. The crew handled the drills remarkably well and professionally.

It surprised no one to see Bob as the OOD for entering port. He kept looking for something unexpected to happen but the surprises were over. He placed *Growler* alongside the pier and the Commodore said, "Good job."

The Maneuvering Watch was secured and the regular in port watch set. The Commodore asked Bob to come to his office in the morning for a written exam on the parts of qualification not covered.

At 0900, Bob reported to Commodore Neeb's office.

"You probably won't know the answers to all the questions, Bob. That's okay. Do your best and I'll see you at 1700." Most of the questions were classified and of the "what would you do if" variety. Thanks to his CO and XO, who enjoyed discussing tactics, he fared well. His hand cramped badly when 1700 arrived. He wrote an answer to each question.

"Go home, Bob. I'll let Captain Henderson know the results."

Next morning, Bob boarded Growler and headed for the wardroom for coffee. He walked into the wardroom and the CO was already there. He raised his head from the newspaper and stared at him.

"Morning, Captain." There was no response. So he poured himself a cup and started out the door.

"Hey, Bob!" A big grin broke on his face and he stood up and shook his hand. "Bob, congratulations, you are Qualified in Submarines."

"Oh, shit, great! Thanks, Captain. What did the Commodore say about my written test?"

The CO grinned even wider. "He said you were the biggest bull shitter this side of the Pecos, but you did show originality. We'll set up a dolphin dunkin' party soon."

Growler's schedule had prevented the opportunity to properly induct her newly qualified officers for a patrol or two, so XO Bob decided to end the drought with a party at his house. Wayne and Dave joined Bob in chugging for the golden fish even though they qualified a couple in-port periods prior. Sanity prevailed at the party when it came to drinking. The CO had a tray of four glasses but only one glass contained the dolphins and the newly qualified officers had to select the glass, the contents of which were unknown. Each glass was wrapped in aluminum foil to hide the contents. Since Wayne qualified first, he selected first and drank a glass of sauerkraut juice with no dolphins. Dave selected next and chugged a glass of sour wine and no dolphins. If Bob's selection was wrong, the tray would return to the house for a refill for the drinking only ended with the dolphins.

He picked a glass and raised it to his lips. It was warm beer with a shot of Vodka. Bob downed it to get it over with. It was a ghastly drink until he heard and felt a clank on his lips. It was the dolphins. The crusade was over!

There was no one prouder in the world that night than the three officers. The road to qualification was tough and demanding but every submarine officer worked equally hard. The help and support of the crew cannot be over stated. All three officers were forever grateful to the wonderful men that made the day possible.

Chapter Eleven
A Failure

In eighty homes and residences on Oahu, and in bunks on board *Growler*, the time had arrived again. Husbands and bachelors alike woke up to face yet another departure day. Good byes and farewell kisses were given to wives, lovers, friends, and children as the men of *Growler* prepared for a long time away from home. Many wives and girl friends would be on the pier later to wave and kiss the submarine crew farewell. Most of the men abhorred the scene and lived through it with swollen eyes and choked throats.

He received a snappy salute from the Marine at the gate and automatically looked to his left breast to make sure the Marine saw the dolphins. As he passed the Exchange and Submarine Museum, he rendered, as always, a salute to the fallen and whispered, "God Bless Them." As he pulled up across the street from Berth #9, he noticed the eastern sky was just beginning to brighten. He patted his Volkswagen bug a goodbye and wished it well with a female driver for the next few months and headed for the boat. The pier was wet from the morning dew and he puffed up with pride at the gallant silhouette of the *Growler* back lit by the lights at the end of the pier.

Even at the early hour, the pier was a bustle of activity with the last minute stores being loaded. It was all food—milk, fresh produce, bread, and—flour!

"Request permission to come aboard, sir."

"Peer-gra, Mr. H. Good morning sir," answered Petty Officer Rauch.

"Yeah, right. I guess so, but I'm getting a little tired of these damned deployment mornings."

"Know what you mean, Mr. H. This is going to be my eighth deployment. How about you, sir?"

"It's only my fifth, but I've only been doing this for five years," he smiled. He slid down the After Battery Hatch and CS1(SS) Kurus handed him a fresh cup of coffee as his feet hit the polished linoleum deck of the Crew's Mess. How many officers were handed a cup of coffee by the cook when he stepped on board? But this was a submarine, a submarine officer, and the *Growler*.

"Thanks, Kurus, I need this."

"You're welcome, Mr. H. Ready to go?"

"Does it make any difference? We're going ready or not. You guys have plenty of lobster for this trip?"

"You can bet your ass on it, sir, and plenty of steaks, too."

"Best news of the day. Thanks again for the coffee."

Below decks, the lighting was still rigged for red and dark. He walked through the dark Control Room, took a sip of his coffee and breathed deeply. He always enjoyed the special smell submariners knew so well. It smelled like home away from home although he doubted any wives would appreciate that thought. In a few hours, Control would be buzzing with activity and continue that way for months to come. A few memories roared through his mind of days from past patrols but he quickly stowed the memories, knowing new ones were to be made shortly.

The Duty Officer was asleep as Bob stepped into his stateroom and stowed his gear. He looked through his locker, full of skivvies, Levis, and sweat shirts. Nothing seemed forgotten, so there would be no last minute call to the wife for a quick delivery.

Carrying his coffee into the Wardroom, he read the result of the previous night's equalizer battery charge.

"Damn." The last hour of charge produced a lot of hydrogen gas again. "I just hope those Fairbanks-Morse engines stay together." Unlike the World War II Fairbanks 38D 8 1/8 X 10 Opposed Piston engines, which successfully propelled half the submarine force, *Growler* was damned with a newer, lightweight, high-speed engine that couldn't stay together. Designed to operate at 1700 RPM, they vibrated themselves apart. The problem was so acute that an extra fireman was required on watch to do nothing more than go around tightening parts. The engines were a mandatory design by some ingenious engineer in BuShips. *Growler* and *Grayback* both had the same engines and never returned with all three engines operable.

It was Bob's third ship since the Academy, and his third tour as a snipe (engineering position). He was flattered by being selected to relieve Wayne Mehl as Engineer, but he knew he faced a sadly overworked engineering system. The responsibility was bearable only because of the great men in the department. Like many Submariners, Bob was superstitious about some things and he made it a point to never visit the engineering spaces just prior to departure on patrol. Thus far it had worked, for he had always returned safely.

Minutes later, the Duty Officer, George Playdon, wandered into the Wardroom wearing only his skivvies and wiping sleep out of his eyes. They exchanged pleasantries over coffee and Bob inquired about how the battery charge had gone the previous evening.

"Pretty routine. Took more time with the battery charge because of hydrogen gas build up. I sure don't envy you with these batteries for a full trip."

"I'm not looking forward to it either. It's not going to be fun." George left to get into uniform, then headed aft to start his below decks inspection. This would be his last inspection as he had orders off *Growler* as soon as the Maneuvering Watch was set. Don Breeding walked in for a cup of coffee, humming, whistling, and happy as could be. He had three teenagers at home and going to sea was a great blessing in his hectic home life.

Bob picked up the message board and started reading. Another Polaris submarine had been launched in the *Layfayette* Class. The *George Washington* Class and *Ethan Allen* Class were already out on patrol in the Atlantic and the *Thomas Jefferson* was close to completion. He mused it wouldn't be long before the Polaris boats would be arriving in the Pacific and Regulus would end. Meanwhile, the Black and Blue crews of Regulus would continue the work of the two Polaris Crews; Blue and Gold. What a dream it would be to ride one of those big floating Hilton Hotels.

Growler would get underway with the Monday morning sortie out of Pearl Harbor. The weather looked good, at least as far as Midway Island, which was to be the top-off stop for food and fuel. The snorkel passage might not be as painful as some in the past.

"Bong bong, bong bong; *Growler* arriving." The skipper came aboard and he only caught a glimpse of the navigator, Horace Leavitt on his way to the Missile Center, which also served to house all the new navigation equipment. Last minute calibration and adjustment would be made to the new SINS (Ship's Inertial Navigation System); a MK 1 MOD 0 Sperry. Few men were more dedicated and entranced with the their work than Horace on the new, state-of-the-art SINS equipment. It was a prototype for *Growler,* but had already made its appearance on the Polaris boats in the Atlantic. Unfortunately for *Growler,* she did not carry all the new, sophisticated support and peripheral navigation position fixing equipment used to update the SINS. *Growler* only had one SINS where the Polaris boats had two or three for comparison and grooming. Robert Norris, one of the new ETNs (Navigation electronic technicians) and Horace were the only two personnel on board that understood the "new compass," SINS. Navigation Electronic Technicians, often called "twichets," were very special people.

On *Grayback* back in 1958, on her cold weather indoctrination run up north, the Loran A stopped working. When on station and for a good share of the transits, overcast skies were usual and Loran A was the only position source available, as inaccurate as it may have been. The Electronic Technicians went to work immediately and continued for a few days without success. QMC(SS) Charlie Napier wandered through the Navigation Center and looked at the Loran A console and tried twisting a few knobs. Suddenly, the Loran A came to life – he had turned the brightness knob clockwise.[1]

SD1(SS) Casuto Bacal, the leading steward, didn't bother asking Bob what he wanted for breakfast. He already knew Bob's gut was in an emotional knot and the last thing he wanted was something to eat. It happened every morning the submarine deployed.

"All hands to quarters for muster and inspection." It was to be a day without inspection, which was not unusual in the Submarine Force. Even when there was an inspection, it wasn't much of one unless it was for a special reason. During this in port period, Jerry Bowman and Lin McCollum had been on their way out the base gate when Horace stopped and offered them a ride. The threesome made it as far as Horace's house where they spent the afternoon and evening eating and drinking. They even tried their hands at fencing—a sport Horace was expert at as a varsity member of the Naval Academy Fencing Team. Time and drink took its toll and Bowman and McCollum ended up falling asleep, waking at an early hour, and catching a taxi back to the boat. Unfortunately, Bowman left his uniform shoes at the Leavitt house. Next morning at quarters, he wore a pair of brown loafers since they were the only other shoes he owned. As the crew mustered and fell in, Horace snuck behind the line of men and slipped Bowman his shoes. One can only imagine what would have happened on a cruiser.[2]

As the men fell in, Bob looked at each of his chiefs for an indication of readiness of their divisions in the engineering department. Each chief flashed him a thumbs up. Engineering was ready to deploy. Each had gone through their respective pre-deployment check off sheets and found everything satisfactory.

"Officers report," ordered the executive officer.

When it was Bob's turn, he responded, "Engineering Department ready to get underway in all respects, sir." There were a few words of wisdom from Bob Owens, then.

"Bob, go to the bridge, you're driving this morning." Bob was elated. He loved to handle the ship, but it also would keep his mind occupied on ship's business instead of feeling remorseful about departing the family again. The crew was given a few last minutes to kiss and hug their families on the pier. The SubPac Band arrived, fell into formation on the pier in the midst of submariners and families and started playing the traditional Navy and Hawaiian music. Bob paused a moment to look at his family on the pier and as usual, tears formed and fell. Then he turned and pressed the button on the 1MC:

"Station the Maneuvering Watch." He looked at his wife as she yelled,

"Good luck, Bob. I hope everything goes well."

Bob laid below to get his binoculars and jacket. Even in the warm waters of

Hawaii the wind could be cool at sea and this was early in the morning. When he got back up to the bridge, QM1(SS) Curbow handed him the pre-underway check-off list. As he went down through the list, one item at a time, the band struck up the Navy Hymn and goose bumps stood everywhere on Bob. There was no other song quite like it except for the National Anthem. Always, the song took him back to the Naval Academy and the thrill he got every time it was played, especially during parades on Wordon Field. Every sailor had his own memories, always fond, of the Navy Hymn. Wives and sweethearts wept on the pier and young children gazed in wonderment, not totally understanding the moment.

"Watch your ears!" It was a warning to the crew that he was about to test the ship's whistle. A deafening roar spat from the front of the sail and everyone jumped on the pier even though they had grown to expect the sound. Bob always wondered why they used the term, "watch your ears." It was physically impossible and made about as much sense as "heads up," when one should be ducking.

"Commander Submarine Force Pacific, arriving." The Captain was at the end of the gangway to meet Admiral Eugene B. Fluckey, the new commander of submarines, to receive his good wishes and any last minute intelligence reports.

"Maneuvering, Bridge. Light off and warm up three main engines. Shutdown with shutdown air," ordered Bob from the bridge on the 21MC. Instantly, #1 engine rattled to life, caught, and roared, emitting a cloud of blue exhaust that drifted across the pier, choking the band momentarily. "God, I love the sound of diesels; always have, always will." Years later, Bob would stop and listen to Greyhound buses or big eighteen-wheelers and think of the days on the diesel boats.

"Commander, Submarine Force Pacific, departing." Bob looked down on deck and the skipper returned his gaze with a smile. One last time, Bob glanced toward the pier and his family. The band swung into another rendition of *Anchors Aweigh*. #3 engine came to life with another growl and roar with attendant blue smoke. He waited patiently for #2 engine to start up but the exhaust port remained silent. He stared at the port quarter for another minute and finally called down on the 21MC,

Maneuvering, Bridge, what's up with #2 engine?"

Bridge, Maneuvering. Wait one, sir."

The gangway was removed and Bob ordered, "Single up all lines."

"Bridge, Maneuvering. I think #2 generator might be flooded, sir."

"Oh, shit," Bob's voice carried across the 21MC as the captain was making his way up to the bridge.

"Permission to come up to the bridge, sir," shouted the Captain.

"Come up, Captain."

"Bob, did I hear that last report correctly?"

"Yes, sir, Maneuvering reports #2 generator may be flooded, sir."

131

"I relieve you Bob. Get your butt down there and find out what's going on." Flying down the ladder from the bridge, Bob landed on the Control Room deck with a resounding bang and headed aft on the run. Out of the corners of his eyes, he saw and felt the crew's eyes looking at him for an answer since they had all heard the report. Literally falling into the Engine Room, he pushed his way through a small crowd of worried gawkers looking into the center bilge.

"Son of a Bitch! It's true." Bilge water was well above the centerline (#2) generator housing, which was the lowest of the three generators. "How bad is it, Chief?"

"It's a zero ground, sir. She's completely shorted out."

"Well, god damn it, Chief, get the bilges pumped down! Then come down to my stateroom, Chief!" He called the CO on the telephone. "Captain, the center bilge is flooded and above the generator housing. I'm afraid the generator is shorted out, sir."

"Okay Bob, what are our options?"

"Well sir, I wish I really knew. The bilge is being pumped and Chief Samuels and I are about to discuss just what we can do. I imagine it's something like flushing the windings with fresh water and drying out the generator. That will give us an indication of how serious the problem is."

"It's serious now, Bob. Have your meeting, then give me your plans." Bob returned to his stateroom practically numb.

"Hi, Chief, What do you think?

"I was standing behind you when you reported to the old man. You pretty well called it, except I've heard there are detergents that can be used to dissolve the salts that cause the grounds. I don't know much about it, but I'll bet the guys over in the shipyard electrical shop have more ideas."

"Okay, Chief, I'll pass that on to the skipper. By the way, how long does this process take?"

"It can take a few days to never, sir."

"Okay, Chief. Understood. Take charge aft and keep me informed." He wearily climbed back up to the bridge where the CO and XO were discussing the matter and alternatives. He explained his discussions with Chief Samuels and what he thought ought to be done.

"Okay, Bob, Guess the first thing I better do is let the Commodore know what has happened and then the Admiral. Bob, go ahead and take the Conn, secure the Maneuvering Watch, then get on the problem."

"*Growler*, departing."

Regulus submarines had departed for patrols previously without everything in commission, but now the problem was a main engine and generator. The engine did them no good by itself since this was a diesel-electric propulsion system. The Maneuvering Watch was secured and Bob went to the Engine Room. The crew was abuzz with questions, rumors, and questions. The bilge was dry and his chief found the source of the flooding. A drain on the fresh water cooling system was left open and permitted fresh water to drain into the bilge. Since the boat had been taking on and topping off fresh water all night, the slow loss was not apparent by sounding a fresh water tank. A quick calculation indicated the water leak had run for at least nine hours.

"My god, what was the Below Decks Watch doing? Well, at least most of he water in the bilge had been fresh, that was a plus. Chief, before we do anything else, let's wait until we talk to the CO and get some advice from the shipyard."

"Sounds good to me, Mr. H.," spoke Chief Samuels, a definite and noticeable note of relief in his voice. He had not encountered this type of problem before, and as chief in charge, he was more than willing to listen to any advice, even from civilian experts.

"*Growler*, arriving."

"All officers assemble in the wardroom," boomed out of the 1MC speakers. A quiet and nervous group of officers mustered immediately as the CO entered the wardroom.

"Gentlemen, you probably know the problem, the question is the options to a solution. The shipyard experts are on their way to give us a hand and advice. As of this moment, our deployment is on hold!"

Bob saw the emotions on the faces of the officers. They were all depressed because they hadn't answered the bell to deploy on time. Fathers and husbands were somewhat pleased because they would be seeing more of their families that night, but the joy was a fleeting moment before failure etched everyone's face. The captain had asked Admiral Fluckey to deploy on just two engines but the admiral refused.

"We will attempt to dry out the generator in place and if it works, we'll take off immediately. *Halibut* is on station, which is fortunate for they are best equipped to handle an extension on station—except for the disappointment of her crew."

So started a period of about two weeks that spelled hope and the prayer that the generator could be repaired in place and quickly. *Growler* remained dockside and tried every idea known to mankind to dry out a generator in place. The generator was flushed with fresh water and detergent. Heaters placed inside the generator hastened the drying process to the windings. Slowly, agonizingly slow, the ground reduced and hope turned to confidence that energizing the windings, very slowly at first, might cure the problem as the heat in the windings dried out residual moisture. By the end of the second week, the shipyard gave the crew thumbs up to deploy. Growler would leave on two engines and follow a prescribed plan of slowly increased loads on the generator, so that by the time they arrived on station the generator should be able to carry a full load. The larger the load, the warmer and drier the windings became.

Growler got underway without fanfare and quietly slipped out of port in the early morning hours. It was early summer and the weather was good. In the Engine Room, the electricians monitored #2 generator constantly and carefully followed the program outlined by the shipyard. The load was slowly increased in small increments and the duration the generator carried the load was increased. Shipyard engineers had computed a curve of expected resistance as the generator dried out and the generator was following the curve exactly. With every ohm of resistance, hopes for success climbed.

The fourth day out of Pearl Harbor they were only a couple days away from Adak. The load on #2 generator was increased to almost a full load as per the shipyard program. *Growler* was on the surface and Bob was standing the afternoon watch on the bridge. He enjoyed the sun and beautiful day as he contentedly listened to all three engines running. About 1500, he suddenly detected an increase in RPM on #2 engine and then it returned to normal. He was an engineer and he thought like one; often listening like one. His throat tightened and his stomach tightened into a knot.

"Maneuvering, Bridge. Anything wrong with #2?" Before he received an answer, the engine shut down.

"Bridge, Maneuvering. Sir, #2 generator just blew to hell—I think, sir. I'll be up to see you in a minute, Mr. H."

"Thank you, Chief." "Captain, Bridge, sir." On the sound powered telephones. "We just lost the generator, sir. I'll have details for you shortly, Captain." There was a long silence. "Captain, did you hear me?"

"Damn it Bob, I heard you. Son of a bitch! I... I know you and your people busted balls to make it, Bob. Call me back when you have the details."

"Chief Samuels. Sir. Permission to come up?"

"Come up, chief." Chief Samuels was in tears, as he had babysat the generator virtually nonstop since the flooding.

"Mr. H., she just sort of flew apart on us."

"I understand, Chief. Take it easy. You certainly are not to blame. I can't think of a thing more you could have done and you couldn't have spent more time with the damned thing."

"Thank you, sir... God. We tried so hard and we came so close."

"I know, as does every member of this crew. Now, Chief, is there anything we can do now or is all lost?"

"Mr. H., there is nothing more we can do at this point. The windings literally blew up. I can repair it in a shop, sir, but not out here. We don't have the equipment."

"I understand, Chief. I get off watch in a few minutes. Please join me to talk with the CO and give him the details." They talked with the CO and he understood.

"Chief, I want you and your men to know I understand what you all went through and all in *Growler* appreciate your effort."

"Thanks, Captain. We really did try very hard, sir."

"I know, Chief. Now I have to tell the Admiral." The CO had to appraise Com-SubPac, so he sent the Admiral a SITREP (situation report) explaining what had transpired. He urgently requested permission to continue on patrol. The answer was to return to port, but the CO tried two more times to change the Admiral's mind. It didn't work.

There were many tears and angry words of unhappiness as *Growler* came about and headed back toward Hawaii. Though they were heading home, there were eighty-five heavy hearts on *Growler* because they had been beaten — they had not answered the bell when called upon. The crew was so miserable that later they could not remember the trip back to Pearl Harbor, including Bob. *Growler* immediately went to West Loch to offload weapons, thence to dry dock at the shipyard. The entire engine/generator set was replaced with an engine used for training. The enginemen and electricians disconnected the engine and generator so Growler was unceremoniously towed to dry dock.

It was during this short trip to the shipyard that the crew witnessed one of the funniest stunts yet to be performed by a submarine. A submarine was entering boat and was either a tear shape *Barbel* Class or a new nuclear fast attack submarine. The stern of the submarine disappeared below the waterline and her rudder was above water a couple dozen feet behind the hull. Atop the rudder, sat a submariner with an Evinrude outboard motor mounted to the rudder and running so as to make it appear the submarine was being propelled by an outboard motor. It served to take a little of the edge off the unhappy *Growler* crew.

The Captain used the shipyard availability to urge the DivCom to seek a new battery since the *Growler's* battery was nearing end of warranty and was already giving the electricians trouble. The replacement didn't arrive in time. Meanwhile, the crew experienced yet another turnover. A brand new Ensign out of Annapolis reported on board in immaculate uniform and gleaming spit-shined shoes. The topside watch had the Ensign escorted below decks and forward to the Wardroom where the officers were just finishing breakfast.

"Ensign Vallentine reporting for duty, Captain," looking directly at Horace and rendering him a snappy salute.

Horace looked up with a rare broad grin, pointed his fork to the other end of the table and said, "Try him."

"Sorry, sir," Gordon blurted out in frustration, and red-faced. He knew the captain of a ship always sat at the head of the table; he just had the wrong end. He backed out of the wardroom, parted the other curtain,

"Good morning, Captain, Ensign Vallentine reporting for duty, sir." Saluting, he addressed Perry Benson, who was thoroughly enjoying the situation and not sitting in the CO's chair..

"Mr. Vallentine, do these silver bars look like I'm the Captain to you?"

"Errr... ah... no, sir. You're a Lieutenant JG."

"Atta boy, Vallentine. Now I'm Naval Academy, like most of these guys, and they taught me not to salute inside. Is that what they taught you?"[3]

"Ahh, yes, sir. Sorry, sir."

"Mister Vallentine, permit me to introduce you to the other worthy officers of this wardroom."

"Thank you, sir, I mean, thank you."

"The ugly guy with his mouth full of food is Horace Leavitt, our Navigator and Operations Officer."

"Sorry for the mistake, sir, nice meeting you, sir."

"What's your first name, Mister Vallentine?"

"Gordon, sir."

"Gordon, eh? Well, Gordo, we are not formal on submarines so we prefer using our first names. I'm Horace."

"Aye, aye, sir, Horace." The Wardroom filled with laughter. Gordo was red-faced, but eagerly greeted each officer.

"And this chubby, old gray-haired man that just walked in is our Executive Officer, Bob Owens."

"Good morning, Commander, sir."

"Damn, Gordo, you don't hear so good do you? Didn't Horace just explain to you that we are on a first name basis in submarines?"

"Ah, er, yes, sir, yes, I heard him, sir."

"Well, Gordo, am I an 'er or an 'ah?"

"Sorry, sir, er, Executive Officer, or , er, ah..., I mean Bob, sir."

"Well Gordo, it sounds like you're gaining on the problem. When you finish breakfast and determine who I am, come and see me."

"Aye, aye, sir, er, Bob, sir." Then the remaining introductions took place. "Hi, Bob... Hello, Don... Nice meeting you, Perry... Hello, Dave... etc."

"And this is your Commanding Officer, Don Henderson," who had just stopped in for a cup of coffee.

"Nice meeting you, Don." Silence filled the Wardroom.

"Sit down, Gordo, and have a cup of coffee while you still can," said Horace.

"Thank you, Horace," answered Gordo, looking a bit perplexed. "Pass the cream please, Don." One could cut the air in the Wardroom. Then the Captain spoke.

"Mister Vallentine, we do use our first names in the Wardroom. My first name is Captain! Do I make myself perfectly clear?"

"Perfectly. Yes, sir, Captain, sir." So began the era of Gordo on *Growler* and it was to be a wild and crazy period.

Gordo's era wasn't more than a few hours old when he made an indelible mark on *Growler*. The XO assigned him as Sonar Officer and tasked him with overseeing the prime project of removing the old BT (Bathythermograph) and replacing it with a new model. SO1(SS) Billy Bob Scott, known to all as "Scotty," explained the project to Gordo and before anyone could stop him, Gordo decided to remove the old BT. With huge bolt cutters in hand, he severed everything connected to the old BT, including a 220VAC power cable. The resulting fireball melted the bolt cutters and slightly burned Gordo. Scotty's next instruction to Gordo was, "You leader—Me worker."[4]

The entire crew cringed as shipyard welders cut a large hole in the overhead of the Engine Room through the inch and a half steel hull. All the piping and electrical systems outside and inside the hull had to be removed around the hole. The major worry, and sometimes a mystery, was how the welders would replace the "soft patch" exactly in place and retain perfect circularity. Despite the despondency of the crew for missing the patrol, some good did come from the delay by getting major work accomplished that should have been done prior to *Growler* deploying. Though young in age, *Growler* was being run into the ground with her arduous schedule. A great deal of work was done that was not absolutely essential but beyond the capability of the crew.

There were few, if any, of the crew that enjoyed being in the shipyard. The exceptions were likely the *Grayback's* Valpoon and *Growler's* Rintz. To them, the shipyard was like a giant shopping mall, and whose small "thefts" often resulted in saving time on station and probably shipmate's lives. Like or dislike the shipyard, no crew members cared much for the shipyard workers and their working habits. Bob encountered a sleeping shipyard worker and awakened him from a drunken stupor. The reaction of the worker and his bellow would have made any self respecting Boatswains mate proud. The worker was sorely pissed and promised Bob he would get more sleep while on the clock. A few mornings later, a routine progress conference was being conducted with the shipyard supervisors and chaired by an Engineering Duty Only Rear Admiral.

"Gentlemen, I am told the ship's crew has not cooperated in assisting the yard to do its work," sayeth the Rear Admiral.

"Admiral, which department experienced the problem?" queried Captain Henderson.

"The Electrical Shop, Captain."

"Thank you, Admiral. What seems to be the problem, sir?"

"Captain, rather than repeating hearsay, let me have the Electrical Shop Supervisor explain his own problem"

"That's fine, Admiral."

"Good morning, Captain. My name is Jim McFarlain and I am the Supervisor of Shop 11. My crews report your crew has not assisted us nor provided adequate prints of the electrical system. It's also reported my lead man has been harassed by the crew and your Engineer, sir."

"Thank you, Jim, I appreciate your candor and I hope we can amiably settle the problem," replied the Admiral.

Captain Henderson rose and spoke, "It was reported to me by my Engineer that the lead man, Badge #317, was found asleep in the middle of his shift. The individual was awakened and asked to get on with ship's work. The lead man informed my Engineer he would sleep even more than work on *Growler* and there was absolutely nothing the submarine could do about it. I tasked my Engineer to set up a log to document Badge #317. It reflects the time he reported aboard and every time he was noticed by *Growler* personnel, indicating what he was doing at the observation time." The Shop Supervisor shifted uncomfortably in his chair. In fact, the Captain had the Supervisor downright squirming. "Admiral, here is our log indicating the lead man did nothing in the past week and slept thirty-one hours out his forty-hour shift."

Red-faced, the Admiral stood up, accepted the log, and glared at the Shop Supervisor.

"Thank you, Captain. I appreciate the completeness of your observation but, in the future, please don't wait until this meeting to report problems. Personally report to me any time you are displeased with the shipyard's work."

"Aye, aye, Admiral, but I don't anticipate any more problems."

A few weeks later, Bob crawled through all the tanks with Rintz and Miller and checked everything below the waterline. He never "dove" the tanks before, so his two leading auxiliarymen were of invaluable help and most informative. He had drawn the systems, and knew what was supposed to be there, but had never had the opportunity to have hands-on experience. The crew took advantage of the opportunity and checked every piece of equipment, every inch of pipe, and valves many times over, especially the vent valves in the tanks and locking rings on the Fuel Ballast Tanks inside the tanks.

Barbero was on patrol when a fuel-ballast tank locking ring backed off a few turns, permitting the vent to creep partially open. It permitted diesel oil in the tank to seep out of the tank. *Barbero* lost fuel oil, but the oil slick on the surface was akin to a rainbow arrow pointing to the submarine. The incident occurred on station and was noticed through the periscope on an exceptionally calm day. The boat made it to Midway to refuel with less than 500 gallons of fuel remaining—less than an hour of running time on one engine.[5] The incident was reminiscent of the *Narwhal*, which leaked 20,000 gallons of fuel oil on her first patrol of World War II.[6]

The vent valve seats looked good and the locking rings were tight below decks.

The crew cleaned up a few rough spots on the propeller blades. The cleaner and smoother the propeller, the less cavitation. All the hull penetrations and stuffing tubes were checked and when all the inspections and checks were complete, the drydock was flooded and *Growler* lifted off the blocks. She returned the Berth S-9 for housekeeping work in preparation for sea trials. Sea trials were mandatory after major hull work or drydocking for a submarine. A custom in submarines was that all shop supervisors where work was accomplished were mandated to ride the boat for the first dive. The CO went a step further and arranged to have the troublesome electrician make the ride.

A week later, *Growler* was underway for operations in shallow waters to conduct sea trials. *Growler* ran on the surface to an area off the coast of Lahaina Island and most of the crew went topside to enjoy a beautiful day on a tropical day off Hawaii. An ASR (submarine rescue vessel) accompanied them and stood by for the first day of sea trials. Gordon was tasked with preparing the trim for the dive as a practical factor for his qualifications. As Engineer, Bob also worked out the trim that was no easy job.

From the time a submarine surfaces until it submerges again, all weight changes are tabulated and the trim tanks adjusted to accommodate the changes. At sea, the time between surfaces and submerges is small and changes are usually insignificant and easily handled each time the submarine submerges. However, *Growler* had been dry-docked and alongside a pier for over a month. She spent time in the shipyard for major repairs, de-fueled the fuel ballast tanks, changed equipments, off-loaded a full load of weapons, and had a major change in onboard supplies. The cumulative weight change was significant.

Gordo submitted this trim plan to Bob shortly after the Maneuvering Watch was set. Bob had completed his trim plan the day prior and he compared the numbers. He was astonished at the large difference in the numbers, hundreds of tons apart. He double checked his numbers and took his trim plan to the CO for approval.

"Wow, we're lighter than hell, Bob."

"Yes, sir, but we are still within the limits to dive."

"How did Gordo's trim look?"

"You think mine is light, we were heavy as a cruiser according to him, sir."

"Okay, Bob, it's Gordo's show so let him trim the boat. If he's in error, we'll bob on the surface like a cork. Just don't let him take more than a few hours out there." It was Gordo's trim so he went to the bridge and relieved the watch. He would then dive the boat. Gordon had the correct numbers accumulated, but had calculated the changes in the wrong direction. Being too light would not endanger the boat or the crew.

"This is Mister Vallentine and I have the Conn."

"Captain in Control," piped Hoffman.

"Relax men. You ready, Bob?"

"Yes, sir. All we have to do is to inform the COUCAL we are diving." Bob choked off his laughter when he reported for he knew they were as light as a blimp and it would be a long time diving. Rintz had also figured out what was going on. He had made way too many trim dives not to realize the *Growler* was light as an air bag.

"Bridge, this is the Captain. The boat is rigged for dive. Dive the boat." The sound of the diving klaxon was followed by Gordo's trembling voice, "Dive, dive!"

"Conn, Radio. COUCAL acknowledges our diving message, sir." Gordo came screaming down the ladder and raced to the diving position and ordered,

"Open the vents on the forward group! Open the vents on the after group! Rig out the bow planes." Air whistled out of the ballast tanks, although the great roar seemed a bit weak. The main engines shut down and the boat became silent. "Straight board, sir," Gordo reported.

"Very well," answered the Captain. "Make your depth 60 feet." The boat remained light, even with all the main ballast tanks open. The decks were dry, not even awash. Gordo began flooding trim tanks, a few hundred pounds at a time. It was like dribbling into the ocean. After an hour, the depth of the keel was at 35 feet—the boat had dropped five feet in the first hour.

"To hell with the pressure, sir," shouted Rintz from the flood manifold, "take her down to 40 feet." Control rocked with laughter for the entire crew knew the score by this time. Bob flinched a bit. The situation was humorous, but he didn't like to see a fellow officer ridiculed too much. The CO felt the same way, even though this was one tight crew and fun was for everyone.

"Conn, Radio. Sir, the COUCAL wants to know if we're going to dive or if we have a problem."

"Bob, take the dive. Ordered depth is six-zero feet." Ten minutes later the boat was at periscope depth after Bob flooded tons into the trim tanks, most of it in big gulps. Next came the serious business of checking the boat for any leaks. The COB took the dive and the CO increased depth in one hundred foot increments. Every member of the crew was constantly checking the boat for leaks except the XO who took reports and the CO who had the Conn. There were no major problems and every item the shipyard worked on was attended by a shipyard worker. The big worry was the soft patch, but it was perfect. The extensive welding done by the shipyard welders caused many sounds and moans of stress relief as the boat delved deeper into the sea. At times, the hull literally screamed.

The unhappy electrician from the shipyard sat in an after corner in the Control Room, wide-eyed and trembling, as the boat increased her descent. An equipment frame or other insignificant piece of steel popped loudly as the hull compressed and the electrician was at the point of panic as he searched the overhead for water. EN1(SS) Jerry Carlson was passing through the space, looked at the electrician, heard the pop, and couldn't contain himself.

"Oh, oh." He whispered in the direction of the yard bird, "sounds like the hull is collapsing." All the anger the electrician had wrought upon the crew evaporated as he thoroughly wet himself and became horribly ill.

They conducted exercises and checked out the new engine and generator. Everything went well. *Growler* was well and ready to go back on patrol. Bob slept the sleep of the dead as all the work and tensions of the past month eased off his shoulders. He knew his men also slept well. They had worked hard to achieve success.

Engineering problems didn't single out just the *Growler* and *Grayback*. It was years later and not a diesel problem, but an engineering problem of significance. The reactor on *Halibut* was depleted of full power run hours. Suddenly, ComSub-Pac was faced with a requirement for *Halibut* to deploy to fill in for the Strategic Air Command. Everyone was aware that if the reactor had to be "scrammed," (shutdown) it could not be restarted until the "xenon" gas subsided. The boat arrived on station following a full power run across the Pacific Ocean when a problem developed and the reactor was scrammed. *Halibut* hovered for three days to save electrical power until the reactor could be restarted. Hovering with little reserve power available was extremely precarious.[7]

"Mr. H., it's 0330, sir, and time for your watch."

"Thanks, Underwood. I'm up." A quick head call, a scrubbing of the teeth, a cup of coffee, and Bob was on his way to the Bridge. The boat was rigged for red and quiet, with only a few men moving on or off watch. He stepped into Control, checked the quartermaster's chart, then headed up the ladder to the Bridge.

"Permission to come up."

"Come up, Bob." It was a beautiful morning. Lights twinkled on the island and the fresh, warm and humid air felt good. They steamed in a local operating area and at the moment, there were no contacts to worry about. He listened to Perry's report to him, asked a couple questions, and felt comfortable.

"Hit the rack, Perry, I relieve you."

"I'll do that, Bob. I stand relieved." Bob looked up into the crystal clear sky and observed the multitudes of stars. MT2(SS) Chris Joas was the starboard lookout and an old timer on *Growler*. He was one of the crew members that had been in Bob's watch section on both patrols, usually as a planesman. They knew each other well; having shared numerous stories in the hundreds of hours they stood watch together. They had discussed just about every topic imaginable and established a special sort of repertoire. Within a few minutes, they were both deep into the "remember whens" and sea stories that always began with, "this is no shit."

The port lookout was a new crewmember and was standing one of his first lookout watches since Submarine School. He was a sponge that sucked up every word the two spoke, occasionally throwing in a, "No shit, sir?"

Don Curbow came to the Bridge preparatory to shooting morning stars, although a star fix wasn't needed since they had good radar and visual bearing lines. It didn't take Curbow long to get the gist of conversation being directed at the newcomer, Larry Noon. Noon was only eighteen years old, but looking at him one would swear he was too young to be a Boy Scout.

"Hi, Mr. H., I meant to ask you why you left that lookout on the Bridge the last time we dove on patrol?

"Give me a break, Curbow. When one is the Officer of the Deck, one has to look at the big picture and consider the boat and the crew below."

"I know, sir, but he didn't even have a life jacket on."

"He didn't suffer long. The water temperature was at or near freezing so he was gone in seconds." Out of the corner of their eyes, they could see Noon was beginning to tremble with fright and question why he had volunteered for submarine duty. The threesome couldn't keep it up much longer so they admitted they were just pulling Noon's leg. He smiled and seemed to relax a bit but didn't appear to be completely convinced.

One of the funnier *Growler* stories was related by Jerry Carlson. It took place on an earlier patrol, when Joe Ekeland was the XO. Ekelund was the commissioning Engineer, then moved up to Navigator, Operations and thence to Executive Officer. Needless to say, the crew knew him well and he had a reputation of being a perfectionist in every manner possible. Every piece of paperwork and log entry had to be done absolutely correct. Enter Jerry Carlson, a quiet and unassuming Engineman and Submariner with a brilliant mind for comedy. One night on watch in Maneuvering, things were quiet and Carlson began whittling on an eraser on the tip of a pencil. It turned out to be a little foot and he found it would work like an ink stamp when inked. That night, when Ekelund signed the navigation log and the Captain's Night Orders, he found a little footprint on the papers. He had no problem voicing his dismay and disapproval. This, of course, encouraged the Submariners and the footprints began to appear everywhere; his napkin, the bottom of the bunk above him, so that when he looked up, there was a footprint. Trails of footprints led nowhere and even appeared in books he was reading on the next page. Ekelund would never find the phantom foot printer until he was a retired admiral at a *Growler* reunion.[8]

Near sunrise, and following Curbow's star sights, God painted a beautiful picture over the eastern skies, with the sky turning blue, and puffy cumulous clouds reflecting oranges and reds from the first rays of light. Noon reported an aircraft to the west and approaching. Noon, Joas, and Bob looked aft and Bob noted it was a C-119 aircraft headed their way at Angels 20, or 20,000 feet altitude. The aircraft then turned and began circling about five miles away. A lesson in observance and imagination was about to occur.

"Sir, a parachute deep on the port quarter. Looks like it came from the aircraft," shouted Noon. Bob whirled and scanned the area with his binoculars. The light to the west was still dark but he did find the parachute near where they had seen the cargo plane.

"Damn, that parachute is right where that aircraft has been circling for the past five minutes. It must have a problem."

"I think you're right, Mr. H. He must have a problem to keep circling way out here so far from land," Joas added. "But I wonder why they're circling out here when they're only about twenty miles to Honolulu International Airport, or are there other airstrips out here on these smaller islands?" No one could see exactly what was attached to the parachute due to the dark skies and distance but they all imagined seeing a person hanging from the shrouds. Bob knew he had to get to the parachute quickly and save the person. Well, *Growler* didn't have a parachute bill, so he bellowed into the 1MC:

"Man Overboard, port side, Man your Man Overboard Stations!" Shifting to the 21MC, "Right full rudder, all ahead standard, steady on course 280°. Curbow, start a plot on 280°, range five miles."

It was prior to reveille and the crew awakened with a start. A few moments later, "Morning, Captain," then looked away from the white legs in undershorts.

"What the hell, Bob, how did we get a man overboard? We dump garbage or something"

"No, sir. We had a C-119 circling ahead of us, out about five miles. Been circling for five to ten minutes. Then we saw a guy jump out in a parachute." Bob handed the CO his binoculars.

"Damn it Bob, I don't see anyone or a parachute. Where they hell is he?"

"We're heading straight for him, sir. Look up about 20° to 30° and he should be ahead a few miles. Where is he, lookouts?"

"I don't see him now." Shouted Joas.

"I lost him, Mr. H."

"Captain, I don't see him right now, but he should be dead ahead or fine on either bow, sir." The parachute and the aircraft were not to be seen with visibility unlimited but a number of huge cumulous clouds in the area.

"Bob, how long you been up?" asked the CO

"Captain, I hit the rack about midnight, sir."

"Bridge, Control. The Man Overboard Party is mustered and requests permission to come on deck through the Forward Torpedo Room hatch, sir."

"Permission granted Control. Open the Torpedo Room hatch and have the party remain on the bow."

"Bob, how much sleep have you had in the past few days?"

"Not much, Captain, busy finishing up all the yard work and stuff. You guys saw the airplane and the parachute, didn't you?" he queried his lookouts. Bob half expected to get his leg pulled but they both acknowledged seeing the event.

"Aircraft, two points on the starboard bow, sir," shouted Joas. "It has the parachute wrapped around its cockpit, sir, what the hell is happening?" They all looked and saw the huge aircraft busting out of cloud cover with a parachute wrapped around its nose. The CO chuckled, but the Bridge Watch found little humor in the laugh.

"Bob, secure the Man Overboard Party and resume steaming in our operating area. You might as well slow to one-third speed as well. We won't be rescuing anybody this morning."

"Aye, aye, sir... but?"

"We've got a Discovery satellite film package recovery coming up next month, which is supposed to land the film near here. NASA is considering snagging the film on a parachute out of the air by aircraft to avoid the lost time in the ocean after splash down, using U-2s and EC-121s to track the package. They're practicing right now, and that's what you're watching." As he finished explaining, another parachute was on its way down and this time Bob could see a capsule, not a human being, on the end of the chute. While he was busy awakening the crew, the parachute had disappeared from view in one of those big, beautiful clouds.

The following Monday, they stood out to sea for the local operating areas to launch another exercise Regulus Missile off Kaena Point. Battle Stations Missile sounded and the boat's personnel hustled to their positions; many of the men changed since the last patrol. Bob ran the missile plot in the wardroom. Perry was concluding his qualifications and it was his turn for the Regulus sauna.

Growler battle surfaced and the chase aircraft were in position. The missile rammed onto the launcher, the engine started, and *Growler* sounded, "Sixty seconds and counting to launch."

"Captain, Radio. FLASH message from SubPac, sir. Cease all missile operations immediately." The message came over PriTac or the Primary Tactical Radio Circuit. ComSubPac Control monitored missile circuits.

"Radio, Captain, pipe PriTac to the Conn."

The CO called the Admiral and explained *Growler* had sounded the minus 30-seconds, and was about to launch. In no uncertain terms, the answer came back to shut down, put the missile away, and return to Pearl immediately. The CO followed orders and the crew was bewildered. The CO went to radio to talk personally with the admiral, but ComSubPac was too busy to speak with him so he returned to the Wardroom.

"Conn, Captain. Surface the boat and head for the barn at best speed. One thousand amp negative float on the battery is authorized." All power generated by the engines and generators, plus another one thousand amps from the batteries, were placed on propulsion alone. Everyone heard the order and wondered what was so god awful important to cancel a missile shoot at the last moment and rush back to port. It was October of 1963.

As *Growler* rounded Barbers Point and headed for "PH," a Top Secret message was received for the CO. The entire crew buzzed with scuttlebutt (rumor), the worst was the beginning of World War III.

"All officers, not actually on watch, assemble in the wardroom." The men in khakis ran to the wardroom. When this was heard, the crew worried, for it usually meant nothing good. The CO sat in his chair sipping coffee with a heavy frown on his brow. The officers looked at each other, knowing the news was not good, not with that frown on his face. They had seen the frown before and it never meant good things.

"Gentlemen, I fear we are on the brink of war with the Soviet Union. We don't worry much about the Atlantic, for we have plenty of our own problems. However, you have read about the Cuban missile build up. Apparently, the President told Khruschev enough is enough and ordered him to remove his missiles from Cuba. For all practical purposes, he placed a Naval Blockade around Cuba. A confrontation with the next Soviet ship will take place sometime tomorrow or the following day. If the Soviets insist on the missiles going into Cuba, we may go to war. I'll be briefed upon return to port. That's when we'll find out what our role will be."

Silence reigned as thoughts whirled through the officers' minds. They looked at each other and not one face provided a sanctuary or solace for the situation.

"Gentlemen, I am going to talk to the crew and tell them what I told you. I won't have anything more to say until I'm briefed. If the men ask questions, do not speculate. Tell them they must wait, like you, to find out what is going on. Any questions?" There wasn't a sound or a movement. "Good. Now let's get ready to enter port and start thinking ahead. We may have a deployment load out facing us within the hour."

Bob had the watch so he went to the bridge. As they neared "PH," the horizon filled with Navy ships, all headed toward Pearl with a bone in their teeth. (slang for making a large white bow wake) There were ships of every size and description, from aircraft carriers to torpedo chasers. It was not to be a submarine force show only. The CO asked Bob to retain the Conn and take *Growler* dockside. *Growler* fell into a long line of ships entering Pearl. They were behind a division of destroyers and in front of a LSD. Every ship home ported in Pearl Harbor and not deployed returned and fast. Bob drove *Growler* like a race car driver, remaining on the tail of the destroyer in front of him.

"Bob, don't mess around with a fancy landing. Put *Growler* dockside as quickly as possible." Then the CO flattered Bob and laid below to talk to the XO while the boat was still off Ford Island. He had faith in Bob's ability to drive the boat. The CO and XO planned the load out and set up a load out program for *Growler*.

The tugboats were busy, but submarines rarely used them, nor did destroyers in those days. Bob turned the corner with the Sub Base in front of him and drove *Growler* into S-9 like submariners in New London. He came in at ahead standard and killed the boat's headway alongside the pier with an "All back Emergency." The lights flickered despite giving Maneuvering a heads up on his intention. The boat shuttered, and the crew on deck looked up to the bridge as if a maniac was driving the boat, not expecting such speed driving from Mr.H. *Growler* came to rest a few feet off the pier and her bow ten feet short of the Quay Wall. One could not moor much faster. The lines went over and with the help of the windlass and a few bells, *Growler* was secured and the gangway across the pier to *Growler*'s main deck.

Bob saw a blur run across the brow and heard the watch announce, "*Growler* departing."

The CO scampered up the gangway and jogged down the pier, headed for ComSubPac's office across the street. The engines were secured, the lines doubled, and the Maneuvering Watch secured. Department heads got together with their chiefs and leading petty officers to discuss requirements prior to rapid deployment. All hands were frightened, but planned for the days to come. A half an hour later, "*Growler* arriving."

"Officers, report to the wardroom on the double." The officers were in their seats before the announcement was completed. The CO entered, asked everyone to be seated, and came up with his nervous grin. "Well guys, it's going to be a long night. The Cuba thing is likely to blow sky high and we must be ready for it. We will receive a message shortly giving us a time to go to West Loch to unload everything exercise and load the real things. Meanwhile, we will load torpedoes here until its time to go. DefCon 2 is set, which means all liberty is canceled and we are in a state of readiness to go to war. You each have a lot of work to do tonight and it's not going to be easy, because everything that floats will try to do the same thing. We have tonight to prepare for deployment. That means arms, fuel, supplies, food, the entire gambit. There will be no calling wives or loved ones. Now I have to tell the troops. You guys get started making up your "to-do lists." This is what we've all trained for. Get the work done, use ingenuity, don't bother me unless you failed every course you can think of. Get 'em, tigers."

The CO went aft where the crew assembled. He gave them the story straight off the chest and asked each of them to support the effort one hundred percent.

"I know it's not difficult to give your officers support to get *Growler* loaded out. I know it will be tough for you 'brown baggers' not to touch base with your wives, but it must be done. If you have any questions, please ask the COB."

All 85 men were experts at something and all 85 went to work. It was Bob's turn to be Duty Officer. It was not to be a small task.

The engineers were in good mechanical shape for a change and concentrated on getting spares, fuel, plus lube oil. The supply officer had a book of requisitions so he and his chief took off to fill as many as possible. Weapons had the biggest job, to offload exercise torpedoes and missiles and load the real things. Horace searched for charts all over the world, and in particular Central America, the Panama Canal, and the Caribbean Sea, including Cuba.

The following hours were some of the proudest in the lives of the *Growler* crew. TMs pulled exercise torpedoes out of the Torpedo Rooms and a couple of torpedo cherry pickers (small cranes) sat on the pier full of war shots carried in trays on either side of the crane. This was unusual, since war shot torpedoes were typically loaded at West Loch, but this was a pre-war setting. As the men heaved around on the lines to pull the big torpedoes, someone started singing a song from wars past... *Pass the Ammunition.* They off loaded all the exercise fish and were ready to load warheads when the word came to go to West Loch.

Bob found enough qualified bodies to station the Maneuvering Watch and got *Growler* underway for West Loch. The Engineers were fueling and left the fuel truck on the pier, with EN3 Hill to insure the truck remained until *Growler* returned.

The Ammo Depot waited for *Growler* with two cranes, which lifted and replaced the missiles one at a time. They followed the check-off sheet, but it was never done faster. One missile came out of hangar #1 and then another. While the launcher and rails were lined up, the first blue bird came aboard and into Hangar #1, and so on. Once the fourth blue bird was on the launcher, *Growler* was underway for S-9 while the final checkouts and housing of the missile took place enroute. *Growler* passed a long line of customers waiting to go alongside the old wooden wharf at the Ammo Depot. The channel to West Loch hadn't seen such activity since December 1941.

In two hours, *Growler* was back at S-9. The fuel truck was there, with an irate driver. The Weapons Department commenced loading war shot torpedoes. The MTs successfully checked out the new birds. Into the wee hours of the morning the crew worked, still singing and chanting. The two load outs prior to patrols took weeks, yet this load out was accomplished overnight. Weapons had a full load of everything *Growler* could carry, and Engineering topped off with fuel, lube oil, and water. It was difficult to tell how well the Supply Department did with spare parts, but a multitude of boxes came aboard and the crew walked on boxes of food again. Credit had to be given the shore establishment for providing such complete support to the forces afloat. It was close to 0400, and the important things were accomplished, so the CO called a halt to work.

"We can't use all our energy preparing; we need rest so we'll be in fighting shape."

Gratefully, the crew fell into their bunks, exhausted, and went to sleep—the deep sleep of hard-working men. Watches were conducted as usual and the officers awakened at 0800.

"My God, it's 0800 and everyone is still asleep. The lights are still on red. What the hell is happening?" Bob thought. He jumped from his bunk and raced topside to see what was up.

"Good morning Mr. H," smiled the TPOW with a snappy salute.

"Morning," he answered and then looked around Pearl in disbelief. "Holy shit," Bob yelled, "where did everybody go?"

"Ships and boats have been leaving for the last couple of hours, Sir!" As far as the eyes could see there was nothing—nothing in submarine black, or in haze gray, except for a couple of tugboats and a YO and YW (yard oil and yard water craft).

"Hey, are they going to start the war without us?" Bob spoke to the wind. "Damn, I better tell the Captain!"

"Good morning, Captain," he said and the CO looked up at Bob like Dracula arising from his coffin.

"Morning, Bob, what's happening?"

"Well, sir, I'm not sure, but there isn't another submarine in port and it looks like all the destroyers and cruisers are gone. I can't see what's around the corner on Ford Island but it's mighty lonesome up there, sir."

"What, they can't start the war without us," he said. The CO hurtled out of his bunk, dressing as he ran topside. It is doubtful that anyone had ever slipped into a shoe while going up a ladder but the Captain did. Bob dutifully followed him topside and his reaction was similar. "Holy shit, where did every one go?"

"I don't know, Captain, but maybe they kept us here to defend Pearl."

"Not funny, Bob," he said, "I'm going to see the admiral and find out what gives. I'll be right back."

"Don't forget your other shoe; your fly, sir."

"*Growler*, departing." Bob went below to talk with the XO and determine what routine he wanted for a day that was anything but routine.

"I think we'll let the crew sleep. Wake the officers and chiefs. Let's get together and make a list of things we still need." It was no trouble getting the officers up, for they were extremely concerned about the situation. About the time all the officers were up and inhaling their first cup of coffee,

"*Growler*, arriving."

The CO entered the wardroom and smiled. He was pleased to see his wardroom engaged in a planning session while the crew continued to sleep, for they needed rest after the previous night's Herculean effort.

"I just talked to the admiral and asked him why the entire Third Fleet departed port without us. The admiral rocked back in his seat and said, "Don, *Growler* is so damned slow if I sent you somewhere and the fight wasn't there, you would miss the entire war."

That got a few grins from the officers, who knew it was true, but they waited for more news. "We will remain here in a ready status until ordered otherwise. We should use this time to our best advantage. Every fleet unit is at sea, so the shore establishment is at our disposal. All we have to do is use them. I understand the XO has you putting together a list of things we need, or have to do, before deployment, so we will concentrate on them. We remain in DefCon Two."[9]

The planning session complete, the officers went their separate directions to prepare for getting underway. The crew was awakened at 1100 and soon were helping the officers. It was eerie with the harbor empty. Later, the CO went back to see the Admiral. When he returned, he told us, "Conditions remain as before, but we can call our wives." Everyone felt better. The officers insisted the enlisted men go first. There were two telephones at the head of the pier and for the next few hours they were in constant use.

A few days later, the readiness condition was dropped to a relaxed DefCon 3 and wives were permitted to bring personal gear to the boat. The following week *Growler* was permitted to go on a standby status, which permitted two-thirds of the crew to go home every night, though they remained on call. So for the following weeks, *Growler* men kissed their wives good-bye in the morning, not knowing if they would return in the evening. For a change, they had it better than the rest of the fleet. The remainder of the Cuban incident is history.

Later, the ships returned to Pearl, along with *Grayback* and a number of other submarines. The boats returned from assigned patrol areas, yet Admiral Fluckey assigned *Grayback* the honor of leading the procession of boats into Pearl. He boarded *Grayback* and asked about the flag flying atop *Grayback*.

"It's the original battle ensign from the first *Grayback*, sir. We fly it every time we leave or return from patrol, and intend to fly it whenever we battle surface to launch the bluebirds."[10]

Chapter Twelve
Caught by a Soviet Nuke

It was an ordinary Wednesday afternoon on board *Growler*, with routine maintenance and repair being conducted. Most of the crew had knocked off ship's work for a few minutes to grab a fresh cup of coffee and trade liberty stories. John Anderson was sitting in the after port side of the Crew's Mess, slowly sipping on a fresh cup of coffee and listening to Hawaiian music on the radio. It was the top of the hour, and a five-minute news report was being made, when his head jerked upward and everyone in the mess stopped dead in their tracks. The news reported the loss of the nuclear attack submarine, USS *Thresher* (SSN-593), while conducting sea trails off Cape Cod. In a flash, but silently, the word spread throughout the boat and the base. Suddenly a carefree day turned sullen. A former *Growler* shipmate, Jim Matulla, had departed a year prior for duty on that submarine so he could be with his family in Portsmouth. The crew whispered to each other reverently; 129 of their own had just been lost. XO Bob Owens quickly noted the despondent crew and knew he had to shake them out of their state of shock.

"Radioman, send off a message to the CNO and request *Growler* be given the *Thresher's* Recreation Fund." It was a completely inane and stupid statement, but it grabbed the crew's attention and made them smile. It wasn't the first boat and crew to be lost and it wouldn't be the last. It was just a part of submarine life. A few prayers were said and the crew returned to preparations for the next patrol.[1]

The sands of time—time in homeport—ran out again. The last party was over; it was difficult to play with the children; and lovemaking seemed to be a last desperate effort of remaining together. In the back of the crew's minds a clock ticked down the last few days in port like sounding the two-minute warning at Lambeau Field. It was a feeling everyone in the Armed Forces felt time and time again. Deploying, for most of the military, is painful and many families cannot cope. But it was a part of military life for which every submariner volunteered.

In a touching Change of Command, Captain Don Henderson was relieved by Bob Owens. Horace relieved Bob Owens as Executive Officer and Stu Merriken reported aboard as the new Weapons Officer. The party was a tearjerker, as everyone loved Captain Don and his wife Billie. They would be sorely missed. Captain Bob had been in the Regulus Program from its inception and knew the missile system extremely well. He also was an "almost mustang" officer, having served in World War II as an enlisted submariner as an electrician. He later earned a degree in Geology and then earned his commission. He was stationed at Point Mugu NAS when the first Regulus missiles were test fired, and worked with *Tunny* and *Barbero* when they first arrived in the Pacific. At the same time, the boat wished Wayne and Helen Mehl farewell as Wayne returned to civilian life. Bob would definitely miss his mentor.

The new CO and his wife Kay were living proof the excellence of Submarine Command was alive and well. Captain Bob loved to laugh and enjoy life, while his wife of many years quickly proved she could cope with problems on the home front.

In the last week before deployment, the Sub Base held a swimming meet and *Growler* entered. A team was assembled, which included Wayne who had been an All American swimmer from Stanford, but that was where the expertise ended. One of the crew swam in high school, and Bob had won some medals for long distance swims. A few enlisted members of the crew signed up for the meet. The Captain encouraged everyone to join in the meet regardless of skill level, for the meet was intended to promote fun and sportsmanship.

Prior to the meet, Wayne taught the *Growler* team some elementary skills of swimming in a pool; how to come off the blocks, and how to make turns at the end of the pool. The day arrived and Wayne swam in all butterfly, breast stroke and back stroke events, winning them all handily. Bob swam in the free style and breast stroke events; he came in second place in one breast stroke event won by Wayne... Bob had two laps to go when Wayne finished. One member almost drowned during the first lap. The kid didn't know how to swim well, but wanted to compete for the boat. When the results were in, *Growler* won and received a prize of ten cases of beer. The beer was gone within the hour.

A few weeks before *Growler* shoved off, *Barbero* returned from patrol, which meant an old friend and classmate was back, Danny Richardson. He was one of few officers who sported both gold wings and dolphins and later was promoted to Admiral. He had experienced the harrowing trip to Midway the previous patrol, when they almost ran out of fuel. The crew entertained thoughts of sewing canvas to be used as a sail.

...and then it was time to go and go they did. *Growler* left for her 7th patrol to relieve the *Halibut*. She departed 14 June 1963. The transit was uneventful, with sinus nosebleeds and a fuel stop at Adak again. The patrol promised to be active, with enemy contacts, and rough weather began in the north. *Growler* surfaced outside Adak Island and made her way into port.

Halibut, following being relieved on one of her patrols, cruised down to White Sands Beach in Okinawa to put on a missile launch demonstration to the South East Asia Treaty Organization (SEATO). She off loaded a blue bird, loaded an exercise missile, and put on the demonstration. Following the demonstration, she returned to pick up her blue bird. When the missile was placed on the launcher and raised for stowing in the hangar, the rail locks failed to close. When the engine was test run up to full power, the missile ran up the launcher, nosed over, falling nose first into the outer hangar door. The problem was quickly solved, by the book, but it was a hectic exercise for the Weapons Officer to "measure" the expansion on a H-Bomb every half hour.[2]

It was a quick stop to top off fuel and stores and they were underway less than eight hours later. The transit west to station was uneventful, as few sailors or fliers ventured out in such bad weather unless absolutely necessary. It was a struggle to snorkel, for the seas were enormous, and they couldn't remain in the troughs for they did not point the way to station.

A few nights from station, the officers were eating the evening meal. It was so rough; they brought out the fiddle boards for the sitting.[3] Fiddle boards were used often in smaller surface ships, but this was the first time they had been used aboard *Growler*. It was a nasty night, and conversation centered around the weather and snorkeling. Don suggested they use the wings again to entertain themselves and everyone eagerly agreed, including Gordo.

Entertainment decided, Gordo said, "What are the wings?"

Don explained with a grin. He drew in a deep breath and, "Every submarine has a set of wings, Gordo. Ours were made by the MTs out of scrap sheet brass a few years ago. They're a foot and a half long and are awarded to the diving officer who flames out—you do know what flame out means don't you?"

"Yes, yes, its when you lose depth control of the boat while snorkeling and go too deep and shut down on five inches of vacuum."

"Good, Gordo. The next guy to flame out wears the wings, which have a piece of old floating wire on them so you can drape them over your neck. You have to wear them until the next flame out occurs, whereupon the offending officer inherits them. Got it?"

"I sure do," responded Gordo, with a great deal of gusto.

"That's good, Gordo," shouted the CO, "because you've got the next watch."

The wardroom roared with, "Ride 'em, cowboy, Gordo, up we go into the wide blue yonder, up we go, go get 'em, Gordo." Gordon laughed and finished his dinner with red goggles on. Gordo excused himself and went out to relieve the watch. Dave also got up and smiled at the rest of the wardroom, whispering out of the side of his mouth, "This is going to be very interesting."

Minutes later, Perry came into the wardroom and reported to the CO he was relieved of the dive by Gordo. He sat down to eat as the head valve closed and they felt the boat take a down bubble.

"He's not going to make it through five minutes of his watch!" The eyes in the wardroom turned to the altimeter on the bulkhead and watched it gain altitude rapidly. Then came the sound of the main engines shutting down while the crew tried to equalize the pressure in their ears.

"Secure snorkeling," came over the 1MC.

The officers marched into Control, where Gordo frantically tried to regain snorkeling depth. The CO stepped forward, "Gordo, it gives me great pleasure to present you with the *Growler* wings. It's the first this patrol, wear them with pride."

With that, the CO draped the wings over Gordo's head and patted him on the back. Everyone chuckled and the officers returned to the wardroom. After they departed, Gordo pulled the wings from his neck and threw them violently to the deck. Thus began a ruckus and loud war between Gordo and the entire crew over the wings.

"I'm an officer and shouldn't be demeaned this way." Soon *Growler* was snorkeling again, but it was an angry sea that night and Gordo flamed out five more times in the four hours. It was rough and most officers would have struggled as well.

Gordo placed *Growler* one officer over the boat's allowance, so there was no bunk for him in Officer's Country. Often times, the extra officer was given the wardroom seats, which was awkward for everyone. On *Growler*, there was an extra bunk in the Goat Locker. He bunked in the Chief's Quarters, which was more comfortable. The shortcoming of living in the goat locker (chief's quarters) was the skill and experience level of seven or eight chiefs was mixed with a brand new, untested, naval officer. It was a good place to start an officer's career if he was a willing listener—but one cannot over emphasis the snoring in the small, enclosed area. Chiefs do know how to snore!

When Gordo went to sleep, enterprising sailors cut dozens of doily wings from paper and decorated his bunk. The next morning, Gordo awakened for his upcoming watch. Suddenly, the entire boat heard,

"Who was the SOB that put up these wings!" A bellow of profanity should not be made by any officer, but to make it in a sleeping "Goat Locker" was unheard of and blasphemous. The incident entertained the crew, but the entertainer must learn to control emotions and have a thick skin. Gordo caught flak from every direction, and each occasion caused yet another angry outburst. Every officer on every diesel submarine suffered the indignity of flaming out, but Gordon was stubborn. He ripped down and trashed the paper wings. At the evening meal in the wardroom that night, the officers didn't bring up the subject since he had received a ration of crap all day from the crew. Gordo agreed to a game and the consequences of the game. When he lost, he backed off his word. That did not sit well with the crew even if it was an officer's game.

Gordo excused himself and relieved the watch. The seas calmed significantly during the day and Gordo swung by the Goat Locker to pick up his jacket. He stepped into Control and put on his jacket. As he swung the jacket over his shoulders, there was a resounding "clank." The crew had riveted the brass wings to the back of his jacket. He was furious and yanked the wings off his jacket but with the wings came the entire back of his jacket. Needless to say, the crew went crazy with laughter again. Gordo finally conceded to wear the wings... but under his sweater.

Gordo didn't have the evening watch on the patrol watch cycle. Following the evening meal, the wardroom prepared for their nightly card game and waited for Perry and Dave to finish supper. The game was Hearts.

The CO named the card game and said, "Even Gordo has to know how to play Hearts." The CO enjoyed playing cards and winning. His competitive spirit was alive and well on top of the wardroom table as well as at the periscope. He was not a bad loser at most things but he was a bad loser at cards. On the very first hand Gordon drew all three Queens of Spades along with some hearts. It was Gordo's first game of hearts since arriving on board. During the course of the first hand, Gordo dumped all three Queens of Spades on the CO, along with a couple hearts. Good card playing, bad choice of dumpee, although the CO did not let it go beyond the table. For the remainder of the patrol, Gordo ate every Queen of Spades the Captain was dealt.

The hangars provided a new challenge for all five boats. *Halibut* likely had the easiest challenge, since she was nuclear power and didn't have to snorkel every night. Her five-bird hangar was huge, but was streamlined and faired into the superstructure to cause minimal problems. The *Grayback* and *Growler* had the two huge hangars on the bow, which caused many a difficulty. Snorkeling was a bitch in heavy seas with the huge hangars so close to the surface. Both boats usually snorkeled with a few degrees down bubble to get the hangars as deep as possible. During *Growler*'s 1961 drydocking and overhaul came a modification that added twelve feet of height to her sail. It was a marvelous idea and made snorkeling much easier, although all the masts and periscopes had to be lengthened to accommodate the height increase. Unfortunately, the engineers decided the extra weight above the center of gravity would make her unstable so saddle tanks were welded outboard the normal ballast tanks. It stabilized the submarine well, but every old salt who rode *Growler* vented frustration as all were banged back and forth at sea. The boat was now heeled over by the waves and seas, but she didn't roll back—she snap rolled back unlike any boat or ship at sea, throwing the most experienced sailor off balance.

Barbero and *Tunny* had their hangars aft of the sail, which caused all sorts of operational changes. Both boats literally battle surfaced with a large down angle to get the hangar out of the water as soon as possible. It was quite a sight watching a submarine surface stern first. On station in the huge and wicked seas *Tunny* found herself top heavy, and tended to roll to port as much as 50°—and then stay there. The hangar acted like an outrigger and prevented her from rolling further, but kept her from righting herself as well. During one storm, she remained at the huge list for days with bulkheads becoming decks.[4]

Regardless of boat, the North Pacific was a cruel sea to master even for boats and crews that practiced in the seas off Dutch Harbor and the Bering Sea. The men hardened to the situation and formed a club that those Submariners are proud of to this day—The North Pacific Yacht Club.

The days snorkeled by and each day *Growler* fought a growing problem with the batteries. The batteries gassed hydrogen badly on every charge, which meant less intense amperage and longer charging periods. The weather remained brutal and, as on any ship, the longer the rolling and pitching continued, the shorter the fuses of the crew. If indeed it can be considered good, weather was an excellent test of stamina and mental strength.

On a gray and dark day, with slush ice forming as far as the eye could see through the periscope, compartments at both ends of the boat experienced ice formation on the deck plates with the outside sea water approaching 29°F. Even the salt water trickling down the periscope left a trail of frost down the finely machined periscope mast. ECM and sonar was quiet, so the CO decided to conduct an equalizer battery charge in the hope it might break up the trees of salt forming in the battery cells, plus the battery was due for its regular 30-day extended charge. Charging batteries on the hydrogen curve took a long time, so the charge began on the 16–20 watch.

The battery lineup was checked and, "Commence snorkeling, two engines," Bob ordered. Perry was his diving officer, and a good one, as he kept *Growler* at snorkel depth despite rough seas topside. The ECM mast was up and signals were as rare as the ships at sea that day. Sonar searched, but the snorkeling noise and sea noise, made listening difficult.

The snorkel charge went well for an hour as the hydrogen meters for both batteries were watched carefully. If *Growler* shut down, the boat was without the ability to exhaust the hydrogen out of the boat, and hydrogen generation didn't stop immediately when the charge stopped. They had to anticipate a shut down, so the crew was more cautious about the buildup than usual.

Suddenly, "Conn, Sonar. Contact bearing 270°, sounds close, sounds submarine, and could be a Nuke, sir."

"Secure snorkeling. Rig for quiet running. Make your depth 130 feet," Bob ordered, then added "Come right to 270°."

Bob pointed the target; the bow was not only the best direction for sonar to listen, but was also the quietest aspect to present the target. The CO and XO were in Control as soon as they heard the order to go quiet. Bob looked at the sonar repeater on the Conn and turned up the UQC-1. It was difficult to see much of the sonar screen since the CO and XO were hunched over in front of the repeater, intently observing the sound spokes.

The instant the engines shut down, they heard a loud, high-pitched whine that everyone connected with the sound of a steam turbine. Bob started to talk to the CO but...

"Conn, sonar. Sir, we definitely have a nuclear submarine. You can hear the turbine whine," Scotty reported, with obvious concern in his voice. With the comment, the turbine whine ceased abruptly. "Conn, sonar. He's shut down after hearing us shut down. I recognize that power plant, Mr. H. Its either one of the missile Hotel class, or their new November class, which is a submarine hunter-killer, sir."

Reports were whispered on sound powered telephone and the battery charge was secured, snorkeling secured, and the boat rigged for quiet.

"Conn, Sonar. We have him at 273°."

"Scotty, shift to sound powered phone."

"Ooops, sorry." "Sonar reports they have the contact. Designate Skunk Alpha. It is definitely a nuclear powered sub. They hear his machinery noise but can't get a turn count (revolutions per minute of the propeller). They think he is showing us his starboard bow."

"Did you get that, Dave?" He manned the TDC.

"Inserted Bob."

"Come right to 275°." Bob had the Conn, but was anything but in charge with both the CO and XO standing below him whispering. The first thing to hit Bob's mind was the report he read on Scott. "If he hears it, he knows what it is." No one every doubted his ability and everyone certainly vouched for his analysis.

"Ask sonar for an estimated range to Alpha." Then, "Curbow, what's the BT showing for a layer?"

"No change, Mr. H, we're passing through it at 130 feet." "Sonar reports the sound of torpedo tubes flooding, sir."

"Oh, shit. This guy is serious."[5]

"Bob, flood tubes 3 and 4, 5 and 6," ordered the CO. "Tell Sonar to have one man concentrate on nothing but listening to the bastard's outer doors. If he hears anything that sounds like them opening, let us know immediately."

"Aye, aye, Captain," Bob said as he became a bit nervous.

The order was passed and then the CO whispered to Bob, "We'll be ready too, Bob. Maybe he won't hear us flooding tubes over his own noise." Then he gave Bob a wink. He had noticed Bob was a bit nervous, as was the entire watch section.

"Captain, do you want to order Battle Stations Torpedo?"

"Make it so, Bob, although I think it's already manned."

"Underwood, pass the word on the 1JV to station Battle Station Torpedo!"

"Sonar reports no range estimate other than they feel he's inside of 10,000 yards from the level of the sound. Another consideration is a large bearing rate to the right even though the Soviet slowed to improve his listening ability."

"Scotty makes sense, Bob. He slowed almost immediately after we secured snorkeling. I doubt he can hear us right now, which is probably making him very nervous."

"I concur, Captain," said Horace, "and I think if we went right back up to periscope depth and began snorkeling eastward, he would think we were nothing more than another trawler with high speed engines. I don't think they know we have the hotrod engines."

"Very interesting, Horace, but what makes you think the Russkies don't know our engines?"

"A gut feeling, Captain. Just a gut feeling, plus I don't recall reading anything in the intelligence reports indicating they have graduated to this level of expertise or thinking."

"What's your gut say about their ability to determine our depth?"

"Captain, I would seriously doubt they have the capability. We can't do that yet, sir, except by interpretation by a professional sonar man."

"Tell sonar to give me a bearing rate," Bob said, which was needed for a firing solution. He was pleased his teeth didn't chatter or his voice break.

"Battle Stations Torpedo manned, sir," reported Underwood. "That took seventeen seconds."

The CO looked at his TDC solution.

"How do you feel about it, Dave," asked the Captain.

"Not too strong yet, sir. Once we get a bearing rate, I can lock him up. I've got a good enough solution to fire a Mk 37-0 or 37-1 forward or aft, though, sir."

"Thanks, Dave. Guess what we've got sitting in those flooded tubes?"

"Sonar reports a right bearing rate of point six, sir."

"Excuse me, sir," Bob said to the CO. "Shouldn't we slide under the layer and hide?"

"Bob, we have a Soviet nuclear powered sub who detected us, so we know he is somewhere between the surface and 130 feet. We know he detected us because he shut down after we went quiet. He is not an idiot and knows we're somewhere between the surface and 130 feet. Horace may be correct in that he does not know about our high-speed engines. That is an unknown. If we go below the layer and he single pings, he'll probably get nothing and he'll know for sure we are a submarine. If we go to periscope depth and he single pings, he'll be sure he has a target, but he won't know it's a submarine. We don't know if he can read depth on his active sonar, but if he can, and we are down here, he will know we're a submarine. Now then, when he knows he has a submarine, he has orders to sink us. He also knows that his submarine target is not another Soviet submarine. What does all this mean? I think Horace has a good solution, as crazy as it sounds. What we have to be sure of is that our distance to him is great enough that he would not see us at that range. And if that doesn't sell you, consider the fact that he is nuclear powered and we are sitting here with a half depleted can."

"Thanks for the pep talk, Captain," quipped Horace.

"My God," Bob thought, "we're sitting here on the brink of disaster and they sound like they're waiting for the next hand to be dealt." The CO walked to the TDC and looked at Dave's solution.

"Hmmm. I like it, Dave. How do you feel?"

"Fairly comfortable, Captain. Everything seems to check. If he was moving faster than eight knots, Scotty would be listening to his cavitation even at this depth."

"Thank you, Dave." The CO and XO chatted for a while and then finally looked up and ordered Bob to, "Come left to 180°. Do not cavitate. Make your depth 80 feet." As they passed through 117 feet, they heard the nuke loud and clear.

The CO laid out his strategy to the crew. He came left to open the range on the Russkie, who was known to be on a course something north of east. His best guess was 070°. The first thing to be accomplished was to attain a range at which the Soviet sub at periscope depth, or on the surface, would be unable to see a trawler mast through his periscope, which meant a range of 20,000 yards or more. Once the range was reached, they would quietly return to periscope depth and commence snorkeling while steering due east. The Russkie would regain his previous target on passive sonar and track them moving eastward. *Growler*'s movement eastward would reduce any Soviet's anxiety. Since they were not in sight, they would believe them to be another trawler and go on about their business.

Everyone trusted the CO's and XO's decision, but there were a lot of assumptions. Nevertheless, their reasoning seemed sound, and to do nothing or hide was worse. The bearing rate increased dramatically to the right, which helped the fire control party refine its solution. In fact, unless he zigged or changed speed, the nuke was in *Growler*'s crosshairs. They traveled south until the target entered the baffles, at which time the CO ordered the boat left to course east. When everyone's solution indicated the nuke outside of 20,000 yards, a careful check for any other contacts was made.

"Bob, make your depth 65 feet. And let's keep it as quiet as we can." The crew was in their stocking feet and all the WT doors were latched open so that no door would slam. Bob chatted with Maneuvering to insure they understand how important it was not to cavitate. Chief Fernandez understood completely and the boat came up without the slightest flutter on the cavitation indicators. As they approached ordered depth, Bob put up the periscope to make sure everything was clear—it was. Snow fell heavily, and the wind was wicked, but he saw no contacts.

"Want to line up for snorkeling, Captain?"

"Yes, Bob, but when we put up the snorkel mast, keep the head valve locked shut and bring your depth to 60 feet. I don't want to blow the entire act with the head valve chattering. Perry, how does she feel?" asked the CO.

"Good, Captain. If a sea is running it is either very small or we're in the trough, sir."

"Good! Let's line up to charge, Bob. I hate to get too many things going at once, but if things go wrong we may need every amp we've got."

The bow planesman was the telephone talker and got a real workout. He maintained depth, steered the ordered course, and was the Control Room talker. He was busy.

Bob found a free moment to comment, "Underwood, good work down there."

"Thank you, sir."

"My pleasure. You've been earning your pay this day. Sure do wish you spoke English, though, instead of that slow Southern drawl"

"Happy to lend a hand, sir. I'm talking as fast as I can, sir!"

The reports were in and Bob bent over the rail on the conning stand and told the CO on the main deck, "Sir, we're ready to snorkel charge at your command, Captain."

"Do it, Bob."

"Aye, Sir. Commence snorkeling, come up to 60 feet, Perry. I'd rather be on the surface today than the head valve chatter."

"You've got it," Perry piped back.

Growler made her move, brazen as it was. They were caught off guard by a single ping from the Soviet nuke. "Pooiing" resounded throughout the boat. You didn't have to be in sonar to hear it. It struck terror into the hearts of everyone. The Soviet nuke had a range on them and everyone looked at Horace, for it was his plan. The range indicated they were outside of his line of sight. There was a solid torpedo solution in the TDC and *Growler* was ready to shoot. The CO picked up the sound powered telephone and told sonar, "Keep one man on those outer doors!"

"We got info on that ping, too, sir. Beautiful print on the N-3, sir. I don't have the captain's name, but I have his girl friend's address."

"Thank you, Scotty. Good work," replied the CO with a grin.

Perry fought to keep the head valve out of the water and he managed, although the planesmen over reacted until Perry settled them down. Hopefully, *Growler* acted like a trawler with engines running and stuffing amps back into the battery. On course east, the Soviet nuke disappeared in the baffles. It was a gut wrenching time as *Growler* played the role and remained on course and speed, unable to hear the Soviet. There was nothing more to do but pray, and pray they did. They prayed the Soviet wouldn't run up behind them to check out their contact.

How long should they keep the charade going? It was to be a gut call by the CO. The extended plan, should the *Growler* still exist, was to shut down, go quiet and deep, reverse course and slide back in closer to the mainland under the Soviet nuke. They must remain within missile range of their targets.

"Conn, Forward Torpedo Room. Be advised we are nearing the time limit to keep the Mk 37 torpedoes spun-up and warm, sir."

"Roger, Torpedo Room. Have Chief Powell see me," answered the CO. The electronics in a torpedo generated heat even with the tube flooded, and that eventually could damage a component. Chief Powell entered Control and went into a huddle with the CO near the Quartermaster's table. A few minutes later, they both nodded their heads in the affirmative, the chief headed forward, and the CO walked over to the conning stand.

"We're going to take one torpedo down forward and aft, blow the tube dry, run a fast self-check test on them, then put them back into the tube but keep it dry. When the first set is done, we'll repeat it for the other two. Then we'll know our fish are good. With that complete, we'll do our 'Zip-it-di-dou-way' game."

"Roger, Captain, but what game?"

"Come on, Bob. We zip up the boat, take it deep, and double back to the coast." He spoke with a twinkle in his eye. He loved the challenge! The Torpedo Rooms reported checks completed. The CO gave Bob the cut-off sign.

"Secure snorkeling, rig for silent running, make your depth 500 feet, slow to turns for three knots, do not cavitate." It was handled easily as the crew knew the plan beforehand. It scared the hell out of the new kids, while a couple of chiefs were heard to say, "That's what I woulda done, too."

Growler shut down, went quiet, reversed course and headed for safety well under the layer. Sonar immediately detected the Russian nuke and kept Plot and the TDC busy with updates. The Soviet submarine had not changed course or speed... "thank God" murmured throughout the crew... and *Growler* silently disappeared under the layer and continued west. An hour later, sonar reported hearing a single ping from the nuke, who was trying to find his high speed engine trawler. The ping came from well off to the northeast. They had escaped!

Everyone breathed easier. The crew settled back into their patrol routine, but no one forgot the few hours they spent tangling with a Soviet nuclear submarine. They remained deep and quiet for a few more hours, then *Growler* slowly rose, passed through the layer and into the sound duct. They searched for the Soviet submarine; above, below, and in the layer, but there was no sign of him. After an hour of searching, the CO was assured he was nowhere near, so *Growler* finished the snorkel charge.

It had been the XO's plan and everyone looked up to him as if he walked on water; or continued to walk on water. Horace was tall, slim, with long black hair and beard, and wore sandals on patrol. In the small morning hours one day, he wandered into the Navigation Center to check on the SINS. His ETN, John Galvin, looked up at him through a faint light, gasped, fell to his knees, and whispered, "God almighty, Jesus is on board."[6]

Although not trained as a Navigation Electronics Technician, Don Curbow, a long time submarine quartermaster, took an interest in the SINS and peripheral equipment and became very adept with the equipment, especially the Loran-C, which was still in its infancy stage in the Northern Pacific.

The seas were calm, with near perfect sonar conditions and passive ranges ad infinitum.

"Hey, Bob, would you like to take me through the Trim and Drain System?"

"Gordo, it would be my pleasure."

"When do you want to go?"

"We're both off watch now. Can you spare an hour?

Let's get it on, Gordo. You are asking me to take you through the system or to be tested?"

"To be tested on the system," replied Gordon.

The two walked to the Engine Room where Chief Wright was replacing cylinder liners on #2 engine. Chief Wright was a huge man in bulk and girth, but particular and careful when he worked. On the upper level of the Engine Room he placed a dozen large #10 tin cans, which contained parts, separated by function and cylinder number of the engine. He was a disciplined and methodical mechanic who never felt it necessary to rush work on his engines.

"Watch out for the cans Gordo. Knock one over and you've signed your death warrant." They climbed down the ladder resting on the lower level deck plates on the port side of #2 engine.

"Let's start at the beginning Gordon, where is the trim pump?"

"Right here, sir, er, Bob."

"Good. Many pumps need to be primed before they can pump well. How is this done?"

"Well, sir, we have a trim pump priming pump right here. When one turns on the pump, the priming pump goes on first to insure the trim pump is primed. The way the priming pump works is this needle valve ..."

"Don't mess with the needle valve!" Bob was too late and the needle valve dropped into the oily bilge water. "

"I'll get it," Gordo responded and his hand went into the oily water searching for the part.

"Hey, Mister H, how's it going, sir?" growled the bull necked chief, working around the corner on #2 engine.

"Just fine, thanks, Chief. Mister Vallentine dropped the needle valve from the prime pump and is looking for it," Bob replied.

"Oh, hell, sir, I'll get it for you," and the chief bent to reach into the bilge.

Evening, Chief," said Gordon.

"Hello, Mister Vallentine," responded the chief. "Did I hear Mr. H correctly? You dropped the needle valve for the prime pump in the bilge?"

"Er, yes, sir, chief," Gordon answered a little scared.

"Sir! What the fuck are you doing screwing around with the needle valve?" Gordon was now without the ability to speak, or to do anything except, possibly, pee in his pants.

"Mister Vallentine, do you realize without the needle valve the trim pump can't work, which means the diving officer can't trim, which means we can't dive!!!"

"Yes, sir, er, Chief. I do understand. I'll find it and put it back."

"Mister Vallentine. This here is maaa engine room, and nobody, but nobody, touches, turns, twists, flips, and yanks anything without maaa approval. Do you read me, sir!"

"Yes, sir, Chief!"

"God damn it, I am not a *sir*, I am a chief!"

"Er, yes s... Chief."

"Now then, I'll find the needle valve and you get your ass out of maaa engine-room."

"On my way out, Chief." In microseconds, Gordon went up the ladder. Bob held his mouth to control his laughter. The Chief looked at Bob, flexed his biceps, pushed his fist toward Gordo, and bent over to search the bilge. Gordon reached the top rung of the ladder but failed to grasp the rail with his oily hands to pull himself up. He lost his balance and performed a beautiful pirouette, followed by a spread eagle flop on top of the chief's cans. Engine parts rained down on the chief.

Growler was fortunate that no Soviets were within listening range, for Chief

Wright let loose with a god-awful bellow. Carpenter fish stopped hammering, Grey whales turned Blue, and the Humpback whales stopped humping. Bob's ears rang as Chief Wright headed topside.

"Easy, Chief, he's just a kid," Bob quietly said in vain. In one long stride, the chief leapt to the main deck level and started after Gordon. Gordo ran forward but the Chief grabbed Gordo by his ass and nap of his neck and assisted him cleanly through the WT door into the After Battery Compartment.[7]

"You dumb son of a bitch, if I catch you here again, I will personally break your fuckin' neck!" Bob watched the chief shake in fury, and was about to say something, until he looked into the chief's red and glazed eyes. He was going to tell the chief to cool it again but, "Sorry we bothered you, Chief," Bob said on the way out.

"No problem, Mr. H. Just don't bring anymo' children back here."

A Naval vessel routine includes the 1200 or noon report. Theoretically from the OOD, but usually put together by the Duty Quartermaster and made by the QM. One boring day, QM1 Taylor decided to liven things up a bit. Most reports begin with, "Good afternoon, Captain. The time is 1200. The Officer of the Deck sends his respects and makes the following report..."

The officers toyed with this QM as he religiously made his reports noon after noon. He waited for the stroke of twelve on the ship's clock in the wardroom to enter and start his report. The officers stopped the chimes, or let the clock only chime seven times, or moved the clock ahead of noon to make it appear he was late. The officers harassed him in jest, but he had the grace and wit to continue with his duty.

He stepped through the curtain into the wardroom, uncovered (removed his hat) and started out:

> "Good afternoon Captain, and the rest of you
> Here's the good word from OOD and the crew.
> The chronometers were wound just about nine,
> then checked and compared with Greenwich Mean Time.
> 1252 is the specific gravity now,
> and since we're submerged its bound to go down.
> The magazines were checked and found to be well,
>
> With the temperature normal, 51 sounds swell.
> Now I don't wear a mask and don't hide my face,
> the noon reports lately have been a disgrace.
> So I'll make this poetic to keep up the pace.
> Now thanks for your patience in hearing me out.
> I'll see you tomorrow, on that there's no doubt."

He got their attention and when he finished, the officers gave him a standing ovation.[8]

Chapter Thirteen
Back Home and the Roach Party

I t was months before Gordo ventured into the Engine Room alone. Chief Wright still seethed with anger, and was so devoted to his work that he was constantly in the Engine Room. Gordo decided to alter the crew's impression of him, hoping to gain the reverence and respect he felt due officers. He missed the point of rank and rate. An officer, as any management figure, must earn respect. A collar device carried one only so far.

A case in point occurred on *Grayback* with EMFN Jefferson. He was an enthusiastic young man just out of high school, boot camp, and sub school. Perchance, he was the only black on *Grayback*'s crew at the time. Submariners seldom see color, but judge by performance. Jefferson worked hard and completed all requirements for qualification in less than minimum time. At quarters, Captain Ekelund joined the crew. Following a brief and complimentary speech about Jefferson, he pinned a set of silver dolphins on Jefferson's proud chest. The crew cheered its approval and demanded a speech. The young man was shy but stepped forward and spoke clearly to the crew,

"Thank you for your help with my qualifications. Each of you, are truly great shipmates. I know some of you think blacks are a bit slow and I just want to say one thing: All niggers on this here boat are qualified!" The crew roared with laughter and cheered loudly, lifted Jefferson on their shoulders, and unceremoniously threw him overboard—a reward given every Submariner when he qualified.[1]

Gordo eventually grew on the crew and was accepted despite a personality the crew forgave. Under all the put-on anger was a good man and officer. Most of the officers believed the crew knew it before Gordo accepted the situation. Gordo never fully accepted the undisciplined mannerism of the submarine, but eventually fit in. He was aggressive and hardworking, which made it with the crew. Gordo was an entertainer, much to the crew's delight, and no one was sure who pulled whose leg. Gordo enjoyed his position as court jester and played it to the hilt.

The days grew longer and the northern lights faded. *Growler* neared the end of a patrol that was cruel for personal comfort. The weather was terrible for most of the trip. Near the end of the patrol, Bob received a message from the DivCom which he had impatiently awaited for weeks.

"CONGRAT ON A BEAUTIFUL BABY GIRL MALIA BORN THIS DATE AT TRIPLER ARMY HOSPITAL. DAUGHTER AND MOTHER DOING WELL."

He was ecstatic for now he had a son and a daughter.

Growler eased to the northeast corner of the patrol area, periodically checking ice conditions, to ensure they didn't go under solid sheet ice. It was imperative they not venture far beneath the ice since they snorkeled daily, and were not equipped to break through thick ice, nor to see ahead and above for ice on sonar while submerged. The injection temperatures remained slightly below 30° F, which was sufficiently cold to form slush ice. The ice formed in small plates a few inches thick.

The *Growler's* newspaper, *The Scuttlebutt*,[2] featured an article by the Editor:

"The past 30 days on station have passed quickly and for the most part, uneventfully. Yet, how many of us stop to realize what really has happened? Some 100 men contained in a 300 by 20 foot steel tube have existed independently, submerged in near freezing water for 30 days. They have consumed 960 gallons of coffee, 90 decks of playing cards, $4,320 worth of food, 3,500 eggs, 320 loaves of bread, and $45,000 from government pay roll and spare parts from Supply. These steel dwellers have not been idle in consumption and production; 21,500 gallons of (fresh) water have been made from 45,000 gallons of salt water; 150 megawatts of electricity have been manufactured. At all times during these 30 days, the capability existed within this steel tube—to intercept enemy electronic signals, observe ship's movements, and destroy four cities the size of Los Angeles.

"These men have plotted themselves over 4,000 (nautical) miles of ocean without the aid of any visual observations arriving at a location and returning another 4,000 miles to family and friends. Certainly, not even Jules Verne's imagination could foretell these accomplishments. And strange enough, only the American Sailor who makes this feat possible, can casually wander away from his steel home after 80 days at sea and become completely absorbed, interested, and forgetful with a $3.50 cab ride to Hotel Street and a 90 cent beer."

During the first few *Growler* patrols, Radioman Pappy Powers kept the crew informed with newsletters consisting of news updates gathered in the Radio Shack.

The XO's Officer Training Program required each officer to put in a day's work on navigation. One night on the surface, Horace was demonstrating the procedures of using a sextant and sighted on a star. Despite his best efforts, he was unable to "swing" one star. Then it became obvious—he was trying to shoot a satellite, probably one of the sputniks.[3]

Intelligence reports indicated a November class nuclear submarine, probably the one encountered earlier, continued eastward and took up station off the southern coast of California. One Hotel class nuclear guided missile submarine was reported departing Petropavlovsk and heading east on a great circle route. The Russkie left a few days earlier and might cross *Growler*'s track somewhere on the journey home.

With the Hotel headed eastward and likely to remain south of the Aleutian Chain, the CO considered it prudent to remain north of the Aleutians en route to Adak. The northern route would be rougher from a weather standpoint. The ice formed in the Bering Sea was hindered from moving south by the archipelago, but could be anywhere north of the islands. The jet stream and storm route usually followed the Aleutians before it bent southward into the Gulf of Alaska. It brought the long and steady stream of storm systems that moved southward along the west coast of North America. A storm center or cyclone moved near the chain with winds that could come from any direction. The reason to favor the south was a shorter wind fetch than north of the islands.

Growler was relieved and slipped northeastward over the Aleutian Ridge. She remained north of the Near Islands past Attu Island and the Semichi Islands. Luck was with her, as a series of storms remained south of the chain, with *Growler* in the lee of the heavy seas. It was a snorkel transit with eastern seas that made depth control tough and battered everyone's sinuses.

Navigation was possible only by Loran-C and was not accurate at higher latitudes. It remained overcast and gray as the boat was buffeted with flying snow and freezing rain, often icing the head of the periscope. The periscope was dipped every few minutes to de-ice the lens. Intelligence reports continued to report the Hotel's progress, which remained south of the Aleutians.

Growler entered Adak Harbor again without the right time of day. On top of the CO's priority list was getting into the PHNSY (Pearl Harbor Naval Shipyard) for major repairs and the replacement of worn-out batteries. Knowing Bob was anxious to see his new daughter, the CO arranged passage for Bob on a P3V flight out of Adak to Barbers Point. He arrived in Hawaii a full week ahead of *Growler*, which gave him time to make preparations with the shipyard for dry docking and battery replacement.

QM1 Taylor was assigned Shore Patrol duty, with a couple other crew members, when they encountered a brand new Marine Second Lieutenant. He stopped his jeep and looked at the bearded, foul weather-clad group with SP brassards on their arms. He asked, "Who the hell are you guys?"

"Shore Patrol from *Growler*, Sir!"

"My God, what is the Navy coming to? You, you... you are... er forget it," and he drove away shaking his head and muttering to himself.

Growler got underway ten hours later, in the midst a raging blizzard. Bob threw off the lines and waved goodbye as his boat slowly twisted through the wind and headed toward the harbor entrance. Seconds later, she disappeared in the snow. He had a knot in his stomach as he watched "his" submarine depart without him.

He hitched a ride to the air terminal and found his flight was to leave within the hour. He joined other passengers on the treacherous walk on an icy tarmac to the aircraft. He was pleased with the luxury and equipment, but these men made their living hunting for submarines no matter what the weather. He then realized he was in uniform and was wearing his Dolphins; a direct challenge to any Naval Aviator.

Bob had a window seat and looked at the long and white runway. A plane crew member asked Bob if he would like a headset to wear, so that he could listen to the aircraft communications. It stopped snowing for the moment and he couldn't believe what was at the end of the runway. A tall, rocky cliff stretched skyward and disappeared into low hanging clouds. The cliff was thousands of feet high; why would someone build a runway toward a mountain?

The four engines synched and sounded smooth. The aircraft rolled down the runway and gathered speed. Then they were airborne and—"My God, he's pulled up the wheels and we're only ten feet off the ground." An eternity went by as the aircraft increased speed but hung ten feet above the deck. Meanwhile, the aviators were having fun with Bob as they talked worriedly about one engine ready to fail and loosing hydraulic pressure. The discussion had Bob more than worried as they continued their plunge toward the mountain. Looking forward, the wall of white rocks rapidly approached. As collision with the mountain was inevitable, the nose pulled up and Bob counted every bush growing on the mountain—one.

"That SOB knew he had a submariner on board!"

The nicest thing he found in Pearl, besides his new daughter, was *Grayback*. She had returned from Subic Bay and extensive repairs, including the repair to the stern planes.

The usual fanfare was observed as *Growler* berthed at S-9 and Bob boarded to take the duty for the next week while the rest of the officers became reacquainted with their families. As Engineer, Bob plunged into the chore of repairing the beaten and sad engineering plant after a multitude of problems on patrol. It wasn't a lack of expertise or preventative maintenance, but just tired equipment overworked on another hectic patrol. The centerline engine was to be replaced again. It was the engine, not the generator that had the problem. *Growler's* record remained intact; not returning with all engines in commission. For some reason, the engines suffered a multitude of injector adaptor failures.

Chief Wright suspected poor quality control in manufacturing as the source of adapter failure. Bob called the manufacturer, Fairbanks Morse, who sent out their best Field Representative, Mr. Monohan, a long time friend of Bob's parents in Wisconsin. The engines were out of commission an inordinate amount of time on patrol. Between the engines and batteries, the patrol was a nightmare for engineers. The Field Representative suspected bad workmanship and took a number of the failed adapters back for analysis in their lab. The answer came quickly; failure of quality control. Bob was sad, since the engines were a hometown product in Beloit, Wisconsin.

A week of liberty with their families and the crew returned to ship's work. *Growler* discharged weapons and entered dry dock. The workload was enormous, yet the entire crew was baffled that two sets of batteries weren't waiting for them in the shipyard. Every time the CO asked about the batteries, innuendoes spouted forth with little content and less fact. The only answer giving the crew hope was they were to receive the batteries scheduled for *Bonefish* and the batteries were in Pearl.

Horace met a couple of U-2 pilots who invited the *Growler* officers to Hickam Air Force Base to watch a U-2 spy plane land. It was amazing, and they were impressed with the aircraft. The plane was a huge glider with a jet engine. An hour after landing, they stood spellbound as the big bird took off, in almost a vertical ascent into the wild blue.

In return, *Growler* invited their hosts for a day to watch a Regulus launch. The pilot's stay was brief. When they realized they were to submerge, they came up with a dozen reasons why they couldn't make the trip. Bob understood; he didn't like flying.

One of Bob's previous destroyers, USS *Richard B. Anderson* (DD-786), pulled into Pearl and he visited the ship that had completed the FRAM Conversion or upgrading. A couple of his chiefs were still on board, so Bob invited them to join *Growler* on the missile launch. They enjoyed the experience and the next day, their CO invited the *Growler* wardroom for a day of underway training against a submarine. The officers accepted and enjoyed a wonderful day at sea. Unfortunately, it was not so wonderful for the destroyer, which was beaten up by the *Bonefish* in a one on one, destroyer versus submarine exercise.

As a last frantic attempt to gain some respectability with the submariners, the destroyer captain held a "Man Overboard" drill. Oscar, a dummy in the shape of a man, was thrown over the side and the exercise began. The crew did everything correctly, manned the motor whaleboat, and launched it, started a plot, extra lookouts took stations, and the OOD executed a perfect Williamson Turn. Everything went right except that they couldn't find Oscar, who was believed to be off

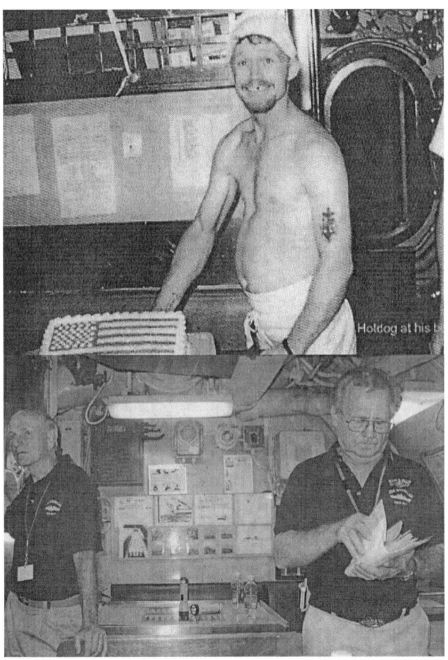

Top: Celebrating the 4th of July 1963 and escape from the Soviet nuke, "Hotdog" bakes a patriotic cake. It was a party complete with gags, skits and songs. Would you eat his cake? (Photo by Al Odette)

Bottom: Duane "Hotdog" Heatwole, on board *Growler*, looks through his old recipe book for the cake he baked nearly half a century earlier. Ron Rousseau reminisces of days past.

Top: L-R: Bob Grogan, Jim Waddell, and Mike Hein enjoy liberty at the NCO Club at Hickam Air Force Base.

Above: Loading a Regulus I missile. This is actually in Port Hueneme, vice West Loch. (NCEL Photo Lab)

Right: *Growler* launches, then runs to be at church on time.

Top: A red Regulus exercise missile being tested on the launcher. Note that boosters are not on the bird, so an explosive hazard is minimal, thus crew on deck. Also, this photo is likely 1960 era, with *Growler* wearing Battle Efficiency "E" and the sail is the shorter version. (Photo by Chuck Mantula)

Middle: The Starlight, Dolphin and Rialto were favorite watering holes for the crew.

Left: The infamous Adak totem pole. The SeaBee image is on top, then an aircraft. At the time of the thefts the SeaBee was not the top image. Note that the pole is mounted in a large block of concrete to preven theft. It didn't work.

Top: Guided Missile Ten, which provided technical support and training to the submarine units.

Left: Mr. H.'s Volkswagen bug in port hanger ready to head for San Francisco.

Below: Panama Canal Zone.

Top: Bill Daak in Adak, returning to Growler in an unusual manner.

Center: Swimming party, enroute San Francisco.

Left: Captain William Gunn, USN (Ret); former weapons officer of USS *Halibut*, Operations/Navigator USS *Growler*, XO/CO USS *Grayback*

Picture of Chief of Naval Operations, Admiral Arleigh Burke, given to *Growler* on the occasion of her commissioning. The photo hung in the wardroom. Author attended his change of command in 1955, and met him again in 1959, during graduation from the Naval Academy.

Above: The only actual launch of a Regulus II missile was by USS *Grayback* (SSg-574). (Photo by Bill Gunn)

Center: Diving stand on *Growler*—the planesmen's watch positions. The right yoke controls the bow planes and helm, while the left controls the stern planes and bubble (boat's attitude).

Right: Sonar room on *Growler*.

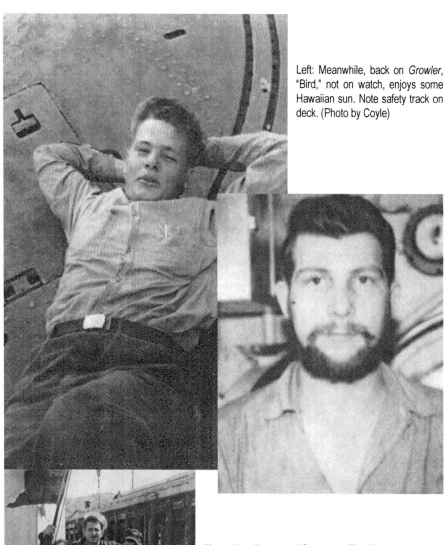

Left: Meanwhile, back on *Growler*, "Bird," not on watch, enjoys some Hawaiian sun. Note safety track on deck. (Photo by Coyle)

Above: A well-groomed Signalman First Don Burrell during Patrol Number 3. (Picture by Burrell)

Left: The fuel gang refueling the boat. Note Bravo flag flying. L-R: Keith Fansler, Ron Rintz, and Duane Lober. (Photo by Robert "Hymie" Hoffman)

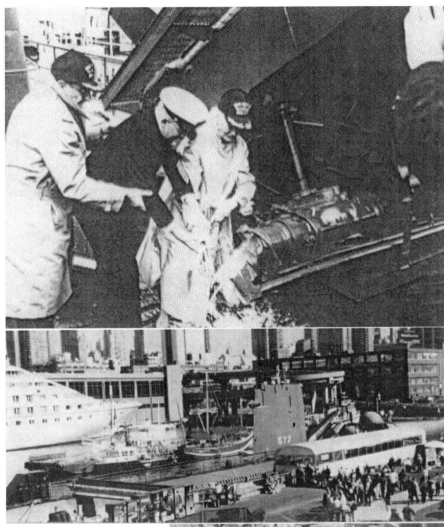

Top: Re-christening the *Growler* at *Intrepid* Museum. L-R: Captain Chuck Priest, COB Stebbins, and Mrs. Fischer, 24 May 1989.

Center: *Growler* today at the *Intrepid* Museum. Over 1,000 people tour the boat daily.

Bottom: Former *Growler* Captain Don Henderson and COB Mike Powell at first reunion in 2000.

Quartermaster Don Curbow, while on *Growler* in the picture, and forty-five years later.

The usual last look at Oahu enroute station.

the starboard side. Captain Owens and Bob got out of the way and went to the port wing of the bridge as the entire boat searched for the dummy to starboard. Bob finished a cigarette and flipped it over the side, watching to insure it made it into the ocean. There, laying alongside the port side of the destroyer, was Oscar. They didn't have the guts to tell the destroyer captain.

Faces changed again, but one set of orders on the *Grayback* pleased everyone. Bill Gunn was selected as CO on *Grayback* to relieve Joe Ekelund. The entire Regulus Force was pleased with the news. Submariners felt one great Submariner relieved another. *Growler* picked up two new officers, Lieutenant Bill "Pecos" Moore, who relieved Horace as navigator, and an Ensign by the name of Jim McCoy, with no sea time. No one was sure if he was one of the Real McCoys. They had a Real McCoy and Ensign Benson.

The patrol schedule permitted *Growler* to remain in port longer than usual, due to the return of *Grayback*. It was a great morale boost to the crew following an arduous patrol. The wardroom was in the mood for a little fun, but no one was prepared for a party extraordinaire awaiting them.

It takes little to entertain a sailor and in particular, a Submariner. The wardroom experienced a party not equaled in suspense in modern times. One night, the officers received a telephone call at home from an unidentified person who whispered to reserve a certain date for a party with the "Roach." At breakfast, the officers talked and the "Roach" subject came up. All officers received the mysterious telephone call and were completely ignorant of who was the "Roach." The date for the party was a month away and the officers kissed off the call as mischief.

One day, the CO found an envelope on his desk that contained an ad for cockroach spray. A week later, the officers received a postcard reminding them of the Roach's party. The officers gained interest in the party yet no one had a clue who was responsible. Reminders arrived continuously with dead cockroaches in the ashtrays, labels, telephone calls, and even in the guard mail. The officers discussed the party and decided to go along with the gag. Final instructions arrived two days before the event and requested everyone report to a small bar off King Kamehameha Highway at 1800 on Friday for cocktails.

Dave was on duty that night, so he was under scrutiny. Some suspected the DivCom and others were certain it was the CO. The wardroom arrived on time and settled in for a cocktail, on the Roach, to await the beginning. The telephone rang for the CO and the Roach thanked him for coming and gave him instructions. They were to proceed to the CO's house to pick up coffee and coffee pots. Each officer was to go to the CO's house via their own home and bring cups and saucers. The wardroom split, picked up cups and saucers, and then mustered at the CO's home. Those suspecting the CO behind the party changed their minds when they arrived at his house and walked in; his dirty skivvies were draped over

169

a stuffed chair; as were his wife's undies.

A red faced Captain picked up and served drinks while they awaited the next instructions. The call was a hint to look in the CO's mailbox for a riddle to be solved for the next clue. After much ado, they decided the clue sent them to the new Honolulu International Airport reflecting pond to look for a Schlitz beer bottle. It was absurd, but they were into the game so they drove to the airport. Gratefully, everyone was in civilian attire as the game-crazy officers and wives waded under the fountain of the pond in front of the airport on a busy Friday evening. The water was 2 feet deep, and everyone was soaked by the cascading water fountain.

Cars stopped to watch the adults run around in the pool. Suddenly, "I've got it," shouted Horace. Everyone gathered around Horace and watched anxiously as he pulled out the bottle cork. A single key fell out. The only clue on the key was a number—#278. Everyone spoke at once with explanations when Captain Bob spoke out.

"I think it appropriate we get the hell out of this pond and away from the fountain."

Everyone nodded approval and moved out of the pool, stopped traffic across the roundabout, but reached safety on the sidewalk.

"Looks like a bank safe box key to me."

"Why would a party maker want to give us a bank key when the banks are closed till Monday?"

"Looks like one of them computer keys to me."

"Come on. We've all been in airports. It's an airport locker key."

"Yeah. That makes sense. We're standing in front of a terminal."

"Hold it! I believe you're right, Pere'. It makes sense it would be an airport locker. Let's go check it out." A dozen rather crazy and wet people walked through the doors of the international airport and started searching for locker #278. After 15 minutes, they found the locker in the United Airlines Terminal and carefully opened the locker. Inside was a single sheet of paper with a map. It showed a route behind Halawa Heights and the treasure was a Chevron Station.

The damp wardroom climbed into their automobiles with cups, saucers, coffee, and coffee maker and headed for an "X" on a treasure map. Bill Moore knew the way, gave everyone instructions, and away they went. In a matter of minutes they ran out of city streets. Everyone gathered around the CO's car lights and checked the map. They followed the map correctly, but the road turned into a narrow dirt road leading into a jungle. The wives wanted no part of entering a jungle, so they got into a couple of cars and remained at the end of the cement road as the men drove into the jungle. The vegetation became thicker and the road narrower.

170

Doggedly, they followed the dirt road, then the dirt path, and then the autos could go no further. They checked the map to insure they hadn't gone astray. They left the CO and Gordo to watch the cars and Horace, Perry, Bill and Bob hiked down the path behind the only flashlight. The mosquitoes were bad, but they were too concerned about the Chevron Station to worry about bugs. They ran out of recognizable path and could have used a machete to cut some of the branches and vines.

"You know, I'll bet we end up coming out of this jungle behind the Chevron Station we passed a few blocks back," said Bill.

"Damn it, Pecos, it was a Texaco Station we passed, not Chevron."

They walked, slapped mosquitoes, brushed aside branches, told jokes, and then whistled the tune to the movie "Bridge Over the River Kwai." Bill carried the flashlight, which started to die.

"Hey, the flashlight's getting dim. We ought to wait until morning and look again," quipped Horace. The light beam caught something white off to the left and Bob yelled, "Bill, put the light over here."

A few feet off the path was an old Chevron gas pump dumped there years ago.

"That's the Chevron station?" Horace asked.

"Hell, how would we know Horace?" Perry gave the old pump a swift kick on the front panel, which fell off, revealing four fifths of excellent Irish Whiskey.

"Can you believe it," Horace said.

"Believe what?"

"This is the treasure. The coffee cups, the coffee maker and coffee, and now this. We've got all the makings for Irish Coffee." There was another note for them in the pump and it read, "Go to Horace and Nancy's Place." They walked back down the trail, turned their cars around, returned to the wives, and headed for Horace's.

After midnight six cars arrived at the Leavitt's, where they found a carton of cream in an ice bucket on the steps. They piled into the house, which also looked like they were not expecting company. Nancy brewed up a huge pot of coffee and they settled back to enjoy the Irish.

The wardroom never did discover the identity of the Roach although the consensus of opinion was Lou Neeb, their DivCom. But whoever did it, gave every officer on Growler a party to remember for the rest of their lives. In the years since, one clue was uncovered. The wardroom on *Growler* was very friendly with the officers on *Halibut*. During World War II, the *Halibut* was once commanded by a Commander Roach, who led a three submarines wolfpack named "Roaches Raiders." Could there be a connection?

During the long patrols, sanity was often maintained by jokes, tricks, and laughter. On *Halibut*, during a quiet mid-watch, the chairs in the Wardroom disappeared and were locked in the ship's freezer. Of course, the officers didn't know where they had disappeared, and the boat's reefer is certainly not a place one would have looked. The XO's order to return the chairs went unheeded. The officers ate by standing or sitting on the deck for a day or so when they finally decided to take the offensive. With the menu indicating steaks for the evening meal, the officers removed all the forks and knives from the Crew's Mess. Trying to enjoy a steak dinner with a spoon made the point and the very cold chairs were returned.[4]

Perry Benson found a wonderful nurse who worked in a Honolulu hospital. She quickly joined the wardroom wives circle and later they decided to get married. They set a date and a time for the wedding that would not interfere with *Growler*'s operating schedule and the planning began. At a point of no return for the wedding date, SubPac decided *Growler* would launch a Regulus on a Saturday morning. *Growler* couldn't tell the admiral the ship had prior commitments. The timing was tight. With luck, the crew could launch and get back for the wedding, so the original plans remained except the time was moved back a couple hours.

Growler stood out to sea early Saturday morning suffering from a bad case of anxiety. Launching the missile wasn't a problem, nor was guiding it to a hit. The problem was to "get to the church on time."

Growler fired, *Growler* hit, and *Growler* ran like hell for port and Perry's wedding. The officers were in Perry's wedding and had left their service dress whites in his "Snake Ranch" (bachelors pad). When *Growler* reached "PH," it was clear it was going to be close. The CO drove the boat right into the berth, doubled up the lines, and the officers took off like rats abandoning a sinking ship. It was no different for the crew, for they were also invited and needed to shower and change clothes. Everyone hurried to "get to the church on time."

It was a mad house at the snake ranch as the officers showered and changed uniforms. They arrived five minutes before the wedding and took their places. Most of the crew had arrived and the CO, Bob, and Perry were in front as part of the wedding party. People grinned.

Perry nudged Bob and whispered, "Look at Pecos." Bob looked down the isle at "Pecos," who was five foot four or less in height. His sword was about the same height. He had clearly picked up the wrong sword. It became clear when they looked at Horace. Horace was six foot four. Pecos's sword dragged on the floor as he seated guests and Horace looked like he wore a dagger.

Bob noticed Dave grimacing in pain as he ushered wedding guests... then he saw why. Coming down the isle, escorting the brides family, was Gordo and he wore two right shoes. He looked as he would veer off to port any moment. Dave wore the two lefts. The wedding was wonderful and the Bensons exited the church under an arch of swords. A wonderful reception followed at the Sub Base Officer's Club and everyone got into their own shoes. The entire crew was at the church and the reception—even for the collapse of a three-tier wedding cake—it was a *Growler* family affair.

Grayback also suffered a problem wearing their own shoes. The boat returned from a patrol and the stewards polished the officer's white shoes for entering port in Tropical White Long uniforms. Lieutenant Gary, the wardroom's loose canon, forgot to bring white shoes so he went through a pile of shoes until he found a pair that fit. Captain Ekelund did not take kindly to the shoe selection.[5]

It was unnerving! The boat received word monetary restrictions necessitated sending *Growler* on one more patrol with her old batteries. The crew was upset, as it placed *Growler* in harm's way. Battery cells were already jumpered out of each battery, and *Growler* was scheduled for a summer patrol with brief hours of darkness. The CO argued heatedly with the Admiral but it did no good. *Growler* would deploy with an old battery and no yard period. Every man worried about insufficient time to conduct good preventative maintenance on equipments such as air compressors, distillers, some pumps, hydraulic systems, etc., usually accomplished by the shipyard.

SubPac replaced the SINS with a new Mk 2 SINS by Autonetics and a new Loran C System. The same SINS was installed aboard the new SSBNs (Polaris Submarines), except they received 2-3 systems, which made calibration easier and system errors more easily detectable. Other than Horace, Bill and a Navigation Tech, no one understood the equipment.

A week before *Growler* deployed, the crews of *Growler* and *Grayback* held a beer ball game. It was a game between friends with lots of beer. Despite being friends, the two teams played with a great deal of competiveness. John Anderson from the *Grayback* and Guy Blades from the *Growler* traded home runs but Bob never saw the final score. Midway through the game, Bob broke his collarbone in eight places.

He was placed into a cast since he had insufficient time to recover from surgery that would have wired the pieces of shoulder bone together. Bob left no doubt in anyone's mind about his position; he was deploying with *Growler*, broken bones or not. Bob got his way as the CO and Admiral agreed to let him make the trip. The day before *Growler* deployed, sickbay recast his shoulder, giving him a little more latitude in the use of his arm—he had to be able to reach his zipper.

It was to be a tough patrol with a bad battery during the summer months, while the Soviets seethed from the Cuban confrontation and hoped to get even. The battery was essentially worn out, and *Growler* departed with little confidence in an engineering plant so tired from the past's demanding schedule, though all equipments worked upon departure.

Chapter Fourteen
The Last Patrol

Most of the officers had been aboard *Growler* for over two years and thought about their next duty assignment. However, preparing for the next patrol curtailed this thought process, and not one officer or enlisted desired to leave the *Growler*. The upcoming patrol was too large a challenge to think of anything except to get *Growler* through the patrol.

SubPac's reluctance to provide new equipment and a battery was a premonition that the Regulus Program's days were limited. The "41 for Freedom" were on their way (41 Polaris boats, with two crews each). ComSubPac sent *Growler* on "Mission Impossible."

The crew was uneasy. *Growler* was a great submarine, and had been cared for as well as the intense operating schedule permitted. The HY-80 steel surrounding the Regulus missiles began to show hairline cracks, although it wasn't dangerous yet. The centerline engine was a new engine, and required a laborious breaking in procedure as they headed for the patrol area. The engine was untested, with minimum test runs conducted at the factory.[1] And there was a multitude of other problem equipments.

Bob was on duty and the CO remained on board as he studied the OpOrder for the upcoming patrol. They met in the wardroom while pouring coffee. They sat to chat. Qualification was the subject and Bob said he never believed the stories about an officer diving the submarine by himself until he faced it during the ORI.

The CO loved to top one's story and said, "You did well, Bob, but if you think that was tough, let me tell you what I did on my underway."

"Okay, Captain," Bob answered.

"I dove the boat myself as you did, then the boat simulated detection by antisubmarine aircraft and I had to leave the area, submerged, and in reverse."

Bob said, "I didn't know they had airplanes when you qualified!"

It earned Bob a thump on the side of the head.

The crew was shocked with another disaster prior to departing on patrol. Don Breeding was the duty officer. About 0300 the temperature alarm in the port hangar sounded. Don tumbled out of bed and raced to the alarm panel. He "reset" the alarm, but it continued.

"My God, we've got a fire in the hangar," he shouted. The duty section flooded the port missile hangar despite the missiles, equipment, and supplies inside. Sixty movies were destroyed, a bunch of food ruined, but worst of all, they flooded two nuclear weapons. It was determined later the temperature sensor was faulty.

Damage, or potential damage, to a nuclear weapon is called an "incident," and an "incident report" or "Bent Spear" must be filed. The loss or destruction of a nuclear weapon is called a "Broken Arrow," as in the recent John Travolta movie. An incident causes great commotion at every level of hierarchy. The hierarchy then looked for "someone" to blame, and in this case went for Don. When one thinks about a fire in a hangar with jet fuel and engines, JATO boosters, and nuclear warheads, it is difficult to fault the duty section's response by energizing the sprinkler system when the fire alarm rang.

The investigation faulted the duty section, as no one had felt the hangar for heat, or opened the hatch to look inside the hangar. It was a piece of 20/20 hindsight. Feeling the hangar for heat was logical, but one had to go topside to feel the hangar. One could not physically touch the hangar from inside the boat, except for the access hatch. Opening the hatch could cause a conflagration if there was a fire, and if the warhead was damaged, permit the spread of radioactivity. Most submariners concurred the duty section acted correctly.

The incident was time consuming, and generated unbelievable paperwork. *Growler* returned to West Loch to offload the wet missiles and reload. The other items lost in the hangar were meaningless compared to potential warhead damage. It is unknown if the warheads were damaged or just in a wet environment.[2]

Halibut had a less dangerous incident materially but not personally. During a missile check out and engine run-up, TM1(SS) Jim Lacy walked in front of the running Regulus Missile and too close to the jet intake. The suction grabbed him and started dragging him toward the intake. Jim Pope instantly grabbed Lacy by the legs and tried to wrestle him to the ground under the missile while the crew shut down the engine. Luckily, Lacy was not injured.[3]

Growler got underway for patrol number #8 on 14 October 1963 despite her problems. The send off was quiet, and families sensed their husbands were not leaving on a routine trip, but on a mission. The band didn't show due to another commitment and the Admiral was away on business. The sun didn't show, which was unusual, while the wind howled, with huge seas beyond the harbor entrance. It was a premonition of gloom and doom. But if there was a crew that could take

Growler through the patrol, it was the present crew.

The crew was seasoned with years of submarine experience and qualified on *Growler*. No one with lesser qualification was aboard, except for the newest men from sub school. It was a team in the Super Bowl Game akin to the Green Bay Packers.

Don Breeding had orders and Stu Merrikan replaced him as the Weapons and Missile Officer. The boat's numbers and name were painted over again and the last stores and spares came aboard. On the unusually cold and rainy autumn day, *Growler* and her "Black and Blue" Crew got underway. Late due to the incident, they made up the time in transit.

The excitement and sorrow attendant with departure on deployment was subdued. Cockiness and confidence was replaced with a quiet tentativeness. Deployment was never a great experience, and one time the *Grayback* wondered if they were going to get underway. The morning they were to depart, quarters was held. Half the crew was missing! It was determined that the enlisted bachelors were missing, except those on duty. Suddenly, Valpoon appeared, running down the dock clad only in his shorts and yelling up a storm.

"Mr. Gunn, Mr. Gunn. I've got to see Mr. Gunn!" The COB and Bill grabbed him and asked him what was wrong. "Our crew's been captured. Luckily, I managed to escape, sir!"

"Escape from what, for god's sake."

"From the brig, sir!"

"What the hell were you doing in the brig?"

The bachelors had held an all night party in the enlisted barracks prior to deploying the next day. By sunrise, the party turned rowdy. The Sub Base Duty Officer was called to the barracks, along with the Shore Patrol (SP). As the SPs rounded up the crew members, Valpoon decided to return to the boat and report what happened. He made a dash for the door, blocked by the Duty Officer. Valpoon lowered his head, caught the officer in the stomach, and ran over him. He headed for *Grayback* while the officer placed the crew in the brig. Bill Gunn came through again as he faced an irate duty officer, but managed to have the remainder of the crew delivered to the dock and sent below decks. *Grayback* was underway on time, but Bill Gunn was bugged for months by the SPs desiring to know how the discipline was administered to the men.[4]

It was a good feeling—the feel of the sea under foot—and it was good to get away from paperwork and the daily crises that marked every day in port. *Growler* steamed up the west side of Oahu on the surface, and the crew ritual topside was repeated. The seas and winds were quiet in the lee of the island, and the men were equally quiet on deck, and below decks, as the last silhouette of Oahu and Waimia Point disappeared. Then the winds and seas kicked up.

Growler reached Adak without incident, and with plenty of exercises under their belts. Memories rushed back to Bob as he thought of his first call at Adak and how nervous he was about fueling. Now he was the Engineer and supervised the event.

Liberty call resulted in only a handful of crew crossing the gangway. They had never been in Adak before, or carried orders from crew members for toiletry items at the Exchange. The crew was on a mission and thought of little else than getting the job done and returning home in one piece.

The break-in run on #2 engine was a long and tedious chore. Chief Wright lived in the Engine Room as each step was carefully followed. At his right hand constantly was Engineman Don Bosetti, who likely knew the engines better than anyone on board. The engine was run a dozen times en route Adak, the last and longest for one minute. All went well and the spirit of the enginemen was on the rise. The engine was one of many problems the engineers faced, and men from other departments walked aft and asked if there was anything they could do to help. The *Growler* was a pitiful example of readiness, but an excellent example of a team.

Growler moved out of Adak on her way to station. They snorkeled along the northern edge of the Aleutians and kept a wary eye for friendly aircraft. The CO conducted drills during the transit, but the seasoned crew displayed little enthusiasm. The officers knew the CO understood, but he wanted to keep the crew busy rather than permit them to sit and worry.

A few days out, the first disaster struck *Growler*. On one of the dives, the stern planesman placed dive on the stern planes before receiving the report that the planes were off the block. The result was the stern planes' operating rod, moved by a hydraulic piston system, moved upward prior to the complete retraction of the block. This caused the operating rod to be bent roughly 30°. The stern planes were placed on a large dive angle and the shaft was partially straightened as it was forced through the cylinder, but tore up the packing in the cylinder. Hydraulic oil spewed in every direction. By the time Bob and Chief Wright got the word, the boat submerged and the diving planes ran the bend through the cylinder a number of times. When Bob arrived in the stern room, he couldn't believe the rod continued up and down with such a large kink. He asked the watch to minimize the use of the stern planes.

Perry ordered the stern planes kept in neutral to prevent more movement, yet the cylinder still spewed hydraulic oil at an uncomfortable rate. The measured hydraulic oil spill rate was ascertained and they would run out of hydraulic oil in 40 days. Bob discussed the problem with Chief Blades and Rintz. They decided to straighten the operating shaft by using torpedo chain falls (block and tackle). The operating rod could not be moved while they straightened it. The shaft was machined to a few thousandth of an inch tolerance, was about 2 ¾ inch diameter, and made of stainless steel. They could not attempt the effort submerged. The stern planes had to be rendered inoperable.

The first obstacle was convincing the CO that they must broach and place the boat in a position where it was unable to submerge. Fortunately, he had plenty of hands-on experience and understood the problem and recommended fix. The concern was to remain undetected. *Growler* was a few days out of Adak and feared detection by anti-submarine aircraft. It bothered the CO, but he realized there was no choice. After a careful sonar and ECM search, *Growler* broached and lay to. The ballast tanks remained flooded and the trim tanks filled for diving. Only surface adhesion kept her on the surface. The stern planes were hydraulically disconnected and trailed astern. Both periscopes were manned and the ECM mast was raised to search for radars. Repair time was estimated at three hours.

Auxiliarymen would straighten the operating rod and replace the packing around the shaft that was shredded.

"Stern Room, Control. Permission granted to commence working on the stern planes operating gear." The auxiliarymen went to work.

"Control, Stern Room. We are about to straighten the shaft and the planes are secured." The Auxiliarymen set up the chain falls and started to pull. The rod straightened almost perfectly. The rod was in line except for a slight "S" curve where the rod was initially bent.

"Conn, ECM. We have an ECM contact, signal strength one, bearing due east, evaluated as American APS-20 surface search radar."

"Damn it," hissed the CO, "has to happen when we're sitting on the surface like a lame duck. Ask Bob how they're coming and explain the ECM contact."

The operating rod ran through the cylinder with little effort but chewed up the new packing and hydraulic fluid spewed out again. They replaced the neoprene packing with graphite flax.

"Mr. H, Control says they have an airborne surface search radar out of Adak. They want to know how much longer you're going to be."

"Tell Conn we are at the point of no return, but if this flax works we can be back in commission in an hour."

"Captain, the Engineer reports that..."

"I know, I heard it," snapped the CO. "Damn it, all we need is a bunch of fly boys buzzing around us all the way to station. Taylor, get me an American Ensign!"

Perry contemplated bringing Ensign McCoy to the conning stand, but it wasn't the time to fool with the CO. He wanted an American flag and got it.

"Pere', I'm going to the bridge with this ensign. Feed me the ECM reports. If he sees us, I'll wave this flag at him and hope that will get him off our ass."

"Will do, sir. Do you want to take the QM with you?"

"Damn it, Pere', I'm old, but I'm sure I can still manage the hatches."

The flax packing was installed and worked better, but they began the patrol with limited use of the stern planes. The men watched the stern planes move through their arc of movement and calculated the planes could be liberally used from nine degrees dive to full rise. Ten degrees dive or greater on the stern planes was an emergency measure.

"Conn, Stern Room. Job completed. Stern planes are in commission, but in a limited status, sir." That relieved the CO ands he silently danced a little jig up on the bridge.

"Stern Room, this is the Captain. Good, Bob. Pere', I'm coming down, then we'll get our asses below." The signal increased to three, remained there for a while, then slowly diminished to the southwest. *Growler* slipped below the waves and resumed the transit. Later, Bob told the CO that the job was done beautifully through the skill of Ron Rintz and Carrol Miller.

Jim McCoy was the newest officer and assumed the position of the boot officer and brunt of attendant jokes. However, Jim looked so innocent that few pulled jokes on him without feeling guilty.

In the Engine Room, the new engine continued its break-in. The engine completed all the unloaded tests well within specifications. Bob was in the Engine Room through many of the tests as an observer, and to provide moral support to his men. Chief Wright and Don Bosetti conducted the tests and Bob made sure they had plenty of coffee.

The seas settled down to 5–6 foot waves with a long period swell from the south. Sonar and ECM had no contacts in the area, which was unusual considering the season. Normally, the area was actively fished during the late summer and early autumn months. The unseasonable cold temperatures and high winds of the past days apparently kept the fishermen in port. Bob was on watch and ordered the boat rigged for a snorkel charge. The batteries gassed badly, so the charging rate followed the hydrogen curve.[5]

"Conn, Maneuvering. Request permission to commence battery charge, two engines, sir."

The engines bogged down a bit as the charge placed a load on the generators. Bob stared through the periscope as he looked for anything, yet hoped he saw nothing but ocean and sky.

"Conn, Maneuvering. Battery charge in progress sir, 750 amps per."

Growler was due on station by noon the following day to relieve *Tunny* and *Barbero*. At their present speed, they would arrive on station about ten hours early.

"Conn, Maneuvering. Request permission to light off #2 engine as part of the break in procedure, sir."

"Permission granted, Maneuvering," Bob answered and said a short prayer. This was the telling test run. If the engine did well, the boat would be back to three engines—what a wonderful thought. He listened carefully and heard the engine roll over with air and kick in... and then suddenly stop. He didn't want to think why the engine shut down and patiently awaited the report.

Bob watched the stern planesman handle the seas. In calm seas, there was no problem holding ordered bubble with less than five degrees of use. The real test would be in the heavy seas they expected in the following weeks.

"Conn, Maneuvering. We lost #2 engine, sir. No reason yet."

To keep from worrying, he checked the baffles for sonar contacts. The course change didn't vary the depth control situation as *Growler* remained generally in the trough of the swell, so the sternplane use remained similar. A few minutes later.

"Conn, Sonar. Everything clear astern, Mr. H. I don't even have a noise spoke out there tonight."

"Conn, aye, sonar. Wouldn't it be nice to have an entire patrol of this?"

"Mr. H., I'm surprised at you. I always thought you thrived on excitement."

"Scotty, I think this trip I'd like to peak my excitement on a cribbage board."

Chief Wright, walked to the conning stand,

"Mr. H., I'm afraid #2 engine has had it, sir."

"Had it! How can a brand new engine 'had it' with twenty or so hours on it, Chief."

"Sixteen hours, sir. Exactly sixteen hours, give or take a few seconds."

Bob kept the periscope moving, but his mind was in the Engine Room. He couldn't understand how they lost the engine.

"Chief, I'm not sure I understand what happened. You followed the script, right?"

"Not one deviation. We followed the book line by line. She sounded perfect, sir, just perfect on the previous runs. She sounded good rolling over with start up air, she caught and started firing, and all of a sudden it was like she hit a wall. The entire engine seized up in one big bang. Sir."

"But what would cause that, chief?"

"I don't know, sir, but I've heard the sound twice before in my life and each time, the engine was totaled."

"What caused them to be totaled?"

"Sir, when you've got an engine starting up and catching, her RPMs run way up there for an instant, and then it stops like right now; the crankshafts usually turn out to be a mess, let alone the timing chain and god knows what else. We'll tear her down, Mr. H., and see what we've got, but I'm not very optimistic. I'll call you as soon as I find something, sir."

"Thanks, Chief." "Curbow, inform the CO #2 engine failed and may be down for the duration."

Bob expected to see the CO in Control but,

"Captain has the word, sir," reported Curbow. *Growler* continued the transit on two engines as the crew's morale dropped another notch. It was dark as a bat

180

house and overcast, so there were no stars to observe. Bob wondered why one looked for blinking running lights on aircraft, when it made sense that no Soviet aviator flew with running lights on if looking for submarines. Anyway, it was dark out there.

"What's the hydrogen reading, chief," Bob asked.

"About 1.2, sir," he answered. Bob figured they should slow the charging rate within the hour.

The watch ended and Bob stepped off the conning stand. Control was dark and eerie, with the glow of a few red lights, and silent as a tomb. Even the evolution of watch relief was silent. People spoke in subdued voices as oncoming watch standers sucked up what the off going watch said and cringed with the word an engine was down. It was so quiet that the sound of hydraulic valves shifting as the helmsman and planesman moved their controls could be heard, with attendant swishing as the fluid was redirected. Faintly came the hushed silence of the audio output from sonar and UQC. Even the continuous "beep beep" from Radio sounded stifled and slow.

Bob stuck his head through the curtain in sonar,

"Thanks for another quiet watch, Scotty."

"You're welcome, Mr. H. Hope your engine is okay!"

Bob winced a bit as he looked over the ECM operator's shoulder and left Control. Temporarily blind as he stepped into the After Battery and mess decks, he was greeted by the cook, Ma Irwin, and returned the greetings. His watch section, already relieved, were enjoying a bowl of hot soup before hitting the rack.

When he entered the Engine Room, he saw half his enginemen working on #2.

God, they are a great bunch of men and they never complain, he thought. He hurt inside for them, for it was no fun in the bowels of the boat with engines running on either side. It was hot, sweaty, and dirty.

Bob chatted with his men and heard bad news. Both upper and lower crankshafts were torqued out of alignment. Just as he climbed back up, Latham cried out, "Damn. Here's the culprit."

He held shrapnel in his hand, most of it brass. "Look at this if you want to know why the engine stopped?" He shined his flashlight on the main drive gear and bull gear. Between the steel teeth of the gears were hunks of brass that fell into the gear train and compressed between the teeth. In the engine is a flex pack that absorbs shock when the engine first catches and starts to run. The flex pack failed and flew apart. As Chief Wright said; it was "totaled."

Growler arrived on station and relieved *Tunny* and *Barbero*. They had started patrols in better shape. A little light did enter Bob's life a week into the patrol, when he received a message from the DivCom stating he was promoted to full

Lieutenant. He forgot it was time for a promotion and didn't bring new insignia, as if it mattered. An insignia would look out of place on a sweatshirt.

Weeks passed and the patrol went well, with the exception of the stern plane limitations and the battery situation. Of concern was the number of battery cells jumpered out of the electrical system because they were grounded. The battery plates came apart, filled electrolyte with floating particles that eventually joined with chemical trees, and shorted out the battery between plates.

Bob was on watch and *Growler* rested gently on the layer at a depth of 140 feet, making minimum way to conserve the battery. Scotty called him from sonar.

"Conn, Sonar. Mr. H., if you're not busy, I'd like you to listen to something, sir."

"What's up, Scotty?"

"Hi, Mr. H. Listen to a sound you've probably not heard before."

He sat down, put on earphones, and couldn't believe what he heard. It was a screeching and moaning sound so shrill, it sent shivers down his back.

"What the hell is that?"

"What do you think it is?"

"If it's whale noise, one of them is either being raped or killed. I don't know. What is it?"

"You are listening to ice. It's forming up again. The noise you hear are pieces of ice coming together. When ice forms, as when it comes apart, the small sections are called rafts and they make a hell of a noise as they rub against each other. You remember two patrols ago when it was late in the winter. We heard the big stuff then, this is thinner ice. We're at the end of summer and a cold snap can temporarily generate ice, as in winter months."

"I don't know how you sort all these sounds out and remember them."

"You have to, sir. My job is to detect anything harmful or threatening to *Growler*. Ice can be a big threat, although I guess we'll be looking for Soviet shipping pretty soon moving between Murmansk and here. It's that time of year when the northern route is still open and the ships appear as they make their last moves before winter traps the Northern Route."

"I've been thinking about that, too, Scotty but I don't know how we'll be able to go in there with the battery on its butt."

"We should start hearing the pressure ridges coming apart again."

They were on the layer and things were quiet, so Bob wandered into Radio to see what was new. They monitored a number of radio stations; one of them was the Voice of Moscow. They listened to the station often, because their world news reports seemed superior to the Voice of America. One listened with a bias in the opposite direction from Moscow's politics to find some measure of reality. He listened for a few minutes when suddenly the Soviets interrupted their own program.

"This is the Voice of Moscow. It has been confirmed the President of the United States was assassinated in Dallas, Texas this 22nd day of November, 1963. The President was in a motorcade in Dallas when a sniper opened fire, killing the President and seriously wounding Texas Governor Connelly. The motorcade..."

The news took seconds to reach the crew. The Radiomen usually patched one of the worldwide broadcasts on a speaker circuit throughout the boat so the crew could stay in touch with current events. Within seconds, the crew was up, thoroughly stunned by the news. Bob called the CO, who went into Radio to monitor the radio circuits. The boat became deathly silent. The crew filed into the Crew's Mess to listen to the broadcast. Others stood outside the radio shack, waiting for someone to come out with additional news. The XO went into radio and the officers gathered in Control.

Radio shifted to the Voice of America, which was broadcasting news, but only reported baseball scores, league standings, and other sports news for the weekend.

"Shit, its another commie trick. Who the hell would kill the President? And if it did happen, why isn't the Voice of America talking about it?"

Shock gave way to relief and anger at the Soviets for putting on another propaganda show.

"This is really a cheap shot!"

"Somebody ought to respond with a big mushroom cloud. "

"How stupid do they think we are?"

The CO stepped out of Radio with face drawn and hard. Captain Bob had a look on his face none of the crew had seen before. A dozen voices popped up,

"Hey, Captain, what's up? Its just a gag isn't it, sir?"

"Well, men, we haven't heard anything yet, except on the Voice of Moscow. We checked to make sure we didn't miss anything on the last Fox Sked, and we haven't missed a thing.[6] I haven't got a bit of news for you, there isn't even a hint in the classified traffic."

"So what do you think personally, Cap?"

"Men, I know no more than you and I don't want to speculate, but I can tell you this; if the President was killed, the radio circuits would be filled with Flash traffic and the DefCon Condition would probably be raised. None of that has happened. At least not yet."

"He's right," someone muttered. "If President Kennedy was assassinated, we definitely would be going to a higher DefCon, especially after the Cuban Crisis."

At the top of the hour, the Voice of Moscow news was back on the air. They continued the assassination news, but backed off the President was dead. Instead, they said, he had been hit by sniper fire at least twice and rushed to a nearby hospital. The radio elaborated that Lyndon Johnson was on hand at the hospital and explained how the change of command took place. Then a background on Johnson began, and how he was considered an old school politician who was narrowly defeated by Kennedy in the Democratic Convention. They discussed Johnson's attributes and attitudes, especially toward Communism and Russia. The bottom line seemed to be Johnson would be less difficult to deal with than Kennedy... so sayeth the Soviets.

The crew felt a mixture of emotion, including fear, shock, disbelief and anger. If the story was true, life might change drastically on *Growler*, for she was the front line of the Cold War. They listened to the Voice of America and again were disappointed—or relieved. The crew was in such an emotional state, they forgot to change the watch and remained glued in their positions awaiting further word.

"Captain to Radio, Sir," came over the 21MC.

"Oh, shit, here it comes. Now we'll get the word."

The CO flew out of the wardroom and into Radio as the crew waited with 'bated breath to hear what he learned. It was a Flash message, encrypted, so it took a few minutes to break. Their wait seemed endless as they talked in hushed voices and rumors abounded.

The radio shack door opened slowly and the CO walked out with a message in a trembling hand and streaks of wet ran from his eyes. His lips quivered as he made his way to the conning stand and picked up the 1MC. Not a word was spoken by anyone, for everyone knew.

"This is the Captain speaking. We just received word from CinCPacFlt as follows: This afternoon the President of the United States, John Fitzgerald Kennedy, died as a result of gunshots wounds to the head. The reins of leadership have passed on to President Lyndon Baines Johnson aboard Air Force 1. All commands are elevated to Condition 3 DefCon Condition for Conus and at sea. Standby for further instructions." (Message read similar to this.)

A stunned silence filled the ship, except for an occasional sob of sorrow and a few whispers of prayer. Then, on the 1MC, the Captain said,

"Men, please follow me in a prayer: Our Father, who art in Heaven, hallowed be thy name. Thy kingdom come..."

The sound of prayer began in a whisper and slowly built into a crescendo of male voices that reached from stem to stern in a plea to God for help. No one wanted to believe what happened for this was America and such things did not occur. The officers were touched by the crew's reaction to the Cuban crisis, but that was honor, loyalty and Country. This was pure and unmitigated grief.

The crew followed every word on the Voice of America in the following days and shared in their Country's sorrow through the funeral that was broadcast to the fleet. Big and strong men, masculine super men who never shed a tear in their lives, bent in sorrow and wept like babies. And when the funeral was over, they picked themselves up and went back to defending America.

Following the mid-watch Dave made his tour through the boat, and when he entered the Forward Torpedo Room he noticed a flashing light on the Navol monitor. He quickly checked and found the Mk 16 torpedo in #1 skid of torpedo tube #3 was gassing excessively. He called the watch, who acknowledged the abnormal reading on the torpedo.

"For god's sake, why didn't you report this before?"

"Sir, it's still within the allowable limits of gassing, sir."

"Yes it is, but it's the change that is meaningful." The TM checked his hourly log and determined the torpedo went from normal to marginal in less than one hour.[7] Dave called the CO and by the time he arrived, the gassing had increased another twofold.

"Hit the collision alarm," ordered the CO. "Brown, get the Mk 37 out of torpedo tube #3 ASAP and load this Mk 16. The fish is running away and we only have minutes."

"Navol runaway, Forward Torpedo Room. Battle Stations Torpedo. All hands man their battle stations."

"Conn, Captain. Come to course east. Check for contacts!"

The Mk 37–0 torpedo came out in record time and the Mk 16 was loaded in its place. By the time the fish was in the tube and the tube secured, the torpedo was so hot the torpedo tube, made of steel instead of brass as in previous submarines, began to change colors—first it was blue and then green and...

"Good work, men, I'm going to Control. Chief flood tube #3 now."

"Captain in Control," piped Hoffman.

"Any sonar contacts, Perry?"

"None, sir."

"Good, I've ordered #3 flooded."

"Yes, sir, they gave us the word, Captain, and we've trimmed for it."

"Good. Open the outer door on #3."

"#3 outer door indicates open, sir."

"Very well. Fire #3!"

"#3 fired electrically, sir," and the boat shuddered.

"Sonar, Conn. Follow that fish."

"Aye, sir, running hot straight and normal, sir. Looks like she's heading due east, sir."

"Come right to course 220°."

The CO explained the MK 16 navol tank was degenerating rapidly and he fired the torpedo to rid the threat to Growler, and to the east away from listening Soviet ears. He turned away to the southwest to open the distance from the time bomb, while keeping the torpedo out of the baffles so Sonar could track it.

"Conn, Sonar. The torpedo stopped running. Range looks like about 20,000 yards to the east, sir." Minutes later, sonar reported an explosion off the port quarter. So ended the threat. It was time to clear the area, for someone certainly heard the explosion and would want to know who and why.

It didn't take long for the Soviet's reaction. Aircraft were in the area within the hour, but *Growler* finished the daily battery charge. With the first ECM contact, *Growler* dropped to the layer and remained in communications via the floating wire. At 0400, Bob and Jim went on watch as the boat lay on the layer at dead slow turns. It was rough topside, with a storm to the south. There were heavy swells but small waves, so sonar conditions remained good. They continued to the south as they exited the explosion area.

Scotty reported no contacts, but had friendly Carpenter fish acting up ahead. Bob called the CO and told him of the noise spoke. He, like most officers, was a believer the fish were an early warning signal.

"I understand the situation, Bob. Come right to 270°. We'll open the explosion area and be closer to our targets." They turned west and put distance between themselves and the explosion, yet kept an ear on the fish.

Bob walked into Sonar to listen to the fish.

"Mr. H,, look at this," Scotty whispered and pointed to the sonar printout. The noise spoke to the south split into two, one remained and the other moved slowly west. The fish became more active, which Scotty interpreted to mean the contacts were approaching the fish. "Sir, I don't hear anything near the fish, but I've seen this before, and the split meant multiple targets."

"You don't hear anything?" Bob asked.

"No, sir, but look at this." A pattern was taking shape out of the random noise spoke.

Bob called the CO and told him what they saw in sonar.

"Captain, my gut tells me we're going to see a contact or two come out of this noise spoke. Scotty agrees, sir."

"Okay, Bob, what is your best estimate of range?"

"I don't have the slightest, but let me massage it a bit with Scotty."

"Okay, Bob. I'll be out there in a minute."

"Scotty, the CO's interested in the range."

"Sir, there's not enough bearing rate here to make me think its close, but the fish are getting loud. My best swag (sweet ass guess) is 20,000 yards or greater." Bob reported the guess to the CO and went back to sitting, looking, and listening with Scotty.

"Hey, I thought I heard a noise level right here, Scotty," he said.

"I think we do have something there, sir. Look at the printout. The computer agrees with you." Then the printout went blank and a dozen scans went by without the slightest hint of an ink mark; and then it was back again for just a few sweeps. "Sir, remember a few patrols ago when you got caught on the surface by that Russki?"

"Geezuz, how could I forget that?"

"Well, after we got into port in Pearl, I took the tape of that episode over to the *Permit* and ran it on their system. I taught the chief sonarman over there in school. Sir, I got a trace on the printout just like this one. We didn't have this feature then. Well sir..."

"You think we have a drifting tin can?"

"Well, sir, I wouldn't bet my entire pay check on it but..." *BOOOING* echoed throughout the boat.

"Shit, they tagged us," Bob yelled, heading for the conning stand. The CO and Bob ran into each other by the QM plot as they headed for the conning stand.

"What the hell was that?" shouted the CO, even though he knew damned well what it was. Bob took one look at the sonar scope when the single ping hit and saw the spoke at 240° or thereabouts.

"All ahead two-thirds, make your depth 300 feet, come right to 240°," he ordered. Bob got his acknowledgement back and explained to the CO, "I think we've got a drifting destroyer, Captain, at 240°. I'm ducking beneath the layer and pointing him to show him our bow."

"Good, Bob, lets rig for silent running and man the torpedo tracking team. Bob, make that Battle Stations Torpedo! This is the Captain, I have the Conn."

"Sir, sonar reports screw noises close aboard, but has no accurate bearing because of the layer depth."

"Bob, where is the break in the layer?" Bob ran to the BT and looked carefully.

"About 135 feet, sir."

"Make your depth 120 feet, all ahead standard, do not cavitate."

"Battle stations torpedo manned and ready, sir. No solution at present, Captain."

"I know, damn it. I'm working on it," hissed the Captain. "Sonar, I'm coming up to 120 feet. You should hear better. If not, let me know ASAP. I like to know where my enemy is and I'll never know under the layer."

"One hundred twenty feet, Captain."

"Very well, slow to one third. Sonar, this is the Captain, what do you have?"

"I've got him, Captain. Bearing 280° sir, turns for 12 knots, a destroyer type. Sounds like he is changing his aspect right now, sir—sir, he has zigged towards."

Aye, right full rudder, come right to 290°."

Captain, he's launched something. I heard a splash in the water." Before the Captain could react or answer, Scotty came back in a calm and confident voice, "Torpedo in the water, bearing 278°. Torpedo is not actively pinging, sir!"

"All ahead standard, do not cavitate, ten degrees down bubble, make your depth 250 feet."

The appropriate replies came back and *Growler* ducked back below the layer. "Flood #1 and #2 torpedo tubes. Give me a solution, gang." The torpedo was so close, its noise penetrated the hull... and every crew member's soul.

"Captain, he is close aboard to starboard, sir, very close, and we do not have a solution."

"Conn, sonar. Target close aboard. Torpedo passing overhead and still not pinging, sir."

"No shit, sonar, I can hear him." The men in Control could track the torpedo from the sound coming through the Growler's hull. Then they heard the ship itself, close aboard and on the starboard bow. Most of the crew had heard the sound before during underway training, when they took turns shooting at each other. There is no sound so terrifying to a submariner than the sound of a torpedo running when the pointed end is pointed at him. They listened to the torpedo pass overhead as *Growler* quietly slipped below the layer. Most of the men in Control looked up and flinched as it went by. The crew relaxed a bit just as the sound of the destroyer, evaluated by Scotty as a *Kynda* class Soviet destroyer, boomed through the hull. For a moment, Bob had visions of Cary Grant, John Wayne, Glenn Ford, and Ward Bond looking up at the overhead of their submarines, waiting for the next depth charge. One could not see through the inch and a half thickness of steel hull, but one unconsciously looked toward the source of noise.

Then it was over. The torpedo missed, and the destroyer, for some reason, continued on to the east.[8] Why would the Soviet steam away after his torpedo missed? The crew cautiously waited for the destroyer to return or another destroyer to arrive on the scene.

They slipped away from him, but they would never know what the Soviet saw on his sonar after the single ping. Perhaps he felt they saw some anomaly that did not reappear; maybe it was just an exercise torpedo; no one knew but they were happy with the end result.

Chapter Fifteen
The Final Days of the Last Patrol

Secure from Battle Stations, Torpedo," boomed on the 1MC. There was a pause, a click, a chuckle unmistakably the Captain, and, "Secure from Silent Running!"

Everyone breathed and relaxed again.

"Conn, Sonar. Noise spoke and machinery noises to the south, sir. I think it's the other half of the split target we saw." Their breath sucked back in and butts puckered as Bob and the CO stared at the sonar repeater.

"Damned but if there weren't two of the bastards," murmured the CO. "Sonar, Captain. Evaluate!"

"Aye, sir. Sounds like another tin can just started up, sir. Don't have any bearing rate yet, but I think he's way out... 10,000 yards or more. Screw beats, sir, increasing speed."

"Bob, on the 1JV phones, remain on Battle Stations Torpedo, stand easy on station, and rig for quiet. Let's stay on top of the layer. Come left to south. I'll be in sonar."

Growler steered course 180° and sonar analyzed the target. It was another Soviet destroyer that had laid to and listened while vectoring the first destroyer on the torpedo attack. As the Soviet destroyer picked up speed, he turned east to rejoin the first destroyer.

Intelligence reported the last Soviet convoy of the year was breaking through into the Bering Sea behind the icebreaker *Moskva*. The convoy was known to include the Submarine Tender *Atrek* and possibly one Hotel class nuclear submarine. The ice would close shortly, so *Growler* was ordered to confirm the make up of the convoy. *Growler* was to intercept the convoy where the ice didn't stretch much more than four hundred miles from land. SubPac didn't want Growler under ice too far, but to make contact with the convoy, count ships, identify, tape all the vessels, and get out.

Horace and Bill plotted a track to intercept the convoy in six days. They had to avoid detection, for *Growler* had no stamina to play games with another submarine, especially a Soviet nuke. They snorkeled most of the transit, shutting down every hour to clear baffles, then resume the transit.

The transit went well for three days as ice noise became intense and frightening. They kept a zero float on the battery, snorkeling on one engine.[1]

"Conn, Maneuvering. Lost #1 engine, sir."

"Secure snorkeling." "Maneuvering, Conn. What's the problem with #1 engine," inquired Perry who had the Conn.

"Don't know yet, sir. We have an indication of high temperature in the cooling water."

"Captain in Control," piped John Anderson.

"What's up, Pere'," asked the CO.

"Not sure yet, Captain. Bob just whistled by headed aft, so we'll find out soon, sir."

"Okay. Have sonar look around while we're shut down. Might as well go below the layer and listen for a bit, too. Keep heading west at one-third speed." The CO walked into sonar to listen.

"How's things sound, Harrison?"

"Pretty noisy, Captain. Lot's of ice noise, and it sounds like we're near a school of shrimp—hear that snapping noise?"

"Sure do. Those deep fat fried?" That brought a smile to both watchstanders. "Do you think we'll be able to pick up an ice breaker at any great distance?"

"Don't know, Captain, I've never heard one working ice before, sir. I imagine it's pretty noisy with the water pumping back and forth plus the ice breaking. We've got her fingerprints ready to check though."

"Thanks, son. Keep listening." The CO stepped out of Sonar as Bob came forward from the Engineroom.

"Got a leak on #1, Captain. Not sure yet where, but its likely another adaptor."

"How long to repair it, Bob?"

"My best guess is a couple of days, sir. A lot of hand work filing out the adaptor threads."

"Can we get #3 on the line right away?"

"Yes, sir. She's fine, Captain—knock on wood."

"Okay, Bob. Thanks." He ordered periscope depth and prepare to snorkel on #3 engine. Ten minutes later, *Growler* was back on the transit, but the crew was nervous. There was no longer a backup engine. The problem in #1 engine was a cracked adaptor, and the enginemen struggled to remove it. It wasn't difficult, but the job took meticulous work and time.

Growler approached the intercept point and changed habits; they snorkeled for 30 minutes and listened. Bob and Jim were on watch. The crew couldn't sleep; they were awake and quietly discussed the mission. Deep moans and shrill groans emanated from sonar as they approached thick ice. Bob spent most of the time on the periscope looking straight ahead, fearful of floating ice striking the periscope or snorkel mast as happened in earlier patrols.

On *Grayback's* 6th patrol, she spent significant time fighting through ice and freezing temperatures. One night they snorkeled in subzero temperatures and ice built on the snorkel valve seat. As the ice built up, it permitted spray to pass into the submarine's air induction system which in turn, froze and aggravated the situation. Eventually, they faced a situation of flooding in the Engine Room as water entered the induction piping system. The conning officer ordered a large up bubble to get the snorkel valve clear of the water and before Captain Ekelund could prevent the up bubble, the water in the Engine Room ran aft and flooded out the centerline generator.

The Captain blew the after group to get the angle off the boat but it was too late and #2 engine/generator was lost. Bill Gunn was involved in the disaster and froze both his feet. Only through the efforts of the Enginemen and Electricians, who built an incubator, and the care of Hospital Corpsman Edwards, were his feet saved. Bill was totally involved in stopping the flooding and received frost bite on both feet in the process. Operating in ice and cold temperatures requires an entirely different train of thought from normal submarine operations.

"Conn, sonar. Noise spoke developing almost due north, sir. I can't hear anything, but you can see the noise spoke on your scope."

"I see it, Scotty. You're looking in the right direction for the convoy. Stay on it. I'm going to ask Harrison and Coffman to give you a hand in there. Use them as you see fit."

"Conn, ECM. I picked up a few sweeps of surface search radar to the north and I'm getting some conversation on VHF, sir," reported Chief Ekenberg. "Looks like the Soviets don't expect us around with all their careless electronic mistakes."

"Conn aye. Thanks, Chief." "Hymie! Tell the CO we hold the convoy on sonar and ECM to the North, as expected."

"On my way ,Mr. H."

"Secure snorkeling."

Growler assumed the nuke would be leading the convoy and running under the ice. The CO kept his mind focused on three problems; the Soviet nuke, the ice, and the state of the battery. *Growler* had lost a periscope to ice in the very same area on her first patrol.

"Captain in Control," reported Hymie.

"Whatsha got, Bob?"

"ECM reports surface search radars to the north, signal strength under one, plus we've got Soviet chit-chat going on. Sonar is watching a noise spoke to the north—see the spoke right here, sir? I secured snorkeling because I don't know the range to those units, especially the Hotel."

"Good, Bob. This jives with intelligence reports. It's the convoy, and I want to stay as far away from them as possible while getting the job done. Hymie! Call the XO up here. How's the battery holding up Bob?"

"Okay, Captain. It's topped off, which means about a half a can. We isolated two more cells forward this afternoon, sir."

"We found 'em, huh, Captain," mumbled Horace.

"Yup. They're in range of sonar and ECM. We have a huge thermal layer here today and I plan to use it. I'm going down to the layer, sit there, and count sheep. If something goes wrong, we can slip under the layer. I hope we have enough battery to last through the count. Comments, please!"

"Jim, make your depth 140 feet. Easy on the down bubble. Lower the ECM Mast, Chief." Then he walked into sonar.

"Scotty, this ought to be interesting."

"Mr. H., I wondered how long it would be before you wandered in. I was about to call you. Look at 295°. It's a spike in the noise spoke and we're hearing it. Here, put on the ear muffs."

He listened for a minute or two and said, "I hear a turn count."

"Bingo. Damn, I trained you well. Look at the fingerprint—and here is the print on a Hotel class."

"Shit, Scotty, its identical. That SOB did pull out in front of the rest of the convoy. Is this the rest of the convoy up here at 335°?"

"You've got it, sir. Once he had a clear run under the ice to home plate, he took off, probably for Petro." The CO was in Control, so Bob gave him a quick update from sonar. Then he offered a suggestion:

"Sir, it might be wise to go to a quiet condition. It would be a shame to mess up by making detectable noise. Besides, it will save the can."

"Good thinking. Make it so."

"*Growler* rigged for silent running, went deep and listened to a parade of Soviet ships cross in front of her. They confirmed that the submarine tender and the icebreaker did make a lot of noise. There were a couple *Riga* class destroyers and the Missile Range Ship *Sibir* in the group, adding to the Soviet Pacific Missile Range capabilities. There were six auxiliary type ships, or merchant ships. By midnight, all the ships passed CPA (Closest Point of Approach) and opened. It was over. The mission was accomplished and all that remained was to get back on station.

Growler reversed course and headed back to station and the crew gave a united sigh of relief. The past week had been a strain on everyone's nerves.[2] She moved slowly atop the layer for a few hours to clear the area, then came up to periscope depth to look around,

"Commence snorkeling."

Number 3 engine rumbled as it turned over with starting air, then caught with a mighty roar. But before a load could be placed on the generator, "Conn, Maneuvering. Secured snorkeling sir."

"Conn, aye. What's the problem?" queried Stu.

"I think it's a loss of lube oil pressure, sir. We'll be back to you with a full report." Bob steamed through Control, headed aft, and the CO walked into Control. "What's the problem Stu?"

"Maneuvering thinks a loss of lube oil pressure to #3 engine. No details, but Bob headed aft."

The CO momentarily showed the strain, not just annoyance.

"God damn it, we're a throw and a spit from the Soviet Union with a battery on its ass and don't even have an engine. Holy shit, what the hell are those guys doing back there?" He stalked back and forth in front of the conning stand a few times.

"Captain, I'm sure the snipes are doing everything they can, sir. Its just that everything's tired," Stu spoke lowly.

"I know it, damn it, Stu. I know they've been bust'n butt this whole trip. I just needed to vent. How's depth control, Gordo?"

"Good, Captain. Must be flat as hell up there."

"Okay. Stu, stay here at periscope depth for the moment. Have Bob see me when he gets his shit together."

Bob reached the Engine Room and pushed through a crowd of snipes to get to the lower level and Chief Wright. The men looked exhausted and now there were two engines to work on. One had to be back on the line and quickly.

"Whatcha got, Chief?"

"Hi, Mr. H. We've got a split in the lube oil tubing to #3 engine and a messed up lube oil separator, which I don't understand. The only thing I can think of is the separator drain got clogged and backed up pressure in the separator. Shit, sir, things are falling apart faster than we can mend 'em," the chief voiced apologetically.

"I know it, Chief, but we've just got to keep one plant running back here. How long to repair #3?" asked Bob.

"An hour, two max, unless we have some more good luck'."

"Good, Chief. Concentrate for the moment on getting #3 back on the line. And, Chief... your men look tired as hell. There's a point where you lose efficiency if the men get over tired."

"Son-of-a-bitch, sir! You think I just got borned yesterday?"

"Easy, Chief. I'm worried about you more than anyone."

"No god damned Naval Academy graduate is goin' to tell me how..."

"Chief! Shut up for a moment. You get #3 back on the line and then hit the rack... and that's an order!"

The chief didn't answer but nodded his head in acknowledgement. Within two hours, #3 engine was on the line and not too soon. The deep cycle on the battery grounded out six more cells. There were twenty-eight grounded cells. The following day, #1 engine was back in commission and the crew relaxed a bit, knowing they now had a backup engine.

It was a secondary duty of the Regulus submarines to carry out intelligence gathering operations. Sometimes, the effort was scary. *Halibut* was observing a Soviet ASW exercise (anti-submarine warfare). They had been tracking the exercise for days and the battle stations tracking team was almost continuously at work. The *Halibut*'s skipper turned to the XO and said,

"Your qualification for command exercise is to take *Halibut* under a Soviet submarine and photograph the under side." The exercise was concluding and the units were beginning to disperse. Sonar reported a submarine contact blowing her ballast tanks. The submarine was either a Zulu, Golf, or Foxtrot class submarine (Soviet diesel submarines). Surprising everyone, a Golf class submarine surfaced almost in front of the *Halibut*. The XO closed her before she got on speed and took some beautiful underwater photographs of the submarine. The intelligence gained certainly didn't hurt the career of the officers on board, as five of them, including the CO and XO, eventually were promoted to Admiral.[3]

Before long it was the last night on station, and the tempo of the crew was upbeat again as thoughts shifted east to home. It was the last night of snorkel charging on station. In the wardroom, the officers finished a round of Hearts and started another movie.

"Secure snorkeling!" Bob was watching the movie and picked up the telephone next to him to listen in on why they secured.

"Maneuvering, Conn. What's the problem back there?"

"Conn, Maneuvering. Wait one, sir. The enginemen shut down both engines, sir, and I don't know why yet."

"Conn, Engine Room. Dial the wardroom, please." It was an excited voice broken by coughing and great deal of heavy breathing.

"Engine Room, why don't you dial yourself?" asked the conning officer—a damn stupid statement to make. He could find out later why the Engine Room made the request.

"Conn, I can't see the dials because of the smoke, sir!"

Bob was on the run, crushing Perry's cigarettes and stomping the CO's coffee cup on the wardroom table as he ran across the table and out heading aft.

"Fire, fire in the Engine Room. All hands man your battle stations," barked the 1MC. Before watertight doors (WT) slammed shut Bob made it half way through the After Battery. He opened the WT door into the Engine Room as Chief Wright ran up his back, coming from the Goat Locker in his skivvy shorts.

"Bosetti, where the hell are you?" Bob shouted for his watch's leading engineman.

"Over here, Mr. H, I'm securing the induction valve."

"Good. Flege, where are you?" he yelled again.

"Down here trying to get to the fire, sir." Bob saw flames licking up from the lower level; probably the oil in the bilges.

"Get out of there, Flege—and be careful. There's electrical shorts sparking down there."

"I see them, sir. Both high pressure air compressors went."

"Okay, okay. Now get your ass out of there and now."

"On my way, sir," called Flege, and Bob saw his shadow through the smoke coming up the ladder from the lower level.

"Where the hell is Austin?" Bob shouted. Silence was his answer. "Bosetti, where is your wiper?"

"I sent him down below, sir, and ..."

"Austin, do you read me," Bob yelled again and again nothing.

"Oh, shit, I'm going down to get him. Chief, get me an OBA ready!" Bob started down the ladder when he felt a vise-like grip around his neck and was literally pulled right back to the upper level.

"You stay here, sir, and get that OBA. I'll get the little twerp!" Two hundred fifty pounds of muscle dropped into the lower level and disappeared in the smoke. (OBA is Oxygen Breathing Apparatus)

"Geezuz, Chief, be careful of those broken wires."

"You worry about getting me an OBA and I'll take care of me... sir." Bob found the OBA in the cabinet in the Engine Control Booth.

"Bosetti, get on an OBA and call for three more. Carlson, glad you're here. Get on an OBA and call for the doc." "Chief, how you doing? I've dropped the OBA at the bottom of the ladder. Have you found him yet?"

"Christ, sir. One question at a time. Fine, thanks, and not yet."

"Mr. H,, Conn wants to know if we should surface."

"Not yet. I think we can handle this. Tell Maneuvering to kill all power to the Engine Room except emergency lighting." "Chief, any luck yet?"

"No, sir."

"Try the forward starboard corner. The explosion may have scared the shit out of him and made him run for cover."

"I got him, I got him, sir. You're right. Coming right up. He's out, sir!"

"Roger, Chief. Bosetti called for a stretcher and a half a dozen more CO_2 bottles."

"Mr. H,, the doc's here."

"Doc, Doc, over here... that's it. Chief's coming up with him right now. He's out doc and I've called for a stretcher. Here's an oxygen bottle."

"Good, Mr. H. I'll go below and help the chief."

"No, no. You stay here. Chief Wright can handle it." There was a thud next to him. It was Austin, as the chief slung him up to the upper level like a sack of potatoes. The chief coughed badly and looked pale. "Chief, get your ass forward."

"I'm staying here, sir."

"Chief, god damn it, out of here and that's an order. I don't want you down, too. Beat it and now," Bob bellowed and he obeyed.

Carlson and Bosetti wore OBAs and went below to fight the fires. Doc got Austin on a stretcher and sent him into the After Battery. A firm hand grabbed Bob by the arm and twirled him around.

"Okay, Bob, good work. I'll take over now. You go forward and get some fresh air."

"But, XO..."

"Move it, Bob!"

Bob fell through the watertight door and felt sick even though he wore an OBA. The crew helped him into the crew's mess and laid him on a table. Doc pushed an oxygen mask into his face and he took in some of the good stuff. Then he heard, "Conn, Engine Room. XO reports the fire out. Requests we evacuate the Engine Room using number one engine, sir."[4]

Bob smiled. Horace was one hell of a sub sailor. He heard the engine start up and felt the vacuum suck all the smoke out of the boat through the snorkel exhaust mast.

They secured from Battle Stations. Bob was feeling much better and returned to the Engine Room to see the damage. The XO was still there and the CO had joined him. A quick glance around the lower level told the entire story. They had suffered an explosion in at least one high-pressure air compressor, and the hot high-pressure air turned the piping into wet noodles that whipped the lower level. The piping severed electrical cable runs in a number of places, which then arced and started the oil in the bilge on fire. A piece of piping severed the drain line, which placed the entire drain system out of commission. They could cross connect to the trim system and pump and trim forward, but not in the Engine Compartment or the Stern Room.

Instrumentation on the Control Panel in the Engine Room was out, but worst was the loss of high-pressure air. They lost some air from the accident, but Miller the AOW in Control, saw the problem and secured air from the high-pressure air flasks in the ballast tanks. His action saved *Growler* from losing all its air and not being able to blow ballast tanks or start the main engines. In summary, the battery was low and the air pressure was down to 2000 psi instead of 3000 psi with no way to replenish the air supply.

Hours later, *Growler* was relieved on station by *Halibut* and headed back toward Adak; maybe limped off station. The major problem was snorkeling for the snorkel valve opened and shut with air pressure. If they were ultra-conservative, they might have sufficient air to make it to Adak, but they would have to do an airless surface; running up to the surface as fast as possible, catching as much air in the tanks as possible, and then removing the remaining water with engine exhaust. The engineers set about the work of returning equipment to working order.

Between the remains of the two compressors, the enginemen found enough parts to make one complete compressor but the high-pressure air piping was totaled. A few minutes of submariner ingenuity solved the problem. The genius came from the missile techs. They had hundreds of feet of high-pressure aeroquip hose carried for emergency startups of the missiles. A few fittings here and there and the piping was replaced, with the head valve functional, as was #2 air compressor. However, the boat lost watertight integrity from the Engine Room to Control due to hoses running through WT doors. Snorkeling was conducted without loss of air pressure in the air flasks and the boat charged batteries.

The response by engineering personnel was typical of the men who wear dolphins. They did not consider themselves heroes but only submariners doing their job. If one wanted a hero, one only had to look at Bill Gunn on *Grayback*.

Grayback was enroute her 7th patrol between Pearl Harbor and Adak. As customary, she was snorkel transiting in a heavy sea when she suddenly took a very heavy roll to port. For some reason, the After Main Battery Circuit Breaker shorted out, spraying the After Battery with sparks. The circuit breaker was located amidst the crew's living quarters. A fire began near the breaker, which set up a barrier of sparks and fire between the fore and aft passageway through the compartment, and the alley of bunks to port in Hogan's Alley. Soon the space was filled with acrid and choking smoke generated by burning linoleum and mattresses. Captain Ekelund took the Conn and Bill ran to the scene of the fire. The smoke filled the living space so quickly, most men choked before realizing there was a fire.

When Bill arrived on scene the space was devoid of the crew, but filled with dense smoke. The door between the living space and the mess deck was shut. Bill heard someone banging on the other side of the bulkhead and muffled voices yelling. He opened the fire door, and with two crew members, entered the living space to look for shipmates. During the emergency, the CO secured snorkeling and evacuated the Engine Room. EN1 Valpoon was back in Maneuvering and volunteered to go back into the Engine Room, start an engine, and begin emergency ventilation procedures.

Bill went into the space without an OBA and found burning mattresses and bedding. *Grayback* surfaced, and Bill received permission to open the After Battery hatch to get rid of smoldering bedding. Several men were helped to safety, but one young Seamen, James Jenson, was too frightened to pass the arcing breaker and crawled under his covers to seek safety. By the time Jensen was found, he was out cold. Every effort was made to resuscitate the young man but all efforts failed. Bill and his two shipmates were almost overcome by the smoke themselves and had to be helped by the corpsman. That is heroism. Seaman Jenson was the only Regulus Missile Program fatality.[5]

Grayback reported her predicament to ComSubPac, who in turn ordered her back to Pearl for repairs. In two weeks, she was underway to relieve *Tunny*. It was not her last battery problem. *Grayback* received a new battery following her 7th patrol. Shortly after arriving on station they experienced a small explosion in the Forward Battery. Bill Gunn reported the problem to Captain Ekelund and, as they spoke in the CO's stateroom, a larger explosion took place directly under the CO's bunk. The problem occurred during a battery charge that was secured.

The CO went to Control and Bill to the scene of the explosion, which was directly below him. He found fires throughout the battery well where the wooden wedges, which separate the individual cells, caught fire. Two officers accompanied Bill into the battery well with fire extinguishers and put out the fires. This act was pure bravery, as one must crawl on top of battery cells with only a foot and a half of clearance above the cells to the overhead. They found the battery cell cooling system fouled, which had formed ground paths, which in turn had ignited fires as the cells overheated. The boat moved to the eastern border of the patrol area and effected repairs.[6]

On *Growler*, EM1(SS) Ed Bell was taking battery gravities and discovered a dozen more cells shorted out. He bypassed the cells, which reduced the battery capacity and DC voltage. *Growler* was slowly crumbling around herself as her few but difficult years took their toll. The good news was that Austin was fine after a couple days rest.

Departure from station and return to Adak was a Godsend as the crew was exhausted, physically and mentally. The engineers took a beating the entire trip as they repaired or restored one piece of equipment after another, yet stood their watches. One night transiting back to Adak, Bob had the Conn and waltzed Matilda. He recalled all that his department had accomplished, repaired or replaced during the course of the patrol. His men had accomplished a mission impossible in the past months and tears welled in his eyes—damned but if he wasn't proud of them.

Growler pulled into Adak on another windy and freezing morning. When they pulled alongside the fuel pier, a messenger from the ComSta (Communications Station) requested Bob send engineering logs to the facilities. It was a strange request, but he was not one to reject the request of a Captain. Captain Bob thought it strange as well, but told Bob to send the logs with a messenger. The SOSUS[7] Facility desired to compare the engineering activities with what they had observed. The system worked uncannily well.

Only a small liberty party went ashore, for there was much work to be done. When a submariner has work to do, nothing can deter him from his given task. Ensign McCoy went over to the Chief's Club with a couple of the chiefs and no elaboration is needed on what followed. The crew struggled with repairs to insure *Growler* could make it home. There was little Adak could do to resurrect their centerline engine or revive the many battery cells. They did manage to improve the jury rig (temporary repair) on the high-pressure air system, and took on fresh food and lots of fuel oil.

Jim was on the same routine most new officers were given, with the primary duty being to qualify in submarines. He had worked hard all patrol, and in Adak he was rewarded with liberty that transcended into going to the CPO Club with *Growler*'s chiefs.

On the way out, Bob had the Conn on the bridge, and this time the CO agreed to take the narrow passage between Adak and Kagalaska Island, saving them a half day, rather than going around Adak Island. Kagalaska Strait was narrow, with the narrowest section at Galas Point, which is only a few hundred yards wide.

In the early hours of the morning, *Growler* got underway. The wind was strong, but they got off the pier and the big lumbering bow through the wind. As *Growler* cleared the protected harbor, she pitched into a heavy northerly swell. They came right and headed for the passage a few miles away. The XO and Bill navigated below.

It looked as if he was driving *Growler* into a cliff, but there was an opening. The passage reminded him of the narrow stone canyons in Lake Powell National Park as they steamed between sheer walls of rock. Horace and Pecos did a brilliant job of navigating down the straits, which was difficult at best during the pre-dawn darkness. Bob looked aft and noticed the wake reflecting back into the strait. At times he thought the reflected wake might catch up with them as *Growler* slowly plowed southward between the islands. There were no buoys to guide her passage, but the course was clear once inside the strait. For two hours *Growler* ran the passage and the crew felt insignificant as they looked up at the walls of rock. They popped out the south end of the strait and back into the Pacific Ocean. The sun came out, though still very low on the horizon. A slight adjustment and *Growler* was on course for Oahu.

South of the Aleutians, they were in a quartering sea, giving *Growler* a movement of both yawing and rolling. Jim was to relieve Bob as the OOD, but when

Bob saw his face he knew the officer was sick. It was windy, rough, and he could see the green reflecting off his face as emerged from the upper hatch.

"Good morning, Bob. Mr. McCoy ready to relieve you, sir!"

"Are you okay?"

"Yes, sir."

"You're not sick and have your foul weather gear?"

"Yes, Sir."

"Jim, talk to me. You sure you're okay?"

"Damn it, Bob, I'm fine, okay?"

"Okay." So Bob briefed him.

Suddenly, Jim said, "Excuse me," and went to the port side of the bridge acting sick.

"No, Jim, don't blow it on the windward side…" Bob was too late as Jim heaved his bloody guts out to port into the icy wind. The port lookout was behind Jim, mouth open gasping for air in the icy temperature. The barf went out to port, hung in the wind, and returned to the bridge and into the port lookout's open mouth.

"Oh, shit, why did you do that, Jim?"

Jim heard nothing except his stomach roar. The port lookout doubled up and retched uncontrollably and the starboard lookout saw and heard the port lookout and followed suit. Bob organized them to heave over the starboard, or lee side, as his own gut pulsated with the very thought of what he witnessed.

"Oh, this is just great," Bob yelled to no one in particular. "Control, Bridge. Send up a couple of men to take my lookouts and Mr. McCoy below who are ill."

The sick men went below and told the story of what had transpired, who told more people, and in minutes, the entire ship was sick. Booze, a pitching boat, and the vile story of what happened to the lookout made every single man aboard sick. Bob had no lookouts as he struggled desperately to regain control of his own stomach. With his lookouts below, Bob heaved far over the side.

"Bridge, ECM. APS-20 airborne radar contact deep on the starboard quarter. Signal strength one, sir." This was a low signal strength.

"Thank you, Chief. It must be our aviators. Keep an eye on them and keep me informed." The new lookouts arrived and he briefed them, including the ECM contact.

"Bridge, ECM. Bearing is constant and signal strength increased to two, sir."

"Aye, aye, Chief Ekenberg. Please inform the Captain of the ECM contact."

They didn't use wind adjusted temperatures but they steamed into a 40 knot wind, gusting to 50 knots or more and the temperature was +10° F. *Growler* hadn't harassed the airedales this trip, but the pilots had not forgotten the embarrassments of the past. *Growler* was to be introduced to Radar Power Programming.

The aircraft reduced power output of his radar to the point where they barely saw the target on every 6–12 sweeps. On *Growler*, no one was alarmed, for the signal strength deemed to be a far away radar in the direction of Adak. ECM made two more reports with signal strength two so Bob didn't dive. When the aircraft was a mile astern, he throttled back and glided down toward *Growler*.

"Holy shit," Bob screamed. He was illuminated by umpteen million watts of light. It was gray and overcast, so the aircraft's lights lit up *Growler* like Lambeau Field with Dallas in town. "Aircraft on top, dive dive," Bob yelled and headed down the tube. When he landed in Control, the CO looked at him.

"Sir, they nailed us. ECM never reported a signal strength over two. We never saw a thing, and then whaam, we got our picture taken."

"It's called power programming, Bob. They just evened the score on us. Aw hell, Bob, they're on our side, so we ought to let them get a point or two once in a while."

On 4 November 1961, *Tunny* returned to the patrol area on the second leg of a back-to-back deployment. She transited on the surface when caught by U.S. patrol aircraft, a P2V. They transited in a "moving haven," but were not *in* the haven.[8] Instead, Captain Stahl moved faster to accommodate any delay and, as a result, the P2V report was considered to be a Soviet submarine near *Tunny's* area. *Tunny* could not respond due to radio silence to explain her position, so the sighting caused a great deal of confusion for everyone. It was simpler not to be detected.

Growler ran east and returned to periscope depth. It was clear. The aircraft scored and went home to tell their mates how they caught *Growler* on the surface. They snorkeled the next two days and then surfaced. Snorkeling with the make shift piping was an emergency measure to get them out of the enemy's backyard but not worth gambling the welfare of the ship's crew.

Pecos calculated they were well ahead of schedule so the CO followed past procedure. The newest officers conducted "man overboard" drills on fishing balls. Bob spotted a buoy where no buoy belonged.

"Send Mr. McCoy to the bridge for a man overboard drill," Bob ordered.

A few minutes later, Jim arrived on the bridge and Bob pointed out the buoy to him. "I'm going to let you pick it up, Jim, but it's my buoy, you savvy?"

Jim maneuvered the boat and a couple seamen recovered the buoy. "On deck, put the buoy in my stateroom. The next two balls to you guys. Thanks for the help."

After watch, he examined the buoy and decided it was a net marker that broke loose. It was made of solid brass and copper, so Bob passed the remainder of his leisure time to Pearl, limited as it was, cleaning and polishing the buoy. He used all the Brasso on the boat before finishing. It was beautiful.

The CO saw it, "Gee, Bob, that'll look nice on my bar. Thanks."

"HMMMRFF, sir!" The buoy remains on the CO's bar to this day over fifty years later.

Chapter Sixteen
Regulus Ends with a Well Done

The remainder of the transit was uneventful. The officers and chiefs readied for the shipyard and repairs. Paperwork was filled out by the reams. *Growler* was scheduled for a major upkeep period and every crew member longed for a new battery. The electricians were exhausted from taking specific gravity readings continually, watching each cell, and nursing them to perform beyond the warranty. The enginemen were spent, and used the last days of the transit resting from their ordeal. Most engineering department equipment was to be replaced or overhauled. Topside, things were a mess from the beating in ice country and the casualty list continued.

Growler returned to Pearl and the ritual replayed.

"Good morning, Bob, welcome home."

"Thank you, Admiral Fluckey. Believe me, we are happy to be back!"

"Where's your Engineer, Bob, I don't see him?"

"He's in Maneuvering, sir, would you like to see him?"

"Nah, I wanted to show him this glossy. He takes a nice picture with his mouth wide open, doesn't he?"

"Ho, ho, oh my, is that a gem. That's the morning he got caught by the P3V out of Adak. Admiral, may I have this to present at quarters some morning?"

"Its yours, Bob. I would love to see his face when he eyeballs the picture."

There were hula girls, the Navy band, dignitaries, the "well dones," and their families. Everyone smiled, laughed, enjoyed their children and hugged their wives, but something was different this time. To a man, they were physically and mentally drained. Every man had given his all on the patrol and they were exhausted. There was no Bellows Beach cottage, and the men only wanted a good shower, a hot dinner, a few drinks, make love, and sleep, and then to sleep some more. For a week, that's all they accomplished other than watch standing every few days.

Growler anticipated major work in the yard. The most important item was the battery and SubPac had the battery replacement at the dry dock. There was no replacement engine, which meant rebuilding #2 engine. Unbeknownst to *Growler*, Commodore Lou Neeb devised a plan to save ComSubPac and CinCPacFlt money by not installing a new battery when *Growler* needed it prior to the past patrol. The new Polaris submarines were to replace the SSGs before a battery replacement was absolutely mandatory. But the SSBN schedule slipped and no money was forthcoming for a *Growler* battery at the time.[9]

Growler cracked the outer lens on #1 periscope and #2 was due for a routine overhaul. The CO felt they struck ice. It wasn't a first for Regulus or *Growler*. Both periscopes were pulled for work in the periscope shop.

On Sunday, Bob and family attended mass at the Sub Base Chapel and after the services, a young and modern day Chaplain held a blessing of vehicles.

"We bless everything in our lives and we spend a lot of time in our vehicles so it is logical we bless them."

After Mass, the congregation lined up in their vehicles near the chapel and one by one, the cars were blessed. When it was Bob's turn, the chaplain sprayed holy water on the windshields, "*In nomine Patris, et Filii, et Spiritus Sancti,*" he prayed.

Bob turned on the window wipers to clear the glass.

"Damn it, Bob, you don't respect anything," hissed his wife.

"Hell, I thought it would be funny... and looking at our padre, he thought so too." The chaplain was doubled up with laughter.

The day after returning to Pearl, the CO made a verbal patrol report to Admiral Fluckey, supplementing his written report. Admiral Fluckey asked about the weather.

"Well, sir, it was normal for late summer and fall. Snorkeling was difficult, which could have been mitigated with a decent battery."

"Don't be political with me, Bob! Was your weather extremely severe and worse than usual? I know fall and winter weather up there can be grim."

"As I said, Admiral, it was tough but not worse than previous trips. Why the concern about the weather admiral?"

"The USS *Crab*[10] was north of you, as you are aware. The weather was so extreme for *CRAB*, they pulled off station to save themselves from severe damage." Captain Bob was caught between reporting the truth and getting another skipper in trouble, or at least, in doubt.

"Admiral, the weather was bad and our area is unpredictable from one day to the next. There is no way one can accurately compare weather at our location and a point 100 miles north. Remember, sir, Regulus submarines have operated in that neck of the woods for years and are accustomed to extreme weather conditions. It may be more difficult for a boat not used to severe weather and a crew not trained for rough seas."

"A nice diplomatic statement, Bob. I get your point. Thank you."[11]

The following Monday was work as usual and housekeeping was scheduled. A new crew member was cleaning in Control, including scrubbing the conning stand overhead. Unable to reach the overhead, he stepped onto #1 periscope yoke since the periscope was removed for repair. A snorkeling submarine left oily deposits everywhere, including the overhead. He scrubbed the paint work. Suddenly, he slipped and reached to steady himself. He grabbed the hydraulic hoist lever that was tagged Do NOT TOUCH, as were the hydraulic stop valves to the lever. Unfortunately, the stop valve leaked a bit and when the kid grabbed the lever, he pushed it to the raise position. Fifteen hundred pounds of hydraulic pressure raised the yoke into the overhead, with the kid atop the yoke.

A blood curdling scream was followed by silence as his body squashed into a void about 2 feet cubed. The pressure in the system was expended and the yoke could not be lowered. It took the enginemen ten minutes to bleed off the system and lower the yoke. The ambulance was on the pier, and corpsmen were in Control, when they finally lowered him. He could not be moved, as every bone in his body was broken. They finally carried him out in a bag in the crushed position and rushed him to Tripler Army Hospital. He was a new kid, but he was a *Growler* sailor and the crew was stunned. The Army doctors performed miracles and he survived and walked again, but was no longer physically qualified to be in the Navy.

The air compressors went to the shipyard for overhaul, as did the distillers and dozens of other equipments. When Bob looked over the damage caused by the explosion, he said a prayer of thanks that none of his men were hurt or killed.

Despite a dim view of shipyards, the yard at Pearl Harbor performed miracles in repairing the broken equipment. Within a month, *Growler* was back in commission except for the centerline engine and the battery replacement. Replacing a battery is a major job and requires cutting open the hull fore and aft, as well as taking up the main deck level below decks.

Duane "Hotdog" Heatwole received orders to *Blueback*. Food would never be the same again. The remaining cook was Whittington, a huge and wonderful first class petty officer. One night Bob and Whittingham were on duty together and brought their wives and children to the boat for supper. Bob was in the wardroom when Whittingham came through the boat with his wife and daughter. By chance, Whittingham was black and as they passed the wardroom, they exchanged pleasantries. Then Bob's young son Michael piped up, "Gee, Dad, look at the chocolate girl."

Bob was embarrassed but Whittingham and his wife understood and had a good laugh.

205

"My God, if only mankind could look at each other as submariners look at each other, there would never be a mention of color or culture next to one's name." In that light, racial prejudice was basically non-existent in the Submarine Force.

Men from PHNSY Paint Shop talked with Stu and Perry. They had attended a paint school and learned about space age paint technology. They came to assist the boat with repainting the front of the sail following a Regulus missile launch. *Growler* was coated in a vinyl paint and the jet blast burned the paint off the front of the sail aided by the blast of the JATO bottles. Following a launch, a seamen went topside to wire brush the sail and repaint it with primer and black vinyl. The effort took one hour. The shipyard encouraged *Growler* to try the paint approved for space capsules.

Perry prepared for the painting. The sail was sanded until it looked like a mirror. The shipyard placed a base paint down, followed by multiple coats of the space age wonder. Thickness tests were taken between coats and finally the task was completed. It looked very nice but the proof would be the next launch.

A destroyer was scheduled for a Dependents Cruise coincident with a *Growler* missile launch. The two commodores worked out a deal where the destroyer carried the *Growler* dependents as well as their own dependents. In return, *Growler* put on a show for the dependents. It worked well and the submarine wives finally saw what their husbands did for a living. It was a perfect launch.

When *Growler* returned to port, the shipyard people awaited to see how the paint experiment turned out. The paint that protected returning space capsules did not withstand the heat and energy of a Regulus launch. Instead of peeled paint and powder rust, they faced "clinkers" of molten something clinging to the front of the sail. It took two days to grind down the mess. When asked by the shipyard to try something else, Perry politely declined.

There was always an argument available when the accuracy of the Regulus Missile was discussed. The warhead was so big that the missile only needed to be in the vicinity to obtain positive results. However, one day, *Tunny* decided to fire a missile and measure the accuracy by dumping the bird on a target rock. Most submariners remember the rock used to fire live torpedoes and everyone has a picture of their boat observing an explosion on the rock through the periscope. They modified a "red bird" as a "blue bird" to explode on the rock. The chase aircraft followed the missile from launch and watched as it nosed over and headed for the rock.

The conversation with the aircraft went something like, "Rock is in sight and Goldy is disabled. I have pulsed smoke from the missile and we are approaching the rock... steady smoke now as missile heading for the rock... missile just went into terminal dive toward the rock!!... still in dive coming up on the rock!!!... It's headed straight for the rock!!!!... It's going to hit it!!!!!... It's going to hit it!!!!!!...

Damn, it missed it." Then in a very low and distraught voice, "but it splashed it."

Plans for the battery replacement were at hand and an abbreviated yard period was scheduled to accomplish the work. On a Tuesday morning, the officers were in the wardroom enjoying coffee and going over work schedules for the day. There was a knock at the wardroom and the messenger of the watch entered.

"Captain, you are requested to report to the Admiral's office as soon as convenient, sir." The CO looked to see "Sweet Pea," the duty messenger and mess cook.

"Thank you, Noon. Wonder what's up today. Take charge XO and try to finalize the plans for the yard this morning."

The CO reached topside and heard, "Bong bong, bong bong. *Grayback* departing." He stepped on the gangway and noticed Bill Gunn stepping onto the pier.

"Bong bong, bong bong. *Growler* departing."

"Hey there, old man. Where you headed for?"

"I just got called up to see the Admiral," replied Captain Bob.

"Oh, shit, so did I. Wonder what's on his mind this time."

"I heard he was going to override the DivCom and let *Growler* go on patrol instead of you derelicts," responded Captain Bob.

"Damn, Bob, you never give up. The DivCom said the first one ready to go will get the next patrol. We beat you fair and square. Shit, what would you use for a battery anyway, a flashlight?" They strode down the pier, side by side and in step. Captain Bob suddenly gave Bill a shove toward the water in jest.

"Hey, when's the last time you went swimming?"

"Look out, oh damn it, there goes my hat. How the hell can I see the Admiral without a hat?"

CO Bob was roaring with laughter, "Put a handkerchief on your bald spot and pretend you're at mass!" laughed Captain Bob, his belly shaking as he laughed.

"Man, that was a new hat, Bob."

"Bullshit. You don't own anything new."

Minutes later at headquarters, "*Growler* and *Grayback* to see you, Admiral."

"Good. Send them in." Admiral Fluckey rose from his leather chair and walked to the door, hand extended. "Bob, Bill. Please come in."

"Good morning, Admiral," chimed the two skippers.

"Good morning, gentlemen, how goes it?"

"Just fine," piped Bill with a smile.

"Give me the battery, Admiral, and we'll be on our way," retorted Bob.

"Well, Gentlemen, I have some big news for you, but I don't think you're going to like it," spoke the Admiral gently. Both skippers' butts puckered and they waited. "Gentlemen, you are both to cease all refit and repair activities immediately. Every requisition from your boats will have to be approved by the DivCom.

Men, I am sorry but the Regulus Program is over."

The captains were stunned. They knew the day was coming but were not ready to accept the word.

"I know how terrible you must feel but we must face it... Polaris is the game of the future. Please pick up a copy of a message I will release shortly from my aide," added Admiral Fluckey. "I will work on doing the best I can in reassigning your officers and men. That is all."

The CO returned to the ship and mustered the officers in the wardroom.

"Men, the first Polaris boat is on her way here from Cape Canaveral. She will end the Regulus Missile Program. The bank account of the Regulus just went from gold to shit. There will be no more requisitions of any kind without DivCom approval." Silence greeted his announcement.

Finally, "What does it mean, Captain?"

"Let me read you a message the Admiral sent to the Submarine Force:

1. THIS DATE MARKS THE CLOSE OF THE REGULUS CAPABILITY IN SUBPAC. FOR SIX YEARS DEDICATED MEN OF SUBPAC HAVE BEEN ON STATION UNDER THE MOST ARDUOUS CONDITIONS. OUR NATION'S REQUIREMENTS DICTATED A TEMPO OF OPERATIONS FOR THE SSG'S/SSGN SURPASSING EVERY OTHER TYPE OF SHIP IN THE FLEET. SOME DAY IN THE FUTURE, WHEN THE ENTIRE SUBMARINE GUIDED MISSILE STORY CAN BE FULLY TOLD, YOU WILL RECEIVE OUR COUNTRY'S APPRE- CIATION FOR MAINTAINING A DETERRENT DURING THE YEARS WHEN YOU, AND YOU ALONE, KEPT YOUR WARHEADS WITHIN MINUTES OF THEIR TARGETS. THE OUTSTANDING SUPPORT FROM GMU-10 MADE IT POSSIBLE THAT WAR READY MIS- SILES WERE ABOARD EACH DEPLOYING SUBMARINE. WHENEVER SUBMARINERS OF TUNNY, BARBERO, GRAYBACK, GROWLER AND HALIBUT MEET IN THE FUTURE THEY WILL SHARE A COMMON GLORY IN THEIR KNOWLEDGE THAT THEY UNDER- TOOK THE MOST DIFFICULT AND CHALLENGING OF TASKS AND SAW IT TO ITS SUC- CESSFUL COMPLETION. TO THE PRESENT AND PAST CREWS OF THESE OUTSTAND- ING SUBPAC UNITS I EXTEND MY SINCEREST CONGRATULATIONS ON A JOB WELL DONE. RADM E.B. FLUCKEY.

2. COMMANDERS AND COMMANDING OFFICERS ARE REQUESTED TO PASS TO ALL WITHIN THEIR COMMANDS WHO WERE A PART OF THE SUBMARINE GUIDED MISSILE PROGRAM. (Hopefully, this book fulfills at least the telling part of the story)

DTG: UNCLASS

"I feel proud alright, and I think we all deserve to be proud of what *Growler* accomplished. But where does that leave us as far as our future?"

"Well, men, the Admiral said all officers will receive priority assignments. You will be able to pick your next assignment, at least by port. The same is true of the men as far as BuPers (Bureau of Naval Personnel) can handle it."

"Captain, is the Regulus Missile Program going down or just the submarine portion of it?"

"Perry, I'm not sure, but we must understand anything Regulus is being replaced by Polaris, which is a far superior weapons system and will be carried by an all nuclear submarine force. No matter how you cut it, we must admit we are being replaced by a better system. It's just life men, just life. Everything eventually is replaced by a better model. You should concentrate on two things: one be proud of the job we did, and two, think about your next career step."

"Will any of us be making another Regulus patrol, Captain?"

"The way it looks right now, *Tunny* and *Barbero* are on station and will be relieved by *Halibut. Growler* and *Grayback* will return to CONUS (Continental United States) soon for decommissioning. We will not make another patrol."

The officers started talking and speaking their minds and guts.

"Gentlemen, it's time to go to the Club. I'm buying the first round," spoke Horace. To the club they went, and in minutes the wardroom of *Grayback* joined them. Soon the dice were rolling and the liars were buying.

Word came from SubPac that *Growler* was to depart Pearl for Mare Island in a few months. Anything of value to SubPac for other submarines in Pearl was to be left behind. Each man received word from their personnel detailer and found out their next duty station. Bob would go to USS *Catfish* (SS-339) in San Diego. The CO had orders to SubPac staff, and the other officers were ordered to submarines in Hawaii. The XO organized the decommissioning of *Growler* and Bob was assigned the chore as the decommissioning officer. As Engineer and qualified in *Growler*, it was logical for Bob to put her to rest. The planning seemed like a dream no one wanted to accept; their boat was to be decommissioned!

"Pecos" Moore completed requirements for Qualification. Perry qualified, but had not yet had the opportunity to "drink for his dolphins." In days past, this tradition was appropriate but on *Growler*, the party was kept "reasonable." The CO held a wardroom party, which served as the officers last get together, and the night Perry and Pecos drank for their dolphins. It was a sad party in some respects, for it was the last party together as a *Growler* family. Stu and Perry removed the firing panel from the Regulus launch board and gave it to the CO as a memento of the Regulus Missile Program. He loved it. The Captain went through the launch sequence and when the fuel system was pressurized, a spray of water streamed out the front of the panel at the CO's fly. When the firing button was pushed, a flash bulb went off. But Bob kept looking at the Captain's bar and the flashing light on "his" buoy.

Grayback had similar plans for Bill Gunn and celebration of qualifications of their last officers. However, the present they gave Bill was quite different. They removed a stainless steel commode and polished it beautifully. They put chromed hooks around the lip to hold sterling silver cups. Each cup, much like a champagne cup, was engraved with each officer's name. The cups were reasonable but to give your Captain a toilet pushed it a bit. However, the idea was perfect for Captain Bill, since he still was a "wild and crazy guy", and recall the commode was chromed.

Bob's family returned to the States and he moved aboard *Growler*. He still owned the VW Bug and hadn't decided what to do with it. The CO came up with an ingenious idea. While they were at Mare Island, they would need wheels. Why not put the bug in a hangar and take it with them? No sooner said than done. Within the hour, the 1962 Volkswagen sat snug as a bug in a rug in the port hangar.

Bob was the only officer who wouldn't continue duty in Hawaii, so he stood watches for his fellow officers, allowing them to remain with their families during the last few weeks. His family departed a week earlier for San Diego. It wasn't all one way, for the other officers took his watches the last few weeks his family was in Pearl. Only those who have experienced the jolt of being told "their" boat was to be decommissioned can appreciate the emotion of the experience. *Growler* and *Grayback* were only six years old. Beaten to death by severe operating conditions and schedules, they were still young at heart, as were the crews. No one had previous experience of decommissioning duty, so no one was sure how long they would be at Mare Island.

The final day arrived and it was time for *Growler* to depart. A real "blue" Regulus was on the pier with *Grayback* and *Growler* on opposite sides. The band played and accolades were spoken about the accomplishments by the Regulus Submarine Force. Then it was time to leave and everyone will recall, oh so vividly, the departure. The CO drove her one last time out of Pearl. They cast off and all the ships in Pearl Harbor blew whistles as a final salute to *Grayback* and *Growler*. Two Regulus Sub Crews "manned the rail" as the boats got underway and slowly each man's starched whites showed stains as tears fell on their ribbons and dolphins. *Grayback* got underway on her battery since her mufflers were missing and she sounded like a super loud Harley Davidson.

The two submarines stood out to sea and as they passed Pearl Harbor Control, they actually told the truth. They were bound for San Francisco. They passed "PH" for the last time and the regular underway watch was set and Bob was on the bridge. A change of uniforms to the underway section but a new patch appeared on the foul weather jackets. The patch had been around for a while but someone bought enough for the entire crew. Those boats, which had suffered the pains and discomfort of the Northern Pacific, were entitled to wear the "North Pacific Yacht Club" patch whether on the Regulus boats or attack boats.

210

"Left full rudder. Steady on course one one zero."

As the two boats passed Diamond Head, both boats lost engines; the pride of the Regulus Submarine Force were on the battery and trying to get an engine on line. The crews were topside to watch a picture no one forgot. Two war horses limped along with the outline of Oahu barely visible in the setting sun. Both boats got their engines on line and slowly made their way eastward. Bob stood watches coincident with Lieutenant John Anderson on *Grayback*. They were friends on destroyers and they passed the night watches talking by blinking light. The voyage was a carefree thing and the boats stopped for swim calls and even exchanged movies.

Shortly after the first of the year, ETN3 Bill Russell came aboard on permanent duty assignment. He was an expert in electronic navigation but *Growler* was his first submarine. He worked like hell on his qualification card, but there were some things he could only accomplish at sea. The only sea time he had was when the boat went out to watch *Grayback* render a missile into the deep. During the transit to Mare Island, he urgently tried to complete his qualification, but there were no longer some needed opportunities to accomplish the feat. On arrival at Mare Island, he was transferred to the Halibut, where he finished his at sea qualifications and proudly donned the silver dolphins. He was presented his dolphins personally by Admiral Eugene B. Fluckey, ComSubPac.

The movie exchange was conducted by Gordo one sunny afternoon in a life raft. He exchanged the films successfully and both *Grayback* and *Growler* were entertained by terrible movies. The crew of both boats were topside to witness the exchange. Larry "Sweet Pea" Noon and Gordo paddled more circles than the waves in the sea, but after a couple hours, completed their mission successfully.

The crews made use of the time to work with the remaining unqualified members. They worked hard to complete the qualification process, but cut no corners; they just made opportunities available.

Midway to San Francisco, the boats received a Flash message about the 1964 Alaska earthquake, warning them of a potential Tsunami. They would meet the tidal wave on the current mid-watch. Anderson and Bob rode the tidal wave and talked via light. It was no higher than other swells, but its period was extremely long. The tsunami wave likely would not have been noticed had they not been alerted to its arrival. In deep water, a tsunami wave is no threat. It's when it arrives in shallow water that all hell breaks loose.

A crew member on *Growler*, Keith Toms, had an appendicitis attack and was transferred to a Military Sealift Command vessel bound for Honolulu that happened to be near by. It was the same ship Bob and family rode to Oahu three years earlier. With the submariner safely aboard, *Grayback* and *Growler* resumed the transit to California.

On the troopship, the Navy doctor opened up Toms and said, "Oh, no."

He sewed Toms back up with a drain line coming out of his abdomen. The ship had a devil of time getting used to Toms and his uniform smell. When they reached Honolulu he was transferred to Tripler Army Hospital, where he recovered completely.[12]

The crews were acclimated to the warm Hawaii temperatures, so the cool and damp morning weather of the bay area cut through them like a steak knife in warm butter. They picked up the bar pilot and waited. Neither *Growler* nor *Grayback* had sufficient power to fight the maximum ebb tidal current under the Golden Gate Bridge. As they passed under the landmark, everyone experienced mixed emotions. Bob reflected on the day his family passed under the same bridge, but westbound. It seemed so many years ago. My God, how fulfilling the *Growler* experience had been.

They passed Alcatraz Island, picked up the next pilot, and headed for Mare Island. A few people ashore and on bridges waved and displayed welcome signs to the boats as they worked their way upstream.

"My god, we have fans everywhere," Captain Bob shouted.

They arrived at Mare Island and berthed at a pier in the Reserve Fleet area. There were no bands, no dancing or hula girls. The local Submarine Group Commander, Commander Joe McGreivy, met the boats, spoke great words to the crews, welcomed them, and invited them to a party.

They prepared a small party for both crews, consisting of sandwiches and beer. They meant well, but their assets were nil. The submariners partied for a few hours with the locals, and then the locals left. It was time to get serious. The men had completed their last ride on *Growler* and *Grayback*; they were not a happy lot.

"Get out the torpedo juice," ordered one chief, and 100% pure grain alcohol arrived and was mixed with V-8 juice. It tasted horrible, but they drank it to drown their sorrows. A couple hours later, the entire group of officers, still dressed in wash khakis and foul weather jackets, visited downtown San Francisco en mass, including the Hotel St. Francis. They received an escorted exit when they weren't considered friends of the bride at a wedding reception. Likely, Bill Gunn's Scottish beret was a clue.

During the evening, the officers ended up in a bar with telephones at every seat. It provided the customers opportunities to talk with other customers without embarrassment. Bob sat on a couch between Pecos and Bill Gunn. Bill called Pecos on the telephone and spoke in a most provocative feminine voice, pretending to be a blonde at the bar. Bill led Pecos on and Bob struggled mightily not to bust in laughter. Bill invited Pecos to the bar,

"Come up here, baby, and kiss me in my ear and we'll see where we go from here." Pecos headed for the blonde at the bar. He came up behind her and gently kissed her in the ear.

"What the hell are you doing," the blonde screamed and smacked Pecos across the running lights with her purse. Pecos fell backwards and ended up looking up at Bill and Bob. It was difficult to keep from wetting one's pants in laughter.

Never before had a warship been placed out of commission with more tender and loving care than was *Growler*. The remaining crew was convinced *Growler* would reappear on the active duty list. Every equipment and module was carefully wrapped and stored. Bob made a log for the recommissioning officer to use as a check off sheet. Every nut and bolt askew was documented. As time passed, the crew and officers slowly were ordered off the boat to, hopefully, bigger and better submarines. But before the wardroom broke up, they made one last trip.

Wayne and Helen Mehl arranged a last get-together for the wardroom. The place was Bodega Bay (the site of Hitchcock's movie *The Birds*). They piled into a small waterfront cottage with plenty of bunk beds, arriving late on a Friday. They sat around a fireplace all night and talked about days and nights now history. Saturday morning, they went to the bay, took a boat to the mud flats, and went clamming. Most of the officers had never clammed before, but despite the cold, wet, and black mud, they caught lots of clams. Helen made clam chowder in a huge cast iron caldron hung in the fireplace, which they filled with clam meat and vegetables. It was the best clam chowder, and by midnight the kettle was empty. Again, they spent the evening and well into the early morning hours reminiscing about happier days on *Growler*. One of Bob's last and most vivid memories of *Growler* was the night they sat around the flickering fire, sipping wine, eating chowder, and occasionally hugging each other. It was their last night together.

The following weeks were difficult and working days. The physical effort was huge if the job was to be done correctly and it was difficult putting a warrior to sleep, piece by piece. It was painful to watch as they rendered the lady into a floating mothball.

Grayback was preserved on blocks on board a reserve ARD (floating dry dock). Possibly the lack of corrosion by being in the water and her new battery was the difference in the Navy's decision to recommission *Grayback vice Growler*. *Growler's* battery cells were pumped dry of electrolyte and left dry. Placing an out of commission submarine on blocks in an out of commission floating dry dock almost ended in disaster. A problem with a trim tank caused the ARD to tilt precariously close to tumbling *Grayback* off her blocks.

Each day, the submarine became more quiet and inert. Deck tiles were lifted and insulation removed as the boat took on the sound and sense of a tomb. Bob woke every morning in his bunk of four patrols and bounced out ready to start a new day. Then reality registered and his morale sank to the deck plates. He filled his locker with logs and records, along with pre-commissioning check off sheets that he left for the recommissioning party.

Then the day arrived. It was decommissioning day and Bob was the only officer left. He and a handful of enlisted fell in at quarters aft of the sail for the event. There was no band or anyone to tell them how wonderful they had been. The Submarine Group sent a boatswains mate to pipe for them, but Bob sent him back. This was an event to be handled by *Growler* personnel only.

Bob whistled the bosun pipe call and tearfully removed the commissioning pennant from the pig stick. They faced aft and whistled the pipe call again as they lowered the Ensign for the last time. Bob sent the Ensign (American flag) to Captain Bob and the pennant to Horace. *Growler* was now in the history books. Bob went below for one last walk through "my" boat. Each step brought a series of memories and he found himself sobbing out of control. The decks and the bulkheads cried out to him with sounds of the past and the pain of being decommissioned.

He went topside and stopped at the base of the gangway. He turned. There was no flag and no watch, but he saluted anyway. He was crying again, but he really didn't care. On the pier were the last few crew members. They saluted him as he came off the gangway and he proudly returned their salutes for one last time.

"Thanks for everything, men. God bless and I hope your next boat is...

"Goodbye, Mr. H., and good luck."

Captain Gilmore of the original Growler was proud.

DBF! (Diesel Boats Forever)

THE END

Growler was decommissioned on 25 May 1964 and later placed into the Inactive Reserve Fleet in Puget Sound Naval Shipyard in Washington. In 1989, twenty-five years later, she was designated as a financial burden and listed as a target for nuclear submarines. The tests of a new torpedo were not conducted and Zachary Fischer managed to convince Congress on 8 August 1988 to assign *Growler* to the Intrepid Sea Air Space Museum in New York City. She departed Puget Sound under tow in 1989 and began her 6,000 mile trip to New York. It was the longest trip for any decommissioned vessel in the United States.

Following some modifications and repairs in Florida in a shipyard owned by George Steinbrenner of New York Yankee fame, she came to rest at the north side of Pier #86, Hudson River in New York on 18 April 1989. She was re-christened on 26 May 1989 with former COB Tom Stebbins, Captain Charles Priest, and Mrs. Zachary Fisher doing the honors.

Footnotes
Chapter One

1. Merrill, Grayson, Capt, USN(Ret), known as the "Father of Point Mugu."

2. Merrill, *ibid.* Numerous emails and telcons. *Conger Eel,* August 2000.

3. Author's *Submarine Officer's Qualification Notebook,* written in 1962; Merrill, ibid, *Principles of Guided Missile Design: Operations Research Armament launching,* 1956.

4. Drew, Christopher and Sontag, Sherry, *Blind Man's Bluff,* Public Affairs, New York, 1998.

5. Merrill, *ibid.*

6. Bothwell, John R., Cdr, USN (Ret), "Brainstorming Days With Submarine Missiles", *Naval Memorial Series,* Spring 1997 issue.

7. Gunn, William, Cpt, USN (Ret), email 05/28/97: Capgun@aol.com.

8. Bevan, Travis, QMC (SS), USN (Ret), *Growler* plankowner, telcon 5 May 1988. Witness on bridge of original *Growler.*

9. Roscoe, Theodore, *Submarine Operations in World War II,* U.S. Naval Institute Press, various editions.

10. Roscoe, *ibid.*

11. Roscoe, *ibid.*

12. Roscoe, *ibid.*

13. LeVangie, Jim, former *Tunny* crew member, *Tunny Tales,* in writing and emails 2006.

14. LeVangie, *ibid;* Gunn, *ibid;* Stumpf, David K., *Regulus, the Forgotten Weapon,* Turner Publishing Company, 1996.

15. LeVangie, Jim, email 2006.

16. Henderson, Donald, Capt, USN (Ret), during author's indoctrination on board *Growler,* April 1962.

17. Simms, William "Pappy," Capt, USN (Ret), Strategic Systems Projects Office, SP-205, 1965, on board U.S.S. *Polk* (SSBN-645) DASO, Cape Kennedy, Florida.

18. Stumpf, ibid.

19. Owens, Robert, CDR, USN (Ret), telcon 17 May 1997; Bothwell, *ibid.*

20. *Vietnam Magazine*, Spring 1997 issue. Gunn, *ibid*, while warhead officer on Halibut and ComSubPac nuclear warhead officer.

21. Gunn, *ibid.*

22. *Vietnam Magazine*, Spring 1997 issue.

23. *Jane's Fighting Ships*, 1959 through 1965 editions.

24. Powers, Leonard "Pappy", RMC(SS), USN (Ret), letter dated 17 November 2006.

25. A fast cruise is normally conducted following construction, dry docking, or major repairs/work. The crew conducts normal at sea routines while remaining dockside.

26. Conversations with Tom Coffman, Pappy Powers, Carroll Miller, and Tom Crymes.

27. Pope, James, email September 2006.

28. Harrison, Jim, *Growler* plankowner, letter 2001.

29. Harrison, *ibid*; Coffman, Tom, telcon 8 October 2006.

30. Stebbins, Tom, second *Growler* COB, letter 1999.

31. Coffman, Tom, telcon 2001.

32. Pope, James, email September 2006.

33. Crymes, *ibid.*

34. Crymes, *ibid.*

35. Crymes, *ibid.*

36. Sloan, Dennis, Capt, USN (Ret), email August 2006.

37. Numerous verbal and email accounts: Coffman, Carlson, Crymes, Hoffman, etc.

38. Crymes, *ibid.*

39. Crymes, *ibid*; Straka, Dave, Reunion 2004.

40. Gunn, William, Capt, USN (Ret), during 1999 visit.

41. Admiral Weiss Letter of Approval.

42. Harrelson, Jim, November 1998 telcon.

43. Bevans, Travis, QMC(SS), USN (Ret), telcon 1999.

44. Bevans, *ibid.*

45. Coffman, *ibid.*

46. Sloan, Dennis, Capt, USN (Ret), email 2001.

47. Sloan, *ibid.*

48. Smith, Uel, summer of 2000; Heatwole, Duane "Hotdog", April 2006.

49. A technique later taught at Submarine School, New London, Connecticut.

50. Flege, Jim, EN2(SS), April 2000.

51. Hoffman, Robert, LT, USN (Ret), then QM2(SS) during Patrol #5.

52. Miller, Carroll, EN1(SS), conversation Patrol #6.

53. Henderson, Donald, Capt, USN (Ret), indoctrination Patrol #5.

54. Crawford, Robert, Capt, USN (Ret), biography 2001.

55. Murphy, James, Capt, USNR (Ret), biography provided 1999.

56. Murphy, James, Capt, USNR (Ret), letter dated October 1998. Coyle, Phillip, letter dated December 1998.

57. Glacy, Lawrence, PhD, then QM1(SS), March 2000.

58. Combs, Donald, TMC(SS), telcon 1999.

59. Daack, William, TM1(SS), email 2003.

60. Owens, Robert, CDR, USN (Ret), telcon December 2006.

61. Owens, Robert, CDR, USN (Ret), last commanding officer, telcon July 2006.

62. Curbow, Donald, QMCS(SS), USN (Ret), then QM1(SS) on Patrol #5.

63. Gunn, William, Capt, USN (Ret), personal conversation San Diego 1999.

64. Barnett, Thomas, CDR, USN (Ret), then GMT1(SS) and shipmate of Gunn on Halibut; Gunn, *ibid.*

65. Richardson, Daniel, RAdm, USN (Ret), then LT(jg) on *Barbero*, Pearl 1963.

66. Boggess, Roger, former shipmate of Bill Gunn on the *Tunny*.

67. Pope, James, USN (Ret), on *Halibut* crew email, 14 September 2006.

68. Powell, Mike, TMC (SS), USN (Ret), while COB on Patrol #7.

69. Von Allmen, Bob, LT(jg), USN (Ret), conversation, Reunion 2000 in New London; Henderson, Billie, CO's wife, conversation April 1962 in Pearl Harbor.

70. Bender, Jim, email 2000.

71. Meyers, Richard, EN2 (SS), email September 2006.

72. Heatwole, Duane "Hotdog", CS1(SS), telcon September 2006.

73. Terry, Jim, LCDR, USN (Ret), on Patrol #5.

74. Heatwole at Reunion 2002 in San Diego.

75. Owens, *ibid.*

Chapter Two

1. Caswell, David, QM3 (SS), telcon, 11 October 2006.

2. Gunn, William, Capt, USN (Ret), various conversations.

Chapter Three

1. Scott, Billy Bob "Scotty", SOCS(SS), USN (Ret), email, 27 February 1998.

2. Scott, *ibid.*

3. A couple of recollections remember a Soviet destroyer laying to in *Growler*'s path, dead in the water, and likely just listening.

4. LeVangie, Jim, *Tunny* Missile Guidance Officer, personal Submarine notes.

5. LeVangie, *ibid.*

6. Huebner, Richard, CDR, USN (Ret), ltr dtd 10 May 1995.

Chapter Four

1. BT stands for Bathythermograph, a graph that measures ship's draft versus water temperature.

2. Moving the rudder to full causes a large surface across the flow of water over the hull and forces the stern down and the bow up.

3. *Janes Fighting Ships*, 1961 edition. *Riga* class destroyers were relatively small, approximately 1,200 tons, carried guns, torpedoes, and depth charges.

4.   Gunn, William, Capt, USN (Ret), conversation; Huebner, *ibid.*

Chapter Five

1.   *Janes Encylopedia of Aviation,* Crescent Books, New York, 1980.
2.   Sea return is a term given to random clutter on radar scopes created by heavy seas that reflect and return a radar signal. Typically, sea return appears similar to snow or interference on television sets.
3.   A partial battery charge brings the battery to a temporary full charge. "Can" is a nickname for the battery, consisting of two units, one each in the forward and after battery compartments, consisting of 126 cells each.
4.   The methodology was used by Polaris/Poseidon programs. The accuracy is directly related to the fathometer and chart.
5.   Henderson, Donald, Capt, USN (Ret); Gunn, William, Capt, USN (Ret), lectures during Patrol # 5.
6.   Pope, James, STCS(SS), USN (Ret), email September 2006.
7.   Mehl, Wayne, LT(JG), USN; Powell, Mike, TMC(SS), USN (Ret); patrols # 5 and # 6.

Chapter Six

1.   Muir, Donald, MTC(SS), USN (Ret), via telecon.
2.   A Russian fisherman invested as much in his nets as he did in his home.
3.   Captain Crawford encountered a similar situation on a previous patrol with a net and is the basis for this story.
4.   *Navy Times*, newspaper, 9 June 1997.
5.   Puffins are colorful sea birds with a face and beak like a parrot, indigenous to the northern latitudes.
6.   The distance may be exaggerated. Battle Surface is a fast surface with extended time of blowing ballast tanks empty.
7.   Obviously *Growler* was expected, but the two sister ships often used the other's name to stay out of trouble.
8.   Meyers, *ibid.*
9.   There are numerous tales about the theft of Adak's totem pole by Regulus submarines. The *Tunny* is credited with the initial theft. Suffice it to say the totem pole was stolen more than once and an attempt was probably made each submarine call. If all the stories were true, the pole spent little time in Adak.
10.   Heatwole, Duane "Hotdog," CS1(SS), Reunion 2004, Branson, MO.
11.   Gunn, William, Capt, USN (Ret), during 1999 visit to San Diego.
12.   Richardson, Daniel, RAdm, USN (Ret), U.S.S. *Barbero.*
13.   This did not occur but accurately reflects the capabilities and qualification level of a submarine officer, each of which could easily have performed the same shiphandling.
14.   Richardson, Daniel, RAdm, USN (Ret), personal letter.
15.   Pope, James, STSCM, USN (Ret), email, September 2006.

Chapter Seven

1. Crymes, Thomas, QM2(SS), letter 1998.
2. This story is based on the USS *Tunny* 1998 launch against the USS *Shangri-La* (CV-38) and task force.
3. A hard turn command ordered a course change of 2.5° while a soft command altered course by 0.5°.
4. LeVangie, Jim, last missile guidance officer on *Tunny*. *Tunny's* exercise against an ASW force in 1964 fooled the task force. The Regulus speed was increased by modifying the missile exhaust nozzle.
5. This specific exercise was actually conducted prior to patrol #4.
6. Henson, George, LCDR, then XO (SSBN-645) related story in April 1966.
7. Gunn, *ibid.*

Chapter Eight

1. Where the superstructure meets the hull near the stern of a submarine.
2. Leavitt, Horace, Capt, USN (Ret), Executive Officer of *Growler*; Gunn, William, Capt, USN (Ret), email, 8 August 1997.
3. Underwood, Calvin, MT2(SS), email, 7 February 1998.
4. Owens, Robert, CDR, USN (Ret), telcon, 2 September 2006.
5. Harrelson, Jim, from the USS *Grayback*.
6. Richardson, *ibid.*
7. This occurred on another submarine.
8. Gunn, ibid.
9. LeVangie, ibid.
10. LeVangie, Jim, email, July 2006.
11. Curbow, Donald, QMSC (SS), USN (Ret).

Chapter Ten

1. Author's personnel file.
2. Operational Readiness Inspection is conducted annually to test a ship's readiness. In submarines it is conducted by the Division or Squadron Commander.
3. This exercise is conducted by many officers. In this case, some of the exercises were conducted orally.

Chapter Eleven

1. Huebner, ibid.
2. McCollum, Mac, email 2006.
3. Ensign Gordon Vallentine was an enthusiastic young officer and often tried too hard. Some of the antics described herein adds humor to the story. Gordon turned out to be an outstanding officer and submariner.

4.   Scott, Billy Bob "Scotty," SOCS(SS), USN (Ret), Reunion 2000.

5.   Richardson, *ibid.*

6.   Roscoe, Theodore, *Submarine Operations in World War II*, all editions.

7.   Pope, Jim, email, July 2006.

8.   Carlson, Gerald, EN1, reunion 2004.

9.   Defense Condition 2 is one step short of war. The submarine remains manned with no liberty and ready to get underway immediately with all hands on board.

10.   Gunn, *ibid.*

Chapter Twelve

1.   Anderson, John, MTCM(SS), USN (Ret), telcon, 22 September 2006.

2.   Pope, *ibid.*

3.   Fiddle boards are hinged boards placed on top of a table, which divide the table into sections. Each person kept his dish, glass, and silverware inside his section, thereby preventing food and utensils from sliding all over the table.

4.   LeVangie, *ibid.*

5.   A torpedo tube on patrol was usually loaded with a warshot torpedo. Prior to opening the outer door to fire a torpedo the tube had to be flooded and equalized with outside water pressure.

6.   Taylor, John, QM1(SS), email, 11 February 1998.

7.   Wright, John, ENC(SS), USN (Ret), actually guided the officer through the watertight door while giving him an earful. It was not an offense, but he made his point.

8.   The author was present but didn't recall the words exactly. He referred to David Stumpf's book, *Regulus, the Forgotten Weapon*, for the exact wording.

Chapter Thirteen

1.   Huebner, *ibid.*

2.   Author wrote the newsletter and continues to this day.

3.   Leavitt, Horace, Capt, USN (Ret), related story on Patrol # 7.

4.   Pope, *ibid.*

5.   Gunn, William, *ibid.*

Chapter Fourteen

1.   Von Fisher, Walter, senior diesel engineer with Fairbanks Morse & Company.

2.   Karr, William, GMC(SS), USN (Ret), member of GMU 10.

3.   Pope, *ibid.*

4.   Gunn, ibid; Huebner, *ibid.*

5.   A submarine can't permit hydrogen in the boat to reach explosive levels. During a battery charge, the batteries release hydrogen for a period of time after the charging has stopped, so the emission must also be anticipated. The hydrogen release and the volume of the boat is used to compute a safe amount of hydrogen in the boat at any time called the

hydrogen curve.

6. The Fox Sked (schedule) is an hourly message radio broadcast to the fleet with numbered message traffic.

7. Hydrogen peroxide fueled torpedo. Any imperfection in the navol begins an exponential decay, creating heat and eventual fire/explosion.

8. Incident did not occur on *Growler*, but had happened in the area to other submarines. Perhaps it was an exercise launch by a Soviet destroyer.

Chapter Fifteen

1. Zero float is like a trickle charge with no amperes being removed from or added to the battery.

2. Occurred on *Growler* Patrol # 1.

3. Pope, *ibid.*

4. In this context, evacuating means removing the smoke from the compartment.

5. Related by Captain Gunn and Commander Huebner.

6. Huebner, *ibid.*

7. SOund SUrveillance System. Underwater listening system used to observe/listen to vessel movements and operations.

8. A moving haven is an area surrounding the estimated/intended movement of a submarine, usually established to inform other units a friendly submarine is present.

9. Gunn, *ibid.*

10. A false submarine name.

11. Owens, Robert, CDR, USN (Ret), interview 1999.

12. Coyle, Phil, email 2005.

Breinigsville, PA USA
17 August 2010
243749BV00005B/6/P